D1301624

READING THE

Part One of

SHORT STORY ✍

HERBERT BARROWS
The University of Michigan

AN INTRODUCTION TO LITERATURE

by Herbert Barrows, Hubert Heffner,
John Ciardi, and Wallace Douglas

HOUGHTON MIFFLIN COMPANY
Boston · The Riverside Press Cambridge

COPYRIGHT ©, 1959, BY HERBERT BARROWS

𝕿𝖍𝖊 𝕽𝖎𝖛𝖊𝖗𝖘𝖎𝖉𝖊 𝕻𝖗𝖊𝖘𝖘 · CAMBRIDGE, MASSACHUSETTS

PRINTED IN THE U.S.A.

PREFATORY NOTE

(To the Complete Edition)

There are many volumes designed to introduce college students to literature. What novelty can be claimed for this book comes from its plan. The four skilled and experienced teachers who have served as editors were not limited in their work by any imposed uniformity of treatment. They were asked instead to organize their approaches to fiction and drama, to poetry and prose, exactly as they would their own courses in these kinds of writing.

The result is four highly idiosyncratic presentations, ranging from Mr. Barrows's catholic and persuasive survey of the short story to Mr. Douglas's lively polemic for modern prose, from Mr. Heffner's detached and orderly analysis of drama to an examination of poetry marked by all the brilliance and conviction readers have come to expect from that poet and defender of poetry, Mr. Ciardi. The customary teaching materials are here. The characteristics, the conventions, and the special effects of each kind of writing are set forth, and the necessary critical terms are introduced. But each editor has done this in his own way.

Yet the book does have a deeper unity, which derives from certain assumptions shared by the editors. I recall some twenty years ago being a member of a group of graduate students in English to whom Robert Frost offered this advice: "Don't work. Worry!" This was his counsel to poets, he said, and he thought it might apply to us as well. One or two of our professors regarded his words as subversive of discipline, but we took them, I am sure correctly, as a clue to the kind of understanding of literature that makes its study really valuable. In like manner the editors of this book see literature as an unending source of delight, not merely as a "subject" to be pursued systematically like any other. They propose formal analysis to the student, not as an end in itself, but as a means of widening his range of comprehension and deepening his enjoyment of the thing comprehended. The beginning student, eager and curious, but largely unread and uninformed, will find them reliable guides to the "extension of life" which literature uniquely offers.

GORDON N. RAY

CONTENTS

READING

THE

SHORT STORY

THE STORIES IN THE FOLLOWING COLLECTION are offered for study in a college literature class, and this is certainly a different purpose from that for which they were written. That purpose, even though the individual writers represented here might give quite different answers to the question of why they wrote, is in general to give pleasure to an individual reader who has come to the particular story with the hope of being entertained by it. Now, exactly what that entertainment consists in is a complex question, though to discover the answer to it ought to be one of our aims in studying the short story. But first of all it may be helpful to say a word about the relation between "studying" short stories and simply reading them—by ourselves and "for pleasure."

In the first place, *all* our reading of imaginative literature ought to give us pleasure. A sense of delighted absorption in what we are reading is a primary ingredient in our response to the greatest works we read as well as to the most humble. It is true that the greatest works of literature —the Greek drama, for instance, or *The Divine Comedy,* or the plays of Shakespeare—hold their high place because of the power and completeness with which they present a view of the truth about man's life and

1

man's destiny. Yet however austere and profound these works may be, they are not philosophical treatises but works of literature, works of art, and this means that in the rather mysterious way that is common to all works of art they make their effect on us through the mode of pleasure, of delight in an artistic object with all its manifold appeal to our imagination, our feelings, and our senses as well as to our intellect. Such works as these are surely to be counted among the greatest achievements of the human spirit, and it may seem like a betrayal of their ultimate value to say that they must give us "pleasure," using a word that we might prefer to keep for more trivial pursuits and more fleeting impulses. Nevertheless, it is the fact that to be effective for us they *must* do so, that such a work as *Hamlet* or *The Inferno* or *Oedipus the King* will have no value whatever to the reader who plods through it, his imagination and his senses and his human curiosity closed up or shut off, just to see what Shakespeare or Dante or Sophocles was really "saying" underneath the plot, the words, and the tale of specific human destiny.

Now, there are many differences, not only of magnitude but of essential aim, which separate such works as those just mentioned from even the finest of modern short stories. Yet there are certain elements which are likely to be present in the situation of a reader who faces a work of literature that is new to him, almost without regard to the scope of the work. Although we become good readers by actually doing a good deal of reading, over a long period of time, rather than by theorizing about what the process consists in, still it is possible that a frank awareness on a theoretical level of just what is involved may be useful. There is a question—or call it a doubt, a perplexity—that sometimes troubles even the most eager and intellectually curious student when he is first asked to *study* literature, to subject stories or poems or novels to a critical analysis rather than just to read them. Sometimes the question goes like this: "Doesn't it spoil stories—or poems—to tear them apart?" This question should be respected, because it usually springs from honest doubt and because it comes from the student who sees how much there is to spoil.

To find the answer, or to help the student find it, we have to realize that it is in the very nature of works of literature both to offer us something and to demand something from us. We realize, when we first try to read Shakespeare as adults, that we can't just open one of the plays and read it through with perfect ease from the first word to the last, that we have to learn many things about Shakespeare's language, about the background of life and thought in his time. But even aside from such matters, the plays are complex, profound, and subtle, and we cannot take them in all at once in all their dimensions, so we analyze them, we study them; and perhaps, if we perform these operations with a decent respect for the plays themselves and for what we eventually hope to derive from them, it won't seem that we are merely tearing them apart.

But Shakespeare's plays, after all, present rather a special case. Surely it is one thing to read *King Lear*, which offers a formidable challenge to *any* mind and imagination, and quite another to read a short story which may originally have been published in a weekly or monthly magazine. Yet the relevant fact here is that a given short story, for a given reader, may present elements of meaning or technique that are so unfamiliar as to prevent him from taking the story in, from responding to it fully and directly on one reading. The reader then has a choice: he can drop the story completely, turning back to stories he already knows "how to read," or he can try it once more, making a conscious effort to see it for what it is, to discover where its own special values lie—values which he may not have perceived at first because they are so different from those found in any of the stories he has previously been acquainted with. If he does this, even if he does it entirely on his own, he will be "studying" the story in question quite as much as if he approached it in a classroom with the help of a teacher and the cooperation of other students. And his method of study will be the only method there is, analysis: which means, really, no more than attending to one aspect, one feature of the story at a time instead of trying to take it in completely and intuitively at a single reading.

Our acquaintance with works of literature, or with works of art of any kind, involves us, once the initial interest has come into play, in a gradual process of development. At any given stage in this development we have available to us, in general, works of two kinds, those we already know how to enjoy, and those with which we are as yet not entirely at ease but which we feel we could enjoy as fully as the others once we have come to understand them better, to see into their meaning and their form more clearly and sensitively. At any stage of this development, moreover, we should make sure that we are finding a place for both kinds of reading, for both kinds of literary experience. We should continue to read books of the kinds we already enjoy and appreciate, but without being merely self-conscious and snobbish about it, we should also try works that will stretch our capacities, works that are apparently deeper or more subtle than anything we have read so far, or works that present some innovation of form or viewpoint that is baffling at first sight. (And, as a general rule, we should be willing to try *anything*, never mind whether or not it seems to be the right work for us at the present "stage.")

Now, intuition, of the kind that leads to direct appreciation, is better than the kind of response which comes only after more or less painstaking analysis, but the point is that by analyzing a certain story or poem today we are making it possible for ourselves to respond directly and intuitively to another work of the same kind tomorrow. For we should never forget that what we are seeking, in the end, is the *enjoyment* that the work can offer us. In studying literature, in familiarizing ourselves with the methods of critical analysis, what we are really doing is working to increase our capacity for enjoyment, to enlarge the range of works which make their appeal to us directly and fully. And in our eagerness to assimilate new forms of literature, to make the very considerable intellectual effort which they often require, we should not forget what we already know, from our pre-college experience, about the love of reading. The chances are that the love of reading, if we're lucky enough to have it at all, was developed, during our first reading years, on very humble materials: on the exploits of the Hardy boys or Nancy Drew, on western stories or detective stories, on out-of-date best sellers left lying about by older readers, on all kinds of magazine fiction. From such reading as this, undertaken solely for the immediate enjoyment it provided, with no thought of improvement or of learning anything whatever, we may have been lucky enough to learn the most important lesson of all: how the imagination is fed and fostered by the printed word, what it feels like to love reading. A love of reading and a love of good literature are not always the same thing, but it is doubtful that anyone has ever attained the second who did not possess the first. And therefore we should be careful, when we first begin to make a conscious effort to improve our understanding and appreciation of literature, not to assume that, while the new experiences will be austerely improving, they can scarcely be expected to be pleasurable. They can be pleasurable, and eventually they will be so—otherwise they would not be worth bothering with. What we are trying to learn is to see new works clearly enough, both in their inner structure and in their relation to the world they reflect, so that we can respond to them directly and fully and on their own terms: so that we can read them with pleasure.

* * *

The modern short story, as we encounter it in the pages of magazines, in collections of stories by a single author, or in anthologies of stories by several authors, has not had a very long history. It is perfectly true that the story-telling habit is as old as civilization itself, and that it seems to be a deep and permanent instinct to catch hold of an event, an incident that is in any way remarkable, and to share it with someone else, as a way of pointing out how full of unexpectedness—or even of expectedness—the world is, how rich in interest and resourcefulness are the men who inhabit it, how mysterious the workings of the forces which govern it. Now, insofar as they reflect and satisfy this deep-lying instinct by *telling a story*, all mythologies, certain portions of many Sacred Books, and later collections of tales like *The Decameron* or *The Canterbury Tales*, have something in common with the stories of any modern practitioner whatever. Yet though they have something in common, these works are so widely different both from one another and from the modern short story in their scope, in their relation to the societies which produced them, and in their form, that to insist on their one fundamental point of similarity in order to construct for the short story an ancestry as old as the history of literature, is to blur essential values rather than to isolate and establish them.

The effective, relevant tradition of the modern short story goes back scarcely more than one hundred and fifty years, and may conveniently be seen as having been initiated by two writers, one Russian and one American, whose life spans coincided almost exactly: Nikolai Gogol, who lived from 1809 to 1852, and Edgar Allan Poe, who lived from 1809 to 1849. These two writers did not "invent" the short story, but they carried it through the most important stage in its development by virtue of producing a considerable number of excellent stories, thus revealing the potentialities of the form and establishing, in a practical way, its external shape and dimensions. Moreover, because their personal visions, interests, and experience were in many respects so very different, their respective practices of the short story illustrate at the very outset one of the form's most gratifying features: its ability to accommodate the most widely diverse kinds of subject-matter, to present visions of life which lie as far apart from one another as Poe's fantasy-world from Gogol's specifically evoked early-nineteenth-century St. Petersburg.

The history of the short story is the history of what individual practitioners have made of the form, the story of how each of them has made it a vehicle for the presentation of his own individual view of what is interesting, significant, amusing, or moving in the areas of life and the aspects of human nature which have presented themselves to his notice. That history, since to tell it even superficially would be to describe the individual use of the form made by a host of writers in Europe and America, cannot be told here. Nevertheless, another pair of names must be mentioned, since they are the names of the two writers who have thus far come closest to achieving unqualified literary "greatness" as writers of the short story: De Maupassant (1850–1893) and Chekhov (1860–1904). A number of great writers—Henry James, for instance—have devoted a part of their time to writing short stories, and many writers not of the first rank, such as Katherine Mansfield, have made the short story their only form and have practiced it with distinction and grace. But so far only De Maupassant and Chekhov (though both of them owe a part of their fame to their work in other forms) have left a body of short stories which, for realization of the artistic possibilities of the form, for fundamental seriousness and penetration of vision, for scope and variety of content, and for the sheer quantity of first-rate stories which the total work of each writer contains, seems to constitute a major achievement.

There has been a tendency in recent discussions of the short story to make De Maupassant and Chekhov the leaders of rival camps: De Maupassant, on the basis of such inferior stories as "The Necklace," is made to represent the contrived sort of story where more important values are sacrificed for the sake of a surprise ending, while Chekhov is seen as a writer who suppresses interest in plot or narrative in order to capture a certain momentary mood or to present a rather low-keyed vignette of "life as it is." There is some truth in these distinctions, but not a very important truth. Despite their differences of aim and practice, De Maupassant and Chekhov resemble one another in having created in their stories an enormously detailed and vivid world in which human motives, conditions, and hopes are probed with great delicacy and penetration and judged—when they are judged at all—with intelligence and compassion. Many other writers have written single stories as good as any of theirs, and some have written single volumes—one thinks of James Joyce's *Dubliners*—which can rival any single volume by De Maupassant or Chekhov, yet theirs remain the greatest single achievements in the form, and the achievements which have given the widest extension to our idea of what a given writer can achieve within it.

Of course this does not mean that the short story as a form reached a dead-end once the accomplishment of these two writers was complete. Probably the single truth most important to remember about any art form is that merely to have seen what has been accomplished within it in the past is no guarantee of knowing what may be done with it in the future. For example, any general description of the way fiction uses and alters the actuality of experience for its own ends would have to be ever so slightly different after Franz Kafka (1883-1924) had written his novels and stories than it would have been before, because Kafka's work, although it is not entirely without precedent and ancestry in earlier fiction, did present a new emphasis, a new way of combining more or less recognizable elements of realism and fantasy into a new and highly individual vision. Similarly, Hemingway's first volume of stories, *In Our Time* (1925), demonstrated a brilliant new style which seemed to make possible a far more *direct* transcription of sensory and emotional experience than had been possible before, even to Stephen Crane or Joseph Conrad, and it is certain that Hemingway's style has had a marked effect on a great many novels and stories which have been written since his early books appeared, in Europe as well as in America. Yet such innovations as these, powerful and decisive as they are seen to be in retrospect, are often neither understood nor welcomed at first, for readers as a whole, especially older readers who are in positions where they can lay down the literary law, are apt to prefer what they are familiar with to something that demands a new effort, a new response. Yet any art form, if it is to remain alive, will from time to time confront us with works that seem disconcertingly strange, and it behooves us to try to make the appropriate new response.

It may be, then, that some day the short story will undergo changes that are impossible to predict now. Nevertheless, of the short story as it has been in the one hundred or so years of its history and as we know it today, it is possible to offer a generally applicable preliminary description. Granted the enormous and very attractive variety of practice that exists from one short-story writer to another, there are a certain few expectations which we legitimately have of the short story and which, taken together, constitute about as complete an *a priori* description of the form as it is desirable to offer.

❈   ❈   ❈

Put briefly, we expect a short story to be *short*. Second, we expect it, whatever else it does, to tell a story that is worth telling *as a story*. Third, we expect it to offer some kind of illumination, however indirect or oblique, on the experience of life in this world as the author sees it: that is, it has to have significance. And fourth, we expect it to make its effects, to interest us, to tell us what it has to tell us, not by direct expository statement as the essay does, but by the dramatic or narrative presentation of imagined, created characters, moving in surroundings which the writer has described or evoked with sufficient vividness and circumstantiality so that we may have the illusion of standing within it, imaginatively, as we read. Demands of individual readers may vary on this last point, but it may be at least suggested that a basic requirement of fiction is that it take us into a world that is both *possible* (that is, recognizably related to the world as we know it) and *new* (that is, not a statistical replica of any segment of reality).

In one sense, the first of these expectations is merely a matter of definition. We expect the form of literature which we call a short story to run from about three or four pages—any shorter and it becomes an anecdote, or a germ for a story rather than the story itself—to something no more than a hundred pages, and usually not more than fifty or sixty —any longer and it becomes a novella or short novel. But in another sense, this question of the short story's *shortness* involves the essential aesthetic of the form. Moreover, it is the one aspect of the short story which sets it apart from the novel. Much of what we shall have to say about the other three expectations with which we habitually approach the short story will be found to apply about equally well to the novel (though the requirement that there be a story to be told has a special relevance to the short story that does not carry over quite intact to the novel). But in deciding to work within the length proper to the short story, a writer accepts a particular challenge which, if he is capable of meeting it, will bring with it a particular strength, the strength of a unique art form.

Reviewing Hawthorne's *Twice-Told Tales* in 1842 (the review is discussed at some length in the note on Poe to be found on pp. 48–51 below), Poe worked out this point in the aesthetic of the short story once and for all. One of Poe's central principles of poetic composition was that there is no such thing as a long poem, that works to which we apply the term are actually collections of short poems strung together by passages in which there is no sign of the true poetic impulse. The poetic impulse, he believed, is so intense that it can be maintained only for brief periods, and this principle of a brief intensity governs the reading of poems as well as the writing of them. For Poe, in accord with this principle, the highest form of literary composition was the short poem, and the second highest form was the short prose tale. The tale must be short enough to be read at a single sitting, long enough to allow the writer to create for his reader a controlled and unified effect.

The important implication in Poe's specifications is that the short story is *not* to be seen as something loose, anecdotal, and essentially trivial, but as an art form in which the writer carefully calculates his effects in order to make a unified appeal to the total emotional and intellectual nature of the reader: the appeal can be thus unified, and can be made with an intensity that involves a deep emotional response, *only* if the story is kept short. In Poe's estimation, the novel was an inferior form because, too long to be read at one sitting, it could not create in the reader the sustained, self-contained, unified response which he deemed essential to any work of literature which set out to realize the highest possible aims.

Poe's prescription has found the most abundant justification and ex- emplification in the work of many short-story writers who, entirely di- verse in temperament, outlook, and choice of subject-matter, are yet alike in their devotion to his principle: that the short story, as a result of its brevity, has available to it an intensity that resembles the intensity of poetry. This is one of the first lessons we have to learn when we ap- proach the work of many of the best practitioners of the short story— writers like Chekhov or Joyce or Hemingway—: that their work is not loosely anecdotal, each story to be read through idly and quickly with the one aim of seeing "how it comes out," but highly controlled and de- manding the most attentive and sensitive response we are capable of giving. As readers, we must learn to see what Poe saw as critic and writer: that the *brevity* of the short story makes possible an intensity and concentration of artistic effect that, in turn, allow the form to work in a very high range of values and significance.

But since so much has been said about the possibility of concentration which is inherent in the very shortness of the short story, a word must be said on the other side of the question before we go on to consider the other expectations we customarily bring to the reading of short sto- ries. It must not be forgotten that, although the short story can aim at ultimate effects comparable in some degree to those of poetry, these effects must be gained by means appropriate to fiction. A short story is a short story, after all, and not a poem, and if a writer forgets that fact and aims too directly at a "poetic" expressiveness, ignoring or minimizing the properly fictional aspects of his work in doing so, he will produce something that is neither poetry nor a short story and the reader will inevitably feel that he has been cheated.

For we approach fiction—both short stories and novels—with a num- ber of attitudes that are scarcely present when we read poetry. We ap- proach it with an interest in narrative, a desire to watch things happen, a curiosity to see how events turn out, and we want the *details* of a situ- ation, we want to see the situation treated expansively, even discur- sively. All this may seem to be in direct contradiction to what has been said about concentration of effect, but actually it is not. A story like Walter Van Tilburg Clark's "The Indian Well" affords a clear illustration of the compatibility of Poe's demands for unity of effect with the demands for narrative interest and multiplicity of detail which as readers we all make of the short story. When we come to the end of that story, as of any good story, a consistent mood has been created, our consciousness of certain aspects of life has been intensified or even altered, and we are aware of the story as a controlled artistic entity. But Clark has accomplished these ends by making it possible for us to follow his narrative with interest and excitement and to become absorbed in a highly detailed presentation of the specific world in which the action takes place. In this story, as in any really successful story, the ultimate artistic value is achieved as a result of successful attention to the immediate aims appropriate to the medium, and here we come to the other elements—story-telling interest, significance, and specificity—which have already been referred to. In actual practice, of course, these elements will be inextricably woven together, but for the moment let us consider them one at a time.

Whatever else happens to us as we read a short story, then, ought to happen as a result of our being *interested* in the story that is told, of our wanting to read to the end, to follow the events until they have passed through a point of climax and been resolved in such a way as to leave the characters *different* in some way—however externally slight—from what they were at the beginning. The short-story writer must have many gifts and powers at his disposal: he must have a genuine understanding of human nature, he must have a keen eye for significant appearances and an ability to render them in his work, he must have the power to grasp and reveal the meaning of the incidents and experiences which have caught his attention. But first of all, he must have a story to tell. No amount of distinguished writing, no amount of philosophic penetration or social insight will suffice to make a short story in the absence of this primary ingredient. To say this is not at all to reduce the scope or value of the short story to a mere satisfying of curiosity or of a demand for the sensational. From a good short story, quite as much as from any other form of literature, we can derive all the varieties of profit and pleasure that are provided by a writer's mastery of form and style, by his possession of an original mind, a keen understanding of life and human nature—and in fact, if we derive none of these things, in any degree whatever, it won't be much of a story. Yet it is the *primary* requirement of this form of literature, as distinguished from the essay or the prose-poem or the descriptive sketch, that it tell a story, that it make its total effect as a result of capturing our interest for a particular sequence of imaginary events with a beginning, a middle, and an end.

To remain theoretical for just a moment longer, it is possible to describe the general conditions under which this essential story-telling interest is aroused and held. Any incident or narrative which is to interest us in the way we expect of a short story, ought to contain elements both of the familiar and of the unfamiliar. What we like, what we respond to in reading or listening to a story, is to see something a little strange, a little extreme, a little out of the ordinary, taking place under conditions which we recognize as being the conditions which govern life as we know it. Even in fantasy, even in tall tales like those which describe the exploits of Paul Bunyan or Davy Crockett, even in science fiction, there has to be an *ultimate* applicability to human nature, to human life as we know it; the convention between the reader and the writer of such fiction is that credibility should be stretched just as far as it can possibly be stretched without being abandoned altogether. And by the same token, even in stories where the conditions of actual life in a particular time and place are rendered with documentary faithfulness there has to be given *some* little lift of novelty, of the unusual, some intensification of a particular human quality, without which we shall feel that we have not really been offered a story.

Nobody can prescribe for the short-story writer a formula or a method whereby his stories can surely be made interesting, nor are we trying to lay down any such prescription here. But once the story has been written, we shall certainly discover that if it is a *good* story it is an *interesting* story, by which we mean that the writer has achieved the right, engaging balance between what is familiar to us and what is new. As to the familiar: we expect that the particular events and reactions of the story will take place under the general laws which we recognize as governing human nature and human life in this world, since it is this life which concerns us. But we also want to be offered something *new* when we read, not absolutely new, perhaps, because human nature doesn't change very much, but at least a new combination of human traits, a new illustration at least of how human beings behave, of just how much they are capable of—in any one of perfectly innumerable directions. Perhaps it is not too much to say that we expect each story to offer us a revelation, in dramatic, fictional terms, of what human nature and human life are capable of, for good or for evil, and that the story's power to arouse our interest is not going to be a matter of multiplying wildly exciting events but rather one of convincing us that such a revelation has actually taken place.

The revelation takes place, for instance, in one of Katherine Mansfield's best known stories, "The Doll's House," a story which demonstrates how little the short story depends on grandiose subject-matter for arousing the interest essential to fiction. Externally considered, "The Doll's House" does no more than tell the story of two socially unacceptable little girls, in a snobbish middle-class world where the adults' false and cruel social values touch even the children's uncomprehending lives: all that "happens" is that the two children are at first excluded from seeing a new doll's house with all its wonders and then are allowed a brief, ecstatic, and perilous glimpse of it. Yet in this story, as much as in any story ever written, what has happened is made to seem momentous, there is a story to tell. We are taken completely into the little world where being allowed to inspect the splendors of the doll's house is a symbolic act which separates those who have from those who have not, and at the end of the story, when the two little Kelveys have been chased out of the back yard by an aunt with a nervous headache and sit by the side of the road, breathless and humble, thinking over the glimpse of felicity which has so grudgingly and selfishly been offered them, we are present at a revelation which has been arrived at through the means of a dramatic conflict between opposing forces. Within the very slight dimensions of the story, those who have been made selfish and callously inhumane by good fortune are confronted by the humble who have a greater capacity than they both for joy and for pain, and at the end we have seen perhaps not a *new* truth, but at any rate a new and specific instance of an old truth, about how human nature will grasp hold of joy under even the most unpromising circumstances. But however much the story's ultimate value may depend on Katherine Mansfield's grasp of this truth, its *primary* value, the value for which in the first instance we read it at all, depends on her having been able to tell it to us in a dramatically effective way, *as a story,* that is, on her power to present the abstract conflict in a new set of concrete terms, to make us care how these two highly specific little girls will emerge from their uneven struggle. She has been able to take us with her, to involve our sympathy and our judgment, as she leads certain human beings through a crisis in their lives, and it is precisely this which *having a story to tell* will always be found to consist in.

It is virtually impossible to talk about any one of the demands we make of the short story without bringing in the others. In our attempt to describe the basic interest which makes a story worth telling, we have already been obliged to mention the elements of truth and specificity. Perhaps there is only one point that needs to be stressed about the demand for truth in—paradoxically—fiction. That is that while fiction—again paradoxically—ought to tell the truth, it must do so in terms of fiction. When we say that we look for truth in fiction, we mean that we expect the stories and novels we read to be based, however indirectly or remotely, in life and human nature as we know them. This law is obeyed by even the most frankly escapist literature, and the tired housewife who reads a so-called "true romance" is still seeing her world, the world of human relationships, even though she is seeing it not as it is but only as she wishes it might be: it is "romance," but it is "true" romance. In fiction of a higher order, fiction which we read with our whole mind rather than merely with our capacity for day-dreaming, life as it goes on about us and as we ourselves live it is constantly being illuminated, our understanding of it is constantly being confirmed or modified or, it may be, contradicted. But all this the short-story writer must do indirectly, by presenting an *imitation* of life, with characters and situations so conceived that they will present a faithful and revealing commentary on some aspect of life, and the truth of that life, as the writer sees it. Another reader might see a different "truth" emerging from "The Doll's House" than the one sketched briefly above, but the point is that Katherine Mansfield leaves her characters and events to speak for themselves, through the pattern she has given them, and never comes forward in her own person to say "This is what my story means." Moreover, the value of her story is not to be reduced to the ultimate value and applicability of any truth that may be disengaged from it and considered abstractly, but must be seen as inhering in its total power to live and to create in its readers a sense of witnessing the life and the action that it presents.

Again closely related to the requirements already discussed, is the final requirement in our list: that a short story should have a high degree of specificity, or at any rate that one of the most satisfying features of a good many short stories is that they take us into specific areas and circumstances of life which are rendered in faithful and convincing detail. It is one of the great pleasures of fiction that it takes us into more places, more walks of life, more varieties of human activity than we shall ever know directly. Nor do we enter those places as total strangers, for the writer is there to make us aware not only of what is new about them but also of what is perfectly familiar because fundamentally true to human nature in all places and all times. But the very *specificity* with which the writer renders the particular world, the particular circumstances in which his story takes place, is one of the elements which most strongly attract us to reading it. In reading F. Scott Fitzgerald, for example, we enjoy the lively way in which he evokes the brassy, zestful, superficial—and often tragic—life of a certain social class in American cities and European tourist spots in the 1920's, just as with Ring Lardner we enjoy a detailed rendering of the very tone and quality of life at the same time, and in some of the same places, but at a lower economic level and viewed, of course, by a wholly different temperament. These two segments of life are already beginning to be remote from us in time, though they certainly have their counterparts in American society today. But the short story makes it possible for us to feel that we have been given a glimpse of life in places and times that are far more distant from us than Fitzgerald's country clubs or theaters or hotels of the 1920's: they take us, for example, to Chekhov's Russian cities and towns and hamlets in the nineteenth century, or to Hemingway's Spanish cities with the bull-ring at their center, or to Paul Bowles' Indian villages and ancient forests in Latin America. They take us anywhere, in fact, where a short-story writer's knowledge and imaginative power have allowed him to penetrate.

The ultimate importance and value of a story may depend more decisively on one of the story's other elements—on its power to catch and hold our interest as a story told, or on the penetration or subtlety of its grasp of the truth of human nature—but even these elements will depend for their effectiveness on the writer's ability to create in us as we read the illusion of entering a *specifically* imagined world. Even in the most completely naturalistic stories, this world is of course, in one sense, only make-believe, just as even in the most thorough-going fantasies, such as the stories of Poe, or in such a combination of fantasy and realism as we find in the stories of Kafka, the make-believe must be capable of *seeming* real as we read. If we analyze our response to any short story which has given us pleasure, we shall see that it is to be accounted for at least to some extent by the writer's having had the power to create the specifically imagined world which fiction presupposes.

* * *

The study of the short story does not demand that we familiarize ourselves with a long list of technical terms. The words we use in analyzing any short story, that is, in isolating its various facets so that in the end we may have a more articulate and explicit understanding of how it works as a whole, are perfectly familiar to us from their use in other contexts: character, plot, setting, theme, narrative, symbol. Short stories are about people, whom we usually refer to as the *characters* of the story, distinguishing between the central characters, in whom we are chiefly interested, and minor characters who have subordinate or incidental roles. What happens in the story, from beginning to end, constitutes the story's *narrative*. A writer may choose to tell his story in straightforward chronological order, or he may choose to begin it at some point on the continuum other than the very beginning and then go back to the earliest relevant events later in the story. He may choose to describe the events of the story from the point of view of a single character who is taking part in them, or he may alternately adopt the points of view of two or more characters, or he may station himself above the events in the position of the omniscient author. *Plot* may be distinguished from *narrative* by noting that by narrative we refer to events in sequence and by plot we refer to events in their causal relationships to one another. E. M. Forster has given a vividly brief explanation of the difference between the two elements in his book *Aspects of the Novel:* if we say, "The king died, and then the queen died," we have narrative; if we say, "The king died and then the queen died of grief," we have plot. Or think of the intricate causal relationship between the particular events in one of O. Henry's well known stories: "The Gift of the Magi," for instance, which depends so completely for its interest on the deadly clicking into place of all the elements in a very intricate plot. (In this story, a young husband and wife, very poor, wish to give each other a Christmas present. The wife cuts off her beautiful long hair, of which both she and her husband are very proud, in order to buy a watch-chain for her husband's watch, of which they are again both very proud; the husband meanwhile has sold the watch in order to buy an elaborate set of combs for his wife.)

The question of how much emphasis should be placed on plot has often been debated, especially in the years following World War I when a number of the most distinguished story writers seemed to want to minimize plot, in the belief that the somewhat artificial arrangement of events which would lead to a surprise ending was likely to work against the faithfulness, the expressiveness of their rendering of life. This controversy is interestingly presented, from the point of view of a writer who both favors and practices the plotted story, in Somerset Maugham's introduction to his anthology, *Tellers of Tales.* Yet surely the final position of any receptive reader is going to be that there is room for both kinds of story, that each kind, in the hands of a good writer, can and indeed must have both of the aims which some critics seem to feel can only be pursued singly. The most intricate or strikingly arranged plot is only one of the means of presenting life in such a way as to illuminate it, to comment on it in the way that is proper to fiction. And by the same token, no story with any power of life in it will be found devoid of some degree of the interest which begins to arise for us the moment two human wills are seen as affecting or crossing one another, and such an interrelationship of motives is far more essential to plot than is mere coincidence.

One of the results of the increasing sophistication with which the short story has been written in our time is that it has often made use of a wide range of literary techniques known collectively as symbolism. Literature has always used symbol of one kind or another, and the modern short story, from its beginnings in the early nineteenth century, has been no exception to this rule. Poe's tales are consciously and systematically symbolic, and Gogol's "The Overcoat" moves on to a symbolic level to complete its meaning, while Hawthorne's tales could be taken not only as a primer of symbolic devices and practices, but also as an illustration of the suggestive power which symbolism can provide when used by a master whose mind and temperament have a genuine affinity for it. In "Ethan Brand," for example, there is a clear-cut use of specific symbol in the discovery at the end that Ethan Brand's heart has been of a substance hard enough to keep its form even in the fire of the lime-kiln. But virtually all the incidents and objects of that story are symbolic, that is, they have the effect, while they remain themselves, of subtly and suggestively directing our attention to something *beyond* themselves, to a facet of the total abstract meaning which the story *symbolically* presents.

Symbolism differs from allegory in this important respect, that while allegory establishes a definite and unmistakable connection between the abstract idea and its physical embodiment, symbolism makes no such point-to-point connection but merely suggests that such a relationship between seen and unseen, between abstract and concrete, is present, leaving it to our imagination to interpret the exact nature of the relationship. In one of the best known of all allegories, Bunyan's *Pilgrim's*

Progress, we follow a human soul on its way through the dangers and temptations of the world to its goal of Christian salvation, and we know from the very start that that is what we are doing: the hero is called Christian, he encounters Mr. Worldly Wiseman, he falls into the Slough of Despond, and so on. But in Hawthorne's story of Ethan Brand and his search for the unpardonable sin, there is no such explicit tying down of each episode to its specific function in the development of the story's ultimate, inner meaning. What does it mean when the dog suddenly starts to chase his own tail, for instance? Or is there any special significance in the fact that it is little Joe who discovers the calcined heart at the end? Different readers may see specific episodes of the story in different ways, at least within a certain range of likelihood, but taken all together it will be found, I believe, that the successive events of a symbolic story form on the concrete, objective level a pattern of relationships which suggests to us as we read a corresponding pattern of abstract meaning which hovers over them, is created by them, but is not minutely tied down to them as Bunyan's meaning is tied down at each particular point to his events.

Both writers and readers of fiction have become somewhat self-conscious about symbolism in recent years, and for new readers the awareness that a complex—or even an apparently simple—story may contain a good deal more than meets the eye can sometimes be disturbing. Certainly the only rule that ought ever to be offered to a reader is that we must do our best to approach each new work both alertly and imaginatively, allowing it to make *its* effect on us unhindered by any presuppositions about what its effect ought to be. But it may be useful to suggest as a mode of procedure in interpreting a new story, that we ought not to embark on a detailed symbolic interpretation *before* we have exhausted the content of the story on the literal, non-symbolic level. A good story should be interesting as objective, literal narrative, whether it also contains a symbolic meaning or not, and we ought to allow it to make its effect on us *at* the literal level before we start to assign symbolic values to particular incidents or objects that figure in the story. The symbolic meaning ought to suggest its presence as we read on the literal level, ought to open out and complete the meaning of the story as a whole. If without bothering to give the story a careful literal reading, and suspecting the presence of a symbolic level, we start to make arbitrary assignments of symbolic value to isolated elements here and there, the chances are that we shall entirely fail to read the story successfully at *any* level.

There are two ways of reading badly in this regard. One is to refuse to see anything but the literal events in a story which, to a better or more experienced reader, only takes on its full life and power when it is seen that it contains a pattern of meaning which is not stated explicitly but is implied or suggested, and controlled, by the sequence of literal events. Sometimes the symbolist writer will give us hints that he is conducting his story on both levels, by stressing particular words or by drawing our attention to certain objects, or by setting up an awareness of some of the abstract qualities or meanings which the symbolic level of the story will work with. But more often than not he will depend on the relation between events and personages on the literal level to suggest to us a similar pattern of relations on the abstract level so that as we follow out the abstract pattern we are put in possession of his symbolic meaning. For example, in reading Thomas Mann's "Mario and the Magician" we begin by knowing only that we are reading about the vaguely uncomfortable experiences of a German family at an Italian beach resort in the 1920's, events which culminate in their witnessing a grotesque encounter between a sinister hypnotist and a young Italian waiter who offers himself as a subject. But we are gradually prepared, by early incidents which focus perfectly naturally on the growing Italian nationalism of the early Fascist years, to see that besides being given a complete and compelling psychological and social account of events in the lives of an interesting group of characters, we are being given *symbolically* a statement about how a dictatorship works; about the tragic relationship between a dictator and his people. It is a full and satisfying story on the literal level, but it would be a mistake to overlook the added dimension of its symbolic meaning.

The second way to read badly where symbolism is concerned has already been alluded to: it is to become too fascinated with a certain range of symbolism which may actually be present in stories we already admire—sex symbols, religious symbols, the symbols of certain patterns of psychological behavior—until we are finding them in stories where they are not present, at least not in any valid relationship to the story's complete pattern of meaning. By seizing on an incidental element and raising it to the status of a symbol in this way, we can make it impossible for ourselves to see the story for what it is.

In discussing both symbolic and non-symbolic stories, we sometimes use the terms "theme" and "motif." By theme we refer to the presence in the story of an area of abstract subject-matter, of meaning, that comes in for treatment, illumination in the story as a whole. The theme of "Ethan Brand," for example, is one of the questions that deeply interested Hawthorne: the question of man's relationship to his fellow-men, and of whether the worst sin possible to a sinful mankind is not for a man to set himself apart, by pride and hardness of heart, from other men. The same theme is treated, in a different way, in Joyce's "A Painful Case." By "motif" we refer to a less pervasive, more incidental element in the whole array of meaning-elements which we encounter in the story as a whole: perhaps a motif can be thought of as a sub-theme, as a stable and possibly recurrent single element in the total theme which the story is exploring. Again in "Ethan Brand," for example, Hawthorne in bringing in the Jew of Nuremberg with his show-box is introducing the motif of the Wandering Jew, thus establishing by reference to legend one specific aspect of his central theme: how a man may be cut off from other men and their common lot.

* * *

In this introductory account, a certain amount has been said, and perhaps more has been implied, about the difficulties, the problems involved in reading the short story. So let us reiterate what was said at the beginning: we read stories for pleasure. Unlike some forms of pleasure, this one will sometimes leave lasting profit behind it. And again unlike some other pleasures, this one does not always come to us instinctively but must be learned. Any art form works within a complexity of conventions—agreements about how the thing is to be done, rules for doing it —and when we first approach any new art form we have to expend a certain amount of patience on familiarizing ourselves with the conventions. We have to learn not only the general conventions which govern the form as a whole, but also the conventions which govern particular varieties of the form. We have to realize that there is no one formula according to which all story-writers will put the elements—character, plot, narrative, setting, theme—together to form a story. For one writer narrative will be of central importance, and he will present his vision of life by following a man through a sequence of events which is allowed to speak for itself—as Walter Van Tilburg Clark does in "The Indian Well." One writer may be interested in his characters as specific individuals and may present them in such detail that we see all the ways in which they are unique as well as the traits they share with others, while another writer may be interested only in the way a character represents one generalized aspect of human nature. For the writer, there is an endless range of choice in respect to every single aspect of technique and approach, with the result that for the reader there is a correspondingly endless variety in the kinds of story which await his pleasure, if only he is willing to take each on its own proper merits. And it is entirely probable, as was suggested at the beginning of this discussion, that the chief aim of *studying* the short story is to put us into the analytical frame of mind which will make it more easily possible for us to see each new story we read for what it is, not as a disappointing and unsuccessful attempt to do what the last one did. Each of the stories in the following collection has been chosen, first of all, in the belief that it is a good story, capable of giving lasting and significant pleasure. But they have also been chosen with an eye to giving an idea of some, at least, of the ways in which good stories can differ from one another, of some of the special directions in which individual writers have been led by their own special talents and interests. Any such collection can only be a beginning, can only point the way to what one hopes will eventually be, for the reader who uses it, a more detailed and comprehensive familiarity with a form which—happily for a reader who has learned to appreciate it—

is both too vast and too varied in its achievements to be adequately represented in a single volume.

The stories are arranged in approximately chronological order. The prefatory notes, which may certainly be skipped by any reader to whom they prove distracting, are designed to offer a minimum of relevant information about each writer, the direction of his interests, his place in literary history, and occasionally a word or two about the particular story itself. From some points of view, it might have seemed advisable to include extended analyses of the stories, but this collection is intended for the use of teachers and students working together to provide their own analyses, and this is an enterprise which is more likely to be inhibited than helped by the presence of "ready-made" analyses which can not, after all, pretend to any greater authority than those developed in the individual classroom.

NIKOLAI GOGOL

(1809–1852)

Gogol was born at Sorochintsky, province of Poltava, in the Ukraine, on March 20, 1809. His early efforts to find his place in the world included an attempt, in 1828, to become an actor; employment in one of the Government bureaus; and the teaching of history, first at an academy for young ladies and then, with marked lack of success, at the University of St. Petersburg. He had published his first work, a poetic idyll, in 1829, but his first significant publication was the two volumes of tales of Ukrainian life, *Evenings on a Farm near Dikanka,* published in 1831–32. Between 1834 and 1836 he published a number of works, including tales both of Ukrainian and of St. Petersburg life. In 1836 his play *The Inspector General* was first performed. In this year he went abroad, to Western Europe, and remained away from Russia, except for brief returns necessitated by the publication of his books, for several years; he lived in Rome for long periods, but also travelled in Switzerland and Germany. In 1835 he had begun to write his satiric novel *Dead Souls* and continued to work on it after leaving Russia in 1836, publishing the first volume in 1842. During these years abroad he had begun to develop a tendency to religious mysticism which gradually assumed the qualities of an obsession. In 1847 the publication of *Select Passages from a Correspondence with Friends* revealed his absorption in the idea of the necessity for moral purification as well as his commitment to political ideas which were quite the opposite of the progressive principles he had hitherto seemed to stand for. The next year he made a pilgrimage to Palestine, and on his return gave himself up entirely to his fervent moral and religious studies, renouncing his past as a writer and destroying the second part of *Dead Souls.* He died in Moscow in 1852.

"The Overcoat," which was first published in 1842, has long been one of the most celebrated works in Russian literature, and is indeed one of the most famous of all short stories. It is often evoked as an early landmark and abiding influence of such literary movements as Realism and Naturalism, perhaps owing part of its fame to Dostoievsky's remark, "We all come out of the folds of 'The Overcoat.'"

A critical question which is almost bound to turn up in any discussion of Gogol's work is the relative degree of importance assumed in it by realism and by fantasy. However this question may be answered for Gogol's work as a whole, it can be said for "The Overcoat" that the presence in it of both elements is at least partly responsible for its greatness and for its special flavor. It offers an excellent illustration of the way in which the two qualities referred to in the Introduction above, specificity and a generally applicable significance, are combined by one writer in a highly individual way.

It is a very specific world indeed into which Gogol introduces us, the world of government bureaucracy in St. Petersburg in the early nineteenth century. The habits and surroundings of the government clerks and officials are most circumstantially described; these clerks sometimes speak in their local occupational jargon, so that it is difficult to render exactly what they say into another language. Customs, social forms, clothing, streets, vehicles: all are described with great faithfulness, and it is typical of the way in which short stories can absorb and make use of minute detail that at one point the entire tension of a scene is focussed, if only for a moment, on a very particular snuff-box—a snuff-box "with the portrait of some general or other on its lid—just which one nobody could tell, inasmuch as the place occupied by the face had been holed through with a finger and then pasted over with a small square of paper." Similarly, the overcoat itself, which becomes if you like a symbol but is in any event the focal point and motivating force for the life of the poor clerk, is also an overcoat made according to the fashions of the specific time and place, not just an abstract, idealized overcoat. Gogol has created the specific world of his story by using many of the techniques of detailed, faithful observation which have always formed the mainstay of realism.

But what happens to the clerk is not merely something that might happen to a clerk in a certain government bureau of a certain Russian provincial district in the 1830's. That the clerk's story has universal significance is clear at many points throughout the story, but is made thrillingly and powerfully so in its concluding pages when Gogol moves events onto the level of fantasy, of the supernatural. The timid clerk, who dies after his precious overcoat has been stolen, returns to haunt the Kalinkin Bridge, pulling the overcoats off the shoulders of those who come in his way. After he has obtained a coat, the specter no longer appears in the form of the dead clerk, but the injustice which he suffered in life is not to be forgotten—there is still an apparition, taller now, with huge moustaches and a huge fist, which had frightened the watchman before it "disappeared utterly in the darkness of night." Gogol uses fantasy to project his meaning with a thrill of cold horror which is appropriate to it: that the injustice which the meek and innocent must suffer because those who could correct it are too lazy and well-fed to do so, does not die out of the world when the victims perish but goes on growing in the dark places until it will become strong enough to disturb even the most complacent. But even in the early parts of the story, the clerk's pathetic struggles to master the specific conditions of his specific life have their meaning for any reader, whatever his own life may have been, who knows or can imagine what it is like to be powerless, decent, and oppressed.

THE OVERCOAT

In the Bureau of . . . but it might be better not to mention the Bureau by its precise name. There is nothing more touchy than all these Bureaus, Regiments, Chancelleries of every sort, and, in a word, every sort of person belonging to the administrative classes. Nowadays every civilian, even, considers all of society insulted in his own person. Quite recently, so they say, a petition came through from a certain Captain of Rural Police in some town or other (I can't recall its name), in which he explained clearly that the whole social structure was headed for ruin and that his sacred name was actually being taken entirely in vain, and, in proof, he documented his petition with the enormous tome of some romantic work or other wherein, every ten pages or so, a Captain of Rural Police appeared—in some passages even in an out-and-out drunken state. And so, to avoid any and all unpleasantnesses, we'd better call the Bureau in question *a certain Bureau*. And so, in *a certain Bureau* there served *a certain clerk*—a clerk whom one could hardly style very remarkable: quite low of stature, somewhat pockmarked, somewhat rusty-hued of hair, even somewhat purblind, at first glance; rather bald at the temples, with wrinkles along both cheeks, and his face of that complexion which is usually called hemorrhoidal. Well, what would you? It's the Petersburg climate that's to blame. As far as his rank is concerned (for among us the rank must be made known first of all), why, he was what they call a Perpetual Titular Councilor—a rank which, as everybody knows, various writers who have a praiseworthy wont of throwing their weight about among those who are in no position to hit back, have twitted and exercised their keen wits against often and long. This clerk's family name was Bashmachkin. It's quite evident, by the very name, that it sprang from *bashmak* or shoe, but at what time, just when and how it sprang from a shoe—of that nothing is known. For not only this clerk's father but his grandfather and even his brother-in-law, and absolutely all the Bashmachkins, walked about in boots, merely resoling them three times a year.

His name and patronymic were Akakii Akakiievich. It may, perhaps, strike the reader as somewhat odd and out of the way, but the reader may rest assured that the author has not gone out of his way at all to find it, but that certain circumstances had come about of themselves in such fashion that there was absolutely no way of giving him any other name. And the precise way this came about was as follows. Akakii Akakiievich was born—unless my memory plays me false—on the night of the twenty-third of March. His late mother, a government clerk's wife, and a very good woman, was all set to christen her child, all fit and proper.

Translated by Bernard Guilbert Guerney. Copyright, 1943, by the Vanguard Press, Inc. Reprinted by permission of the Vanguard Press from *A Treasury of Russian Literature* edited by Bernard Guilbert Guerney.

She was still lying in bed, facing the door, while on her right stood the godfather, a most excellent man by the name of Ivan Ivanovich Eroshkin, who had charge of some Department or other in a certain Administrative Office, and the godmother, the wife of the precinct police officer, a woman of rare virtues, by the name of Arina Semenovna Byelobrushkina. The mother was offered the choice of any one of three names: Mokii, Sossii—or the child could even be given the name of that great martyr, Hozdavat. "No," the late lamented had reflected, "what sort of names are these?" In order to please her they opened the calendar at another place—and the result was again three names: Triphilii, Dula, and Varahasii. "What a visitation!" said the elderly woman. "What names all these be! To tell you the truth, I've never even heard the likes of them. If it were at least Baradat or Baruch, but why do Triphilii and Varahasii have to turn up?" They turned over another page—and came up with Pavsikahii and Vahtissii. "Well, I can see now," said the mother, "that such is evidently his fate. In that case it would be better if he were called after his father. His father was an Akakii—let the son be an Akakii also." And that's how Akakii Akakiievich came to be Akakii Akakiievich.

The child was baptized, during which rite he began to bawl and made terrible faces as if anticipating that it would be his lot to become a Perpetual Titular Councilor. And so that's the way it had all come about. We have brought the matter up so that the reader might see for himself that all this had come about through sheer inevitability and it had been utterly impossible to bestow any other name upon Akakii Akakiievich.

When, at precisely what time, he entered the Bureau, and who gave him the berth, were things which no one could recall. No matter how many Directors and his superiors of one sort or another came and went, he was always to be seen in the one and the same spot, in the same posture, in the very same post, always the same Clerk of Correspondence, so that subsequently people became convinced that he evidently had come into the world just the way he was, all done and set, in a uniform frock and bald at the temples. No respect whatsoever was shown him in the Bureau. The porters not only didn't jump up from their places whenever he happened to pass by, but didn't even as much as glance at him, as if nothing more than a common housefly had passed through the reception hall. His superiors treated him with a certain chill despotism. Some assistant or other of some Head of a Department would simply shove papers under his nose, without as much as saying "Transcribe these," or "Here's a rather pretty, interesting little case," or any of those small pleasantries that are current in well-conducted administrative institutions. And he would take the work, merely glancing at the paper, without looking up to see who had put it down before him and whether that person had the right to do so; he took it and right then and there went to work on it. The young clerks made fun of him and sharpened their wits at his expense, to whatever extent their quill-driving wittiness sufficed, retailing in his very presence the various stories made up about him; they said of his landlady, a crone of seventy, that she beat him, and asked him when their wedding would take place, they scattered torn paper over his head, maintaining it was snow.

But not a word did Akakii Akakiievich say in answer to all this, as if there were actually nobody before him. It did not even affect his work: in the midst of all these annoyances he did not make a single clerical error. Only when the jest was past all bearing, when they jostled his arm, hindering him from doing his work, would he say: "Leave me alone! Why do you pick on me?" And there was something odd about his words and in the voice with which he uttered them. In that voice could be heard something that moved one to pity—so much so that one young man, a recent entrant, who, following the example of the others, had permitted himself to make fun of Akakii Akakiievich, stopped suddenly, as if pierced to the quick, and from that time on everything seemed to change in his eyes and appeared in a different light. Some sort of preternatural force seemed to repel him from the companions he had made, having taken them for decent, sociable people. And for a long time afterward, in the very midst of his most cheerful moments, the little squat clerk would appear before him, with the small bald patches on each side of his forehead, and he would hear his heart-piercing words "Leave me alone! Why do you pick on me?" And in these heart-piercing words he caught the ringing sound of others: "I am your brother." And the poor young man would cover his eyes with his hand, and many a time in his life thereafter did he shudder, seeing how much inhumanity there is in man, how much hidden ferocious coarseness lurks in refined, cultured worldliness and, O God! even in that very man whom the world holds to be noble and honorable. . . .

It is doubtful if you could find anywhere a man whose life lay so much in his work. It would hardly do to say that he worked with zeal; no, it was a labor of love. Thus, in this transcription of his, he visioned some sort of diversified and pleasant world all its own. His face expressed delight; certain letters were favorites of his and whenever he came across them he would be beside himself with rapture: he'd chuckle, and wink, and help things along by working his lips, so that it seemed as if one could read on his face every letter his quill was outlining. If rewards had been meted out to him commensurately with his zeal, he might have, to his astonishment, actually found himself among the State Councilors; but, as none other than those wits, his own co-workers, expressed it, all he'd worked himself up to was a button in a buttonhole too wide, and piles in his backside.

However, it would not be quite correct to say that absolutely no attention was paid him. One Director, being a kindly man and wishing to reward him for his long service, gave orders that some work of a more important nature than the usual transcription be assigned to him; to be precise, he was told to make a certain referral to another Administrative Department out of a docket already prepared; the matter consisted, all in all, of changing the main title as well as some pronouns here and there from the first person singular to the third person singular. This made so much work for him that he was all of a sweat, kept mopping his forehead, and finally said: "No, better let me transcribe something." Thenceforth they left him to his transcription for all time. Outside of this transcription, it seemed, nothing existed for him.

He gave no thought whatsoever to his dress; the uniform frock coat on him wasn't the prescribed green at all, but rather of some rusty-flour hue. His collar was very tight and very low, so that his neck, even though it wasn't a long one, seemed extraordinarily long emerging therefrom, like those gypsum kittens with nodding heads which certain outlanders balance by the dozen atop their heads and peddle throughout Russia. And, always, something was bound to stick to his coat: a wisp of hay or some bit of thread; in addition to that, he had a peculiar knack whenever he walked through the streets of getting under some window at the precise moment when garbage of every sort was being thrown out of it, and for that reason always bore off on his hat watermelon and cantaloupe rinds and other such trifles. Not once in all his life had he ever turned his attention to the everyday things and doings out in the street—something, as everybody knows, that is always watched with eager interest by Akakii Akakiievich's confrère, the young government clerk, the penetration of whose lively gaze is so extensive that he will even take in somebody on the opposite sidewalk who has ripped loose his trouser strap—a thing that never fails to evoke a sly smile on the young clerk's face. But even if Akakii Akakiievich did look at anything, he saw thereon nothing but his own neatly, evenly penned lines of script, and only when some horse's nose, bobbing up from no one knew where, would be placed on his shoulder and let a whole gust of wind in his face through its nostrils, would he notice that he was not in the middle of a line of script but, rather, in the middle of the roadway.

On coming home he would immediately sit down at the table, gulp down his cabbage soup and bolt a piece of veal with onions, without noticing in the least the taste of either, eating everything together with the flies and whatever else God may have sent at that particular time of the year. On perceiving that his belly was beginning to swell out, he'd get up from the table, take out a small bottle of ink, and transcribe the papers he had brought home. If there were no homework, he would deliberately, for his own edification, make a copy of some paper for himself, especially if the document were remarkable not for its beauty of style but merely addressed to some new or important person.

Even at those hours when the gray sky of Petersburg became entirely extinguished and all the pettifogging tribe has eaten its fill and finished dinner, each as best he could, in accordance with the salary he receives and his own bent, when everybody has already rested up after the scraping of quills in various departments, the running around, the unavoidable cares about their own affairs and the affairs of others, and all that which restless man sets himself as a task voluntarily and to an even greater extent than necessary—at a time when the petty bureaucrats hasten to devote whatever time remained to enjoyment: he who is of the more lively sort hastening to the theater; another for a saunter through the streets, devoting the time to an inspection of certain pretty little hats; still another to some evening party, to spend that time in paying compliments to some comely young lady, the star of a small bureaucratic circle; a fourth (and this happened most frequently of all) would simply go for a call on a confrère in a flat up three or four flights of stairs, consisting of two small rooms with an entry and a kitchen and one or two attempts at the latest improvements—a kerosene lamp instead of candles, or some other elegant little thing that had cost many sacrifices, such as going without dinners or good times—in short, even at the time when all the petty bureaucrats scatter through the small apartments of their friends for a session of dummy whist, sipping tea out of tumblers and nibbling at cheap zweiback, drawing deep at their pipes, the stems thereof as long as walking sticks, retailing, during the shuffling and dealing, some bit of gossip or other from high society that had reached them at long last (something which no Russian, under any circumstances, and of whatever estate he be, can ever deny himself), or even, when there was nothing whatsoever to talk about, retelling the eternal chestnut of the commandant to whom people came to say that the tail of the horse on the Falconetti monument had been docked—in short, even at the time when every soul yearns to be diverted, Akakii Akakiievich did not give himself up to any diversion. No man could claim having ever seen him at any evening gathering. Having had his sweet fill of quill-driving, he would lie down to sleep, smiling at the thought of the next day: just what would God send him on the morrow?

Such was the peaceful course of life of a man who, with a yearly salary of four hundred, knew how to be content with his lot, and that course might even have continued to a ripe old age had it not been for sundry calamities, such as are strewn along the path of life, not only of Titular, but even Privy, Actual, Court, and all other sorts of Councilors, even those who never give any counsel to anybody nor ever accept any counsel from others for themselves.

There is, in Petersburg, a formidable foe of all those whose salary runs to four hundred a year or thereabouts. This foe is none other than our Northern frost—even though, by the bye, they do say that it's the most healthful thing for you. At nine in the morning, precisely at that hour when the streets are thronged with those on their way to sundry bureaus, it begins dealing out such powerful and penetrating fillips to all noses, without any discrimination, that the poor bureaucrats absolutely do not know how to hide them. At this time, when even those who fill the higher posts feel their foreheads aching because of the frost

and the tears come to their eyes, the poor Titular Councilors are sometimes utterly defenseless. The sole salvation, if one's overcoat is of the
thinnest, lies in dashing, as quickly as possible, through five or six blocks
and then stamping one's feet plenty in the porter's room, until the faculties and gifts for administrative duties, which have been frozen on the
way, are thus thawed out at last.

For some time Akakii Akakiievich had begun to notice that the cold
was somehow penetrating his back and shoulders with especial ferocity,
despite the fact that he tried to run the required distance as quickly as
possible. It occurred to him, at last, that there might be some defects
about this overcoat. After looking it over rather thoroughly at home he
discovered that in two or three places—in the back and at the shoulders,
to be exact—it had become no better than the coarsest of sacking; the
cloth was rubbed to such an extent that one could see through it, and
the lining had crept apart. The reader must be informed that Akakii
Akakiievich's overcoat, too, was a butt for the jokes of the petty bureaucrats; it had been deprived of the honorable name of an overcoat, even,
and dubbed a *negligée*. And, really, it was of a rather queer cut; its collar
grew smaller with every year, inasmuch as it was utilized to supplement
the other parts of the garment. This supplementing was not at all a compli-
ment to the skill of the tailor, and the effect really was baggy and unsightly.

Perceiving what the matter was, Akakii Akakiievich decided that the
overcoat would have to go to Petrovich the tailor, who lived somewhere
up four flights of backstairs and who, despite a squint-eye and pock-
marks all over his face, did quite well at repairing bureaucratic as well
as all other trousers and coats—of course, be it understood, when he was
in a sober state and not hatching some nonsartorial scheme in his head.
One shouldn't, really, mention this tailor at great length, but since there
is already a precedent for each character in a tale being clearly defined,
there's no help for it, and so let's trot out Petrovich as well. In the beginning he had been called simply Gregory and had been the serf of some
squire or other; he had begun calling himself Petrovich only after ob-
taining his freedom papers and taking to drinking rather hard on any
and every holiday—at first on the red-letter ones and then, without
any discrimination, on all those designated by the church: wherever
there was a little cross marking the day on the calendar. In this respect
he was loyal to the customs of our grandsires, and, when bickering with
his wife, would call her a worldly woman and a German frau. And, since
we've already been inadvertent enough to mention his wife, it will be
necessary to say a word or two about her as well; but, regrettably, little
was known about her—unless, perhaps, the fact that Petrovich had a
wife, or that she even wore a house-cap and not a kerchief; but as for
beauty, it appears that she could hardly boast of any; at least the soldiers in the Guards were the only ones with hardihood enough to bend
down for a peep under her cap, twitching their mustache as they did so
and emitting a certain peculiar sound.

As he clambered up the staircase that led to Petrovich—the staircase, to render it its just due, was dripping all over from water and slops and thoroughly permeated with that alcoholic odor which makes the eyes smart and is, as everybody knows, unfailingly present on all the back-stairs of all the houses in Petersburg—as he clambered up this staircase Akakii Akakiievich was already conjecturing how stiff Petrovich's asking-price would be and mentally determined not to give him more than two rubles. The door was open, because the mistress of the place, being busy preparing some fish, had filled the kitchen with so much smoke that one actually couldn't see the very cockroaches for it. Akakii Akakiievich made his way through the kitchen, unperceived even by the mistress herself, and at last entered the room wherein he beheld Petrovich, sitting on a wide table of unpainted deal with his feet tucked in under him like a Turkish Pasha. His feet, as is the wont of tailors seated at their work, were bare, and the first thing that struck one's eyes was the big toe of one, very familiar to Akakii Akakiievich, with some sort of deformed nail, as thick and strong as a turtle's shell. About Petrovich's neck were loops of silk and cotton thread, while some sort of ragged garment was lying on his knees. For the last three minutes he had been trying to put a thread through the eye of a needle, couldn't hit the mark, and because of that was very wroth against the darkness of the room and even the thread itself, grumbling under his breath: "She won't go through, the heathen! You've spoiled my heart's blood, you damned good-for-nothing!"

Akakii Akakiievich felt upset because he had come at just the moment when Petrovich was very angry; he liked to give in his work when the latter was already under the influence or, as his wife put it, "He's already full of rot-gut, the one-eyed devil!" In such a state Petrovich usually gave in willingly and agreed to everything; he even bowed and was grateful every time. Afterward, true enough, his wife would come around and complain weepily that, now, her husband had been drunk and for that reason had taken on the work too cheaply; but all you had to do was to tack on another ten kopecks—and the thing was in the bag. But now, it seemed, Petrovich was in a sober state, and for that reason on his high horse, hard to win over, and bent on boosting his prices to the devil knows what heights. Akakii Akakiievich surmised this and, as the saying goes, was all set to make back tracks, but the deal had already been started. Petrovich puckered up his one good eye against him very fixedly and Akakii Akakiievich involuntarily said, "Greetings, Petrovich!" "Greetings to you, Sir," said Petrovich and looked askance at Akakii Akakiievich's hands, wishing to see what sort of booty the other bore.

"Well, now, I've come to see you, now, Petrovich!"

Akakii Akakiievich, the reader must be informed, explained himself for the most part in prepositions, adverbs, and such verbal oddments as have absolutely no significance. But if the matter was exceedingly difficult, he actually had a way of not finishing his phrase at all, so that, quite frequently, beginning his speech with such words as "This, really, is perfectly, you know—"—he would have nothing at all to follow up with, and he himself would be likely to forget the matter, thinking that he had already said everything in full.

"Well, just what is it?" asked Petrovich, and at the same time, with his one good eye, surveyed the entire garment, beginning with the collar and going on to the sleeves, the back, the coat-skirts, and the buttonholes, for it was all very familiar to him, inasmuch as it was all his own handiwork. That's a way all tailors have; it's the first thing a tailor will do on meeting you.

"Why, what I'm after, now, Petrovich . . . the overcoat, now, the cloth . . . there, you see, in all the other places it's strong as can be . . . it's gotten a trifle dusty and only seems to be old, but it's really new, there's only one spot . . . a little sort of . . . in the back . . . and also one shoulder, a trifle rubbed through—and this shoulder, too, a trifle—do you see? Not a lot of work, really—"

Petrovich took up the *negligée*, spread it out over the table as a preliminary, examined it for a long time, shook his head, and then groped with his hand on the window sill for a round snuffbox with the portrait of some general or other on its lid—just which one nobody could tell, inasmuch as the place occupied by the face had been holed through with a finger and then pasted over with a small square of paper. After duly taking tobacco, Petrovich held the *negligée* taut in his hands and scrutinized it against the light, and again shook his head; after this he turned it with the lining up and again shook his head, again took off the lid with the general's face pasted over with paper and, having fully loaded both nostrils with snuff, covered the snuffbox, put it away, and, at long last, gave his verdict:

"No, there's no fixin' this thing: your wardrobe's in a bad way!"

Akakii Akakiievich's heart skipped a beat at these words.

"But why not, Petrovich?" he asked, almost in the imploring voice of a child. "All that ails it, now . . . it's rubbed through at the shoulders. Surely you must have some small scraps of cloth or other—"

"Why, yes, one could find the scraps—the scraps will turn up," said Petrovich. "Only there's no sewing them on: the whole thing's all rotten: touch a needle to it—and it just crawls apart on you."

"Well, let it crawl—and you just slap a patch right on to it."

"Yes, but there's nothing to slap them little patches on to; there ain't nothing for the patch to take hold on—there's been far too much wear. It's cloth in name only, but if a gust of wind was to blow on it it would scatter."

"Well, now, you just fix it up. That, really, now . . . how can it be?"

"No," said Petrovich decisively, "there ain't a thing to be done. The whole thing's in a bad way. You'd better, when the cold winter spell comes, make footcloths out of it, because stockings ain't so warm. It's them Germans that invented them stockings, so's to rake in more money for themselves. [Petrovich loved to needle the Germans whenever the chance turned up.] But as for that there overcoat, it looks like you'll have to make yourself a new one."

At the word *new* a mist swam before Akakii Akakiievich's eyes and everything in the room became a hotchpotch. All he could see clearly was the general on the lid of Petrovich's snuffbox, his face pasted over with a piece of paper.

"A new one? But how?" he asked, still as if he were in a dream. "Why, I have no money for that."

"Yes, a new one," said Petrovich with a heathenish imperturbability.

"Well, if there's no getting out of it, how much, now—"

"You mean, how much it would cost?"

"Yes."

"Why, you'd have to cough up three fifties and a bit over," pronounced Petrovich and significantly pursed up his lips at this. He was very fond of strong effects, was fond of somehow nonplusing somebody, utterly and suddenly, and then eyeing his victim sidelong, to see what sort of wry face the nonplusee would pull after his words.

"A hundred and fifty for an overcoat!" poor Akakii Akakiievich cried out—cried out perhaps for the first time since he was born, for he was always distinguished for his low voice.

"Yes, Sir!" said Petrovich. "And what an overcoat, at that! If you put a marten collar on it and add a silk-lined hood it might stand you even two hundred."

"Petrovich, please!" Akakii Akakiievich was saying in an imploring voice, without grasping and without even trying to grasp the words uttered by Petrovich and all his effects. "Fix it somehow or other, now, so's it may do a little longer, at least—"

"Why, no, that'll be only having the work go to waste and spending your money for nothing," said Petrovich, and after these words Akakii Akakiievich walked out annihilated. But Petrovich, after his departure, remained as he was for a long time, with meaningfully pursed lips and without resuming his work, satisfied with neither having lowered himself nor having betrayed the sartorial art.

Out in the street, Akakii Akakiievich walked along like a somnambulist. "What a business, now, what a business," he kept saying to himself. "Really, I never even thought that it, now . . . would turn out like that. . . ." And then, after a pause, added: "So that's it! That's how it's turned out after all. Really, now, I couldn't even suppose that it . . . like that, now—" This was followed by another long pause, after which he uttered aloud: "So that's how it is! This, really, now, is something that's beyond all, now, expectation . . . well, I never! What a fix, now!"

Having said this, instead of heading for home, he started off in an entirely different direction without himself suspecting it. On the way a chimney sweep caught him square with his whole sooty side and covered his whole shoulder with soot; enough quicklime to cover his whole hat tumbled down on him from the top of a building under construction. He noticed nothing of all this and only later, when he ran up against a policeman near his sentry box (who, having placed his halberd near him, was shaking some tobacco out of a paper cornucopia on to his calloused palm), did Akakii Akakiievich come a little to himself, and that only because the policeman said: "What's the idea of shoving your face right into mine? Ain't the sidewalk big enough for you?" This made him look about him and turn homeward.

Only here did he begin to pull his wits together; he perceived his situation in its clear and real light; he started talking to himself no longer in snatches but reasoningly and frankly, as with a judicious friend with whom one might discuss a matter most heartfelt and intimate. "Well, no," said Akakii Akakiievich, "there's no use reasoning with Petrovich now; he's, now, that way. . . . His wife had a chance to give him a drubbing, it looks like. No, it'll be better if I come to him on a Sunday morning; after Saturday night's good time he'll be squinting his eye and very sleepy, so he'll have to have a hair of the dog that bit him, but his wife won't give him any money, now, and just then I'll up with ten kopecks or so and into his hand with it—so he'll be more reasonable to talk with, like, and the overcoat will then be sort of. . . ."

That was the way Akakii Akakiievich reasoned things out to himself, bolstering up his spirits. And, having bided his time till the next Sunday and spied from afar that Petrovich's wife was going off somewhere out of the house, he went straight up to him. Petrovich, sure enough, was squinting his eye hard after the Saturday night before, kept his head bowed down to the floor, and was no end sleepy; but, found that, as soon as he learned what was up, it was as though the Devil himself nudged him.

"Can't be done," said he. "You'll have to order a new overcoat."

Akakii Akakiievich thrust a ten-kopeck coin on him right then and there.

"I'm grateful to you, Sir; I'll have a little something to get me strength back and will drink to your health," said Petrovich, "but as for your overcoat, please don't fret about it; it's of no earthly use any more. As for a new overcoat, I'll tailor a glorious one for you; I'll see to that."

Just the same, Akakii Akakiievich started babbling again about fixing the old one, but Petrovich simply would not listen to him and said: "Yes, I'll tailor a new one for you without fail; you may rely on that, I'll try my very best. We might even do it the way it's all the fashion now—the collar will button with silver catches under appliqué."

It was then that Akakii Akakiievich perceived that there was no doing without a new overcoat, and his spirits sank utterly. Really, now, with what means, with what money would he make this overcoat? Of course he could rely, in part, on the coming holiday bonus, but this money had been apportioned and budgeted ahead long ago. There was an imperative need of outfitting himself with new trousers, paying the shoemaker an old debt for a new pair of vamps to an old pair of bootlegs, and he had to order from a sempstress three shirts and two pair of those neth-ergarments which it is impolite to mention in print; in short, all the money was bound to be expended entirely, and even if the Director were so gracious as to decide on giving him five and forty, or even fifty rubles as a bonus, instead of forty, why, even then only the veriest trifle would be left over, which, in the capital sum required for the overcoat, would be as a drop in a bucket. Even though Akakii Akakiievich was, of course, aware of Petrovich's maggot of popping out with the devil knows how inordinate an asking price, so that even his wife herself could not restrain herself on occasion from crying out: "What, are you going out of your mind, fool that you are! There's times when he won't take on work for anything, but the Foul One has egged him on to ask a bigger price than all of him is worth"—even though he knew, of course, that Petrovich would probably undertake the work for eighty rubles, nevertheless and notwithstanding where was he to get those eighty rubles? Half of that sum might, perhaps, be found: half of it could have been found, maybe even a little more—but where was he going to get the other half?

But first the reader must be informed where the first half was to come from. Akakii Akakiievich had a custom of putting away a copper or so from every ruble he expended, into a little box under lock and key, with a small opening cut through the lid for dropping money therein. At the expiration of every half-year he made an accounting of the entire sum accumulated in coppers and changed it into small silver. He had kept this up a long time, and in this manner, during the course of sev-eral years, the accumulated sum turned out to be more than forty rubles. And so he had half the sum for the overcoat on hand; but where was he to get the other half? Where was he to get the other forty rubles? Akakii Akakiievich mulled the matter over and over and decided that it would be necessary to curtail his ordinary expenses, for the duration of a year at the very least; banish the indulgence in tea of evenings; also, of evenings, to do without lighting candles, but, if there should be need of doing something, to go to his landlady's room and work by her candle; when walking along the streets he would set his foot as lightly and carefully as possible on the cobbles and flagstones, walking almost on tiptoes, and thus avoid wearing out his soles prematurely; his linen would have to be given as infrequently as possible to the laundress and, in order that it might not become too soiled, every time he came home all of it must be taken off, the wearer having to remain only in his jean bathrobe, a most ancient garment and spared even by time itself.

It was, the truth must be told, most difficult for him in the beginning to get habituated to such limitations, but later it did turn into a matter of habit, somehow, and everything went well; he even became perfectly trained to going hungry of evenings; on the other hand, however, he had spiritual sustenance, always carrying about in his thoughts the eternal idea of the new overcoat. From this time forth it seemed as if his very existence had become somehow fuller, as though he had taken unto himself a wife, as though another person was always present with him, as though he were not alone but as if an amiable feminine helpmate had consented to traverse the path of life side by side with him—and this feminine helpmate was none other than this very same overcoat, with a thick quilting of cotton wool, with a strong lining that would never wear out.

He became more animated, somehow, even firmer of character, like a man who has already defined and set a goal for himself. Doubt, inde-cision—in a word, all vacillating and indeterminate traits—vanished of themselves from his face and actions. At times a sparkle appeared in his eyes; the boldest and most daring of thoughts actually flashed through his head: Shouldn't he, after all, put marten on the collar? Meditations on this subject almost caused him to make absent-minded blunders. And on one occasion, as he was transcribing a paper, he all but made an error, so that he emitted an almost audible "Ugh," and made the sign of the cross.

During the course of each month he would make at least one call on Petrovich, to discuss the overcoat: Where would it be best to buy the cloth, and of what color, and at what price—and even though some-what preoccupied he always came home satisfied, thinking that the time would come, at last, when all the necessary things would be bought and the overcoat made.

The matter went even more quickly than he had expected. Contrary to all his anticipations, the Director designated a bonus not of forty or forty-five rubles for Akakii Akakiievich, but all of sixty. Whether he had a premonition that Akakii Akakiievich needed a new overcoat, or whether this had come about of its own self, the fact nevertheless re-mained: Akakii Akakiievich thus found himself the possessor of an extra twenty rubles. This circumstance hastened the course of things. Some two or three months more of slight starvation—and lo! Akakii Akakiie-vich had accumulated around eighty rubles. His heart, in general quite calm, began to palpitate. On the very first day possible he set out with Petrovich to the shops. The cloth they bought was very good, and no great wonder, since they had been thinking over its purchase as much as half a year before and hardly a month had gone by without their making a round of the shops to compare prices; but then, Petrovich himself said that there couldn't be better cloth than that. For lining they chose calico, but of such good quality and so closely woven that, to quote Petrovich's words, it was still better than silk and, to look at, even more showy and glossy. Marten they did not buy, for, to be sure, it was expensive, but instead they picked out the best catskin the shop boasted—catskin that could, at a great enough distance, be taken for marten.

Petrovich spent only a fortnight in fussing about with the making of the overcoat, for there was a great deal of stitching to it, and if it hadn't been for that it would have been ready considerably earlier. For his work Petrovich took twelve rubles—he couldn't have taken any less; everything was positively sewn with silk thread, with a small double stitch, and after the stitching Petrovich went over every seam with his own teeth, pressing out various figures with them.

It was on . . . it would be hard to say on precisely what day, but it was, most probably, the most triumphant day in Akakii Akakiievich's life when Petrovich, at last, brought the overcoat. He brought it in the morning, just before Akakii Akakiievich had to set out for his Bureau. Never, at any other time, would the overcoat have come in so handy, because rather hard frosts were already setting in and, apparently, were threatening to become still more severe. Petrovich's entrance with the overcoat was one befitting a good tailor. Such a portentous expression appeared on his face as Akakii Akakiievich had never yet beheld. Petrovich felt to the fullest, it seemed, that he had performed no petty labor and that he had suddenly evinced in himself that abyss which lies between those tailors who merely put in linings and alter and fix garments and those who create new ones.

He extracted the overcoat from the bandanna in which he had brought it. (The bandanna was fresh from the laundress; it was only later on that he thrust it in his pocket for practical use.) Having drawn out the overcoat, he looked at it quite proudly and, holding it in both hands, threw it deftly over the shoulders of Akakii Akakiievich, pulled it and smoothed it down the back with his hand, then draped it on Akakii Akakiievich somewhat loosely. Akakiievich, as a man along in his years, wanted to try it on with his arms through the sleeves. Petrovich helped him on with it: it turned out to be fine, even with his arms through the sleeves. In a word, the overcoat proved to be perfect and had come in the very nick of time. Petrovich did not let slip the opportunity of saying that he had done the work so cheaply only because he lived in a place without a sign, on a side street, and, besides, had known Akakii Akakiievich for a long time; *but* on the Nevski Prospect they would have taken seventy-five rubles from him for the labor alone. Akakii Akakiievich did not feel like arguing the matter with Petrovich and, besides, he had a dread of all the fancy sums with which Petrovich liked to throw dust in people's eyes. He paid the tailor off, thanked him, and walked right out in the new overcoat on his way to the Bureau. Petrovich walked out at his heels and, staying behind on the street, for a long while kept looking after the overcoat from afar, and then deliberately went out of his way so that, after cutting across a crooked lane, he might run out again into the street and have another glance at his overcoat from a different angle—that is, full front.

In the meantime Akakii Akakiievich walked along feeling in the most festive of moods. He was conscious every second of every minute that he had a new overcoat on his shoulders, and several times even smiled slightly because of his inward pleasure. In reality he was a gainer on two points: for one, the overcoat was warm, for the other, it was a fine thing. He did not notice the walk at all and suddenly found himself at the Bureau; in the porter's room he took off his overcoat, looked it all over, and entrusted it to the particular care of the doorman. None knows in what manner everybody in the Bureau suddenly learned that Akakii Akakiievich had a new overcoat, and that the *negligée* was no longer in existence. They all immediately ran out into the vestibule to inspect Akakii Akakiievich's new overcoat. They fell to congratulating him, to saying agreeable things to him, so that at first he could merely smile, and in a short time became actually embarrassed. And when all of them, having besieged him, began telling him that the new overcoat ought to be baptized and that he ought, at the least, to get up an evening party for them, Akakii Akakiievich was utterly at a loss, not knowing what to do with himself, what answers to make, nor how to get out of inviting them. It was only a few minutes later that he began assuring them, quite simple-heartedly, that it wasn't a new overcoat at all, that it was just an ordinary overcoat, that in fact it was an old overcoat. Finally one of the bureaucrats—some sort of an Assistant to a Head of a Department, actually—probably in order to show that he was not at all a proud stick and willing to mingle even with those beneath him, said: "So be it, then; I'm giving a party this evening and ask all of you to have tea with me; today, appropriately enough, happens to be my birthday."

The clerks, naturally, at once thanked the Assistant to a Head of a Department and accepted the invitation with enthusiasm. Akakii Akakiievich attempted to excuse himself at first, but all began saying that it would show disrespect to decline, that it would be simply a shame and a disgrace, and after that there was absolutely no way for him to back out. However, when it was all over, he felt a pleasant glow as he reminded himself that this would give him a chance to take a walk in his new overcoat even in the evening. The whole day was for Akakii Akakiievich something in the nature of the greatest and most triumphant of holidays.

Akakii Akakiievich returned home in the happiest mood, took off the overcoat, and hung it carefully on the wall, once more getting his fill of admiring the cloth and the lining, and then purposely dragged out, for comparison, his former *negligée,* which by now had practically disintegrated. He glanced at it and he himself had to laugh, so great was the difference! And for a long while thereafter, as he ate dinner, he kept on smiling slightly whenever the present state of the *negligée* came to his mind. He dined gayly, and after dinner did not write a single stroke; there were no papers of any kind, for that matter; he just simply played the sybarite a little, lounging on his bed, until it became dark. Then, without putting matters off any longer, he dressed, threw the overcoat over his shoulders, and walked out into the street.

We are, to our regret, unable to say just where the official who had extended the invitation lived; our memory is beginning to play us false—very much so—and everything in Petersburg, no matter what, including all its streets and houses, has become so muddled in our mind that it's quite hard to get anything out therefrom in any sort of decent shape. But wherever it may have been, at least this much is certain: that official lived in the best part of town; consequently a very long way from Akakii Akakiievich's quarters. First of all Akakii Akakiievich had to traverse certain deserted streets with but scant illumination; however, in keeping with his progress toward the official's domicile, the streets became more animated; the pedestrians flitted by more and more often; he began meeting even ladies, handsomely dressed; the men he came upon had beaver collars on their overcoats; more and more rarely did he encounter jehus with latticed wooden sleighs, studded over with gilt nails—on the contrary, he kept coming across first-class drivers in caps of raspberry-hued velvet, their sleighs lacquered and with bearskin robes, while the carriages had decorated seats for the drivers and raced down the roadway, their wheels screeching over the snow.

Akakii Akakiievich eyed all this as a novelty—it was several years by now since he had set foot out of his house in the evening. He stopped with curiosity before the illuminated window of a shop to look at a picture, depicting some handsome woman or other, who was taking off her shoe, thus revealing her whole leg (very far from ill-formed), while behind her back some gentleman or other, sporting side whiskers and a handsome goatee, was poking his head out of the door of an adjoining room. Akakii Akakiievich shook his head and smiled, after which he went on his way. Why had he smiled? Was it because he had encountered something utterly unfamiliar, yet about which, nevertheless, everyone preserves a certain instinct? Or did he think, like so many other petty clerks, "My, the French they are a funny race! No use talking! If there's anything they get a notion of, then, sure enough, there it is!" And yet, perhaps, he did not think even that; after all, there's no way of insinuating one's self into a man's soul, of finding out all that he might be thinking about.

At last he reached the house in which the Assistant to a Head of a Department lived. The Assistant to a Head of a Department lived on a grand footing; there was a lantern on the staircase; his apartment was only one flight up. On entering the foyer of the apartment Akakii Akakiievich beheld row after row of galoshes. In their midst, in the center of the room, stood a samovar, noisy and emitting clouds of steam. The walls were covered with hanging overcoats and capes, among which were even such as had beaver collars or lapels of velvet. On the other side of the wall he could hear much noise and talk, which suddenly became distinct and resounding when the door opened and a flunky came out with a tray full of empty tumblers, a cream pitcher, and a basket of biscuits. It was evident that the bureaucrats had gathered long since and had already had their first glasses of tea.

Akakii Akakiievich, hanging up his overcoat himself, entered the room and simultaneously all the candles, bureaucrats, tobacco-pipes and card tables flickered before him, and the continuous conversation and the scraping of moving chairs, coming from all sides, struck dully on his ears. He halted quite awkwardly in the center of the room, at a loss and trying to think what he ought to do. But he had already been noticed, was received with much shouting, and everyone immediately went to the foyer and again inspected his overcoat. Akakii Akakiievich, even though he was somewhat embarrassed, still could not but rejoice on seeing them all bestow such praises on his overcoat, since he was a man with an honest heart. Then, of course, they all dropped him and his overcoat and, as is usual, directed their attention to the whist tables.

All this—the din, the talk, and the throng of people—all this was somehow a matter of wonder to Akakii Akakiievich. He simply did not know what to do, how to dispose of his hands, his feet, and his whole body; finally he sat down near the cardplayers, watched their cards, looked now at the face of this man, now of that, and after some time began to feel bored, to yawn—all the more so since his usual bedtime had long since passed. He wanted to say good-by to his host but they wouldn't let him, saying that they absolutely must toast his new acquisition in a goblet of champagne. An hour later supper was served, consisting of mixed salad, cold veal, meat pie, patties from a pastry cook's, and champagne. They forced Akakii Akakiievich to empty two goblets, after which he felt that the room had become ever so much more cheerful. However, he absolutely could not forget that it was already twelve o'clock and that it was long since time for him to go home. So that his host might not somehow get the idea of detaining him, he crept out of the room, managed to find his overcoat—which, not without regret, he saw lying on the floor; then, shaking the overcoat and taking every bit of fluff off it, he threw it over his shoulders and made his way down the stairs and out of the house.

It was still dusk out in the street. Here and there small general stores, those round-the-clock clubs for domestics and all other servants, were still open; other shops, which were closed, nevertheless showed, by a long streak of light along the crack either at the outer edge or the bottom, that they were not yet without social life and that, probably, the serving wenches and lads were still winding up their discussions and conversations, thus throwing their masters into utter bewilderment as to their whereabouts. Akakii Akakiievich walked along in gay spirits; he even actually made a sudden dash, for some unknown reason, after some lady or other, who had passed by him like a flash of lightning, and every part of whose body was filled with buoyancy. However, he stopped right then and there and resumed his former exceedingly gentle pace, actually wondering himself at the sprightliness that had come upon him from none knows where.

Soon he again was passing stretch after stretch of those desolate streets which are never too gay even in the daytime, but are even less so in the evening. Now they had become still more deserted and lonely; he came upon glimmering street lamps more and more infrequently—the allotment of oil was now evidently decreasing; there was a succession of wooden houses and fences, with never another soul about; the snow alone glittered on the street, and the squat hovels, with their shutters closed in sleep, showed like depressing dark blotches. He approached a spot where the street was cut in two by an unending square, with the houses on the other side of it barely visible—a square that loomed ahead like an awesome desert.

Far in the distance, God knows where, a little light flickered in a policeman's sentry box that seemed to stand at the end of the world. Akakii Akakiievich's gay mood somehow diminished considerably at this point. He set foot in the square, not without a premonition of something evil. He looked back and on each side of him—it was as though he were in the midst of a sea. "No, it's better even not to look," he reflected and went on with his eyes shut. And when he did open them to see if the end of the square were near, he suddenly saw standing before him, almost at his very nose, two strangers with mustaches—just what sort of men they were was something he couldn't even make out. A mist arose before his eyes and his heart began to pound.

"Why, that there overcoat is mine!" said one of the men in a thunderous voice, grabbing him by the collar. Akakii Akakiievich was just about to yell "Police!" when the other put a fist right up to his mouth, a fist as big as any government clerk's head, adding: "There, you just let one peep out of you!"

All that Akakii Akakiievich felt was that they had taken the overcoat off him, given him a kick in the back with the knee, and that he had fallen flat on his back in the snow, after which he felt nothing more. In a few minutes he came to and got up on his feet, but there was no longer anybody around. He felt that it was cold out in that open space and that he no longer had the overcoat, and began to yell; but his voice, it seemed, had no intention whatsoever of reaching the other end of the square. Desperate, without ceasing to yell, he started off at a run across the square directly toward the sentry box near which the policeman was standing and, leaning on his halberd, was watching the running man, apparently with curiosity, as if he wished to know why the devil anybody should be running toward him from afar and yelling. Akakii Akakiievich, having run up to him, began to shout in a stifling voice that he, the policeman, had been asleep, that he was not watching and couldn't see that a man was being robbed. The policeman answered that he hadn't seen anything, that he had seen two men of some sort stop him in the middle of the square, but he had thought they were friends of Akakii Akakiievich's, and that instead of cursing him out for nothing he'd better go on the morrow to the Inspector, and the Inspector would find out who had taken his overcoat.

Akakii Akakiievich ran home in utter disorder; whatever little hair still lingered on his temples and the nape of his neck was all disheveled; his side and his breast and his trousers were all wet with snow. The old woman, his landlady, hearing the dreadful racket at the door, hurriedly jumped out of bed, and, with a shoe on only one foot, ran down to open the door, modestly holding the shift at her breast with one hand; but, on opening the door and seeing Akakii Akakiievich in such a state, she staggered back. When he had told her what the matter was, however, she wrung her hands and said that he ought to go directly to the Justice of the Peace; the District Officer of Police would take him in, would make promises to him and then lead him about by the nose; yes, it would be best of all to go straight to the Justice. Why, she was even acquainted with him, seeing as how Anna, the Finnish woman who had formerly been her cook, had now gotten a place as a nurse at the Justice's; that she, the landlady herself, sees the Justice often when he drives past her house, and also that he went to church every Sunday, praying, yet at the same time looking so cheerfully at all the folks, and that consequently, as one could see by all the signs, he was a kindhearted man. Having heard this solution of his troubles through to the end, the saddened Akakii Akakiievich shuffled off to his room, and how he passed the night there may be left to the discernment of him who can in any degree imagine the situation of another.

Early in the morning he set out for the Justice's, but was told there that he was sleeping; he came at ten o'clock, and was told again, "He's sleeping." He came at eleven; they told him, "Why, His Honor's not at home." He tried at lunchtime, but the clerks in the reception room would not let him through to the presence under any circumstances and absolutely had to know what business he had come on and what had occurred, so that, at last, Akakii Akakiievich for once in his life wanted to evince firmness of character and said sharply and categorically that he had to see the Justice personally, that they dared not keep him out, that he had come from his own Bureau on a Government matter, and that now, when he'd lodge a complaint against them, why, they would see, then. The clerks dared not say anything in answer to this and one of them went to call out the Justice of the Peace.

The Justice's reaction to Akakii Akakiievich's story of how he had been robbed of his overcoat was somehow exceedingly odd. Instead of turning his attention to the main point of the matter, he began interrogating Akakii Akakiievich: Just why had he been coming home at so late an hour? Had he, perhaps, looked in at, or hadn't he actually visited, some disorderly house? Akakii Akakiievich became utterly confused and walked out of the office without himself knowing whether the investigation about the overcoat would be instituted or not.

This whole day he stayed away from his Bureau (the only time in his life he had done so). On the following day he put in an appearance, all pale and in his old *negligée*, which had become more woebegone than ever. The recital of the robbery of the overcoat, despite the fact that there proved to be certain ones among his co-workers who did not let pass even this opportunity to make fun of Akakii Akakiievich, nevertheless touched many. They decided on the spot to make up a collection for him, but they collected the utmost trifle, inasmuch as the petty officials had spent a lot even without this, having subscribed for a portrait of the Director and for some book or other, at the invitation of the Chief of the Department, who was a friend of the writer's; and so the sum proved to be most trifling. One of them, moved by compassion, decided, at the least, to aid Akakii Akakiievich with good advice telling him that he oughtn't to go to the precinct officer of the police, because, even though it might come about that the precinct officer, wishing to merit the approval of his superiors, might locate the overcoat in some way, the overcoat would in the end remain with the police, if Akakii Akakiievich could not present legal proofs that it belonged to him; but that the best thing of all would be to turn to a *certain important person;* that this important person, after conferring and corresponding with the proper people in the proper quarters, could speed things up.

There was no help for it; Akakii Akakiievich summoned up his courage to go to the important person. Precisely what the important person's post was and what the work of that post consisted of, has remained unknown up to now. It is necessary to know that the certain important person had only recently become an Important Person, but, up to then, had been an unimportant person. However, his post was not considered an important one even now in comparison with more important ones. But there will always be found a circle of people who perceive the importance of that which is unimportant in the eyes of others. However, he tried to augment his importance by many other means, to wit: he inaugurated the custom of having the subordinate clerks meet him while he was still on the staircase when he arrived at his office; another, of no one coming directly into his presence, but having everything follow the most rigorous precedence: a Collegiate Registrar was to report to the Provincial Secretary, the Provincial Secretary to a Titular one, or whomever else it was necessary to report to, and only thus was any matter to come to him. For it is thus in our Holy Russia that everything is infected with imitativeness; everyone apes his superior and postures like him. They even say that a certain Titular Councilor, when they put him at the helm of some small individual chancellery, immediately had a separate room for himself partitioned off, dubbing it the Reception Center, and had placed at the door some doormen or other with red collars and gold braid, who turned the doorknob and opened the door for every visitor, even though there was hardly room in the Reception Center to hold even an ordinary desk.

The manners and ways of the important person were imposing and majestic, but not at all complex. The chief basis of his system was strictness. "Strictness, strictness, and—strictness," he was wont to say, and when uttering the last word he usually looked very significantly into the face of the person to whom he was speaking, even though, by the way, there was no reason for all this, inasmuch as the half-score of clerks constituting the whole administrative mechanism of his chancellery was under the proper state of fear and trembling even as it was: catching sight of him from afar the staff would at once drop whatever it was doing and wait, at attention, until the Chief had passed through the room. His ordinary speech with his subordinates reeked of strictness and consisted almost entirely of three phrases: "How dare you? Do you know whom you're talking to? Do you realize in whose presence you are?" However, at soul he was a kindly man, treated his friends well, and was obliging; but the rank of General had knocked him completely off his base. Having received a General's rank he had somehow become muddled, had lost his sense of direction, and did not know how to act. If he happened to be with his equals he was still as human as need be, a most decent man, in many respects—even a man not at all foolish; but whenever he happened to be in a group where there were people even one rank below him, why, there was no holding him; he was taciturn, and his situation aroused pity, all the more since he himself felt that he could have passed the time infinitely more pleasantly. In his eyes one could at times see a strong desire to join in some circle and its interesting conversation, but he was stopped by the thought: Wouldn't this be too much unbending on his part, wouldn't it be a familiar action, and wouldn't he lower his importance thereby? And as a consequence of such considerations he remained forever aloof in that invariably taciturn state, only uttering some monosyllabic sounds at rare intervals, and had thus acquired the reputation of a most boring individual.

It was before such an *important person* that our Akakii Akakiievich appeared, and he appeared at a most inauspicious moment, quite inopportune for himself—although, by the bye, most opportune for the important person. The important person was seated in his private office and had gotten into very, very jolly talk with a certain recently arrived old friend and childhood companion whom he had not seen for several years. It was at this point that they announced to the important person that some Bashmachkin or other had come to see him. He asked abruptly, "Who is he?" and was told, "Some petty clerk or other." "Ah. He can wait; this isn't the right time for him to come," said the important man.

At this point it must be said that the important man had fibbed a little: he had the time; he and his old friend had long since talked over everything and had been long eking out their conversation with protracted silences, merely patting each other lightly on the thigh from time to time and adding, "That's how it is, Ivan Abramovich!" and "That's just how it is, Stepan Varlaamovich!" But for all that he gave orders for the petty clerk to wait a while just the same, in order to show his friend, a man who had been long out of the Civil Service and rusticating in his village, how long petty clerks had to cool their heels in his anteroom.

Finally, having had his fill of talk, yet having had a still greater fill of silences, and after each had smoked a cigar to the end in a quite restful armchair with an adjustable back, he at last appeared to recall the matter and said to his secretary, who had halted in the doorway with some papers for a report, "Why, I think there's a clerk waiting out there. Tell him he may come in."

On beholding the meek appearance of Akakii Akakiievich and his rather old, skimpy frock coat, he suddenly turned to him and asked, "What is it you wish?"—in a voice abrupt and firm, which he had purposely rehearsed beforehand in his room at home in solitude and before a mirror, actually a week before he had received his present post and his rank of General.

Akakii Akakiievich already had plenty of time to experience the requisite awe, was somewhat abashed, and, as best he could, in so far as his poor freedom of tongue would allow him, explained, adding even more *now's* than he would have at another time, that his overcoat had been perfectly new, and that, now, he had been robbed of it in a perfectly inhuman fashion, and that he was turning to him, now, so that he might interest himself through his . . . now . . . might correspond with the Head of Police or somebody else, and find his overcoat, now. . . . Such conduct, for some unknown reason, appeared familiar to the General.

"What are you up to, my dear Sir?" he resumed abruptly. "Don't you know the proper procedure? Where have you come to? Don't you know how matters ought to be conducted? As far as this is concerned, you should have first of all submitted a petition to the Chancellery; it would have gone from there to the head of the proper Division, then would have been transferred to the Secretary, and the Secretary would in due time have brought it to my attention—"

"But, Your Excellency," said Akakii Akakiievich, trying to collect whatever little pinch of presence of mind he had, yet feeling at the same time that he was in a dreadful sweat. "I ventured to trouble you, Your Excellency, because secretaries, now . . . aren't any too much to be relied upon—"

"What? What? What?" said the important person. "Where did you get such a tone from? Where did you get such notions? What sort of rebellious feeling has spread among the young people against the administrators and their superiors?" The important person had, it seems, failed to notice that Akakii Akakiievich would never see fifty again, consequently, even if he could have been called a young man it could be applied only relatively, that is, to someone who was already seventy. "Do you know whom you're saying this to? Do you realize in whose presence you are? Do you realize? Do you realize, I'm asking you!" Here he stamped his foot, bringing his voice to such an overwhelming note that even another than an Akakii Akakiievich would have been frightened. Akakii Akakiievich was simply bereft of his senses, swayed, shook all over, and simply could not stand on his feet. If a couple of doormen had not run up right then and there to support him he would have slumped to the floor; they carried him out in a practically cataleptic state. But the important person, satisfied because the effect had surpassed even anything he had expected, and inebriated by the idea that a word from him could actually deprive a man of his senses, looked out of the corner of his eye to learn how his friend was taking this and noticed, not without satisfaction, that his friend was in a most indeterminate state and was even beginning to experience fear on his own account.

How he went down the stairs, how he came out into the street—that was something Akakii Akakiievich was no longer conscious of. He felt neither his hands nor his feet; never in all his life had he been dragged over such hot coals by a General—and a General outside his bureau, at that! With his mouth gaping, stumbling off the sidewalk, he breasted the blizzard that was whistling and howling through the streets; the wind, as is its wont in Petersburg, blew upon him from all the four quarters, from every cross lane. In a second it had blown a quinsy down his throat, and he crawled home without the strength to utter a word; he became all swollen and took to his bed. That's how effective a proper hauling over the coals can be at times!

On the next day he was running a high fever. Thanks to the magnanimous all-round help of the Petersburg climate, the disease progressed more rapidly than could have been expected, and when the doctor appeared he, after having felt the patient's pulse, could not strike on anything to do save prescribing hot compresses, and that solely so that the sick man might not be left without the beneficial help of medicine; but, on the whole, he announced on the spot that in another day and a half it would be curtains for Akakii Akakiievich, after which he turned to the landlady and said, "As for you, Mother, don't you be losing any time for nothing; order a pine coffin for him right now, because a coffin of oak will be beyond his means."

Whether Aakakii Akakiievich heard the doctor utter these words, so fateful for him, and, even if he did hear them, whether they had a staggering effect on him, whether he felt regrets over his life of hard sledding —about that nothing is known, inasmuch as he was all the time running a temperature and was in delirium. Visions, each one stranger than the one before, appeared before him ceaselessly: now he saw Petrovich and was ordering him to make an overcoat with some sort of traps to catch thieves, whom he ceaselessly imagined to be under his bed, at every minute calling his landlady to pull out from under his blanket one of them who had actually crawled under there; then he would ask why his old *negligée* was hanging in front of him, for he had a new overcoat; then once more he had a hallucination that he was standing before the General, getting a proper raking over the coals, and saying, "Forgive me,

Your Excellency!"; then, finally, he actually took to swearing foully, uttering such dreadful words that his old landlady could do nothing but
cross herself, having never in her life heard anything of the sort from
him, all the more so since these words followed immediately after "Your
Excellency!"

After that he spoke utter nonsense, so that there was no understanding
anything; all one could perceive was that his incoherent words and
thoughts all revolved about that overcoat and nothing else.

Finally poor Akakii Akakiievich gave up the ghost. Neither his room
nor his things were put under seal; in the first place because he had no
heirs, and in the second because there was very little left for anybody to
inherit, to wit: a bundle of goose quills, a quire of white governmental
paper, three pairs of socks, two or three buttons that had come off his
trousers, and the *negligée* which the reader is already familiar with. Who
fell heir to all this treasure-trove, God knows; I confess that even the
narrator of this tale was not much interested in the matter. They bore
Akakii Akakiievich off and buried him. And Petersburg was left without
Akakii Akakiievich, as if he had never been therein. There vanished and
disappeared a being protected by none, endeared to no one, of no interest to anyone, a being that actually had failed to attract to itself the
attention of even a naturalist who wouldn't let a chance slip of sticking
an ordinary housefly on a pin and of examining it through a microscope;
a being that had submissively endured the jests of the whole chancellery
and that had gone to its grave without any extraordinary fuss, but before
which, nevertheless, even before the very end of its life, there had flitted a radiant guest in the guise of an overcoat, which had animated for
an instant a poor life, and upon which being calamity had come crashing
down just as unbearably as it comes crashing down upon the heads of the
mighty ones of this earth!

A few days after his death a doorman was sent to his house from the
Bureau with an injunction for Akakii Akakiievich to appear immediately;
the Chief, now, was asking for him; but the doorman had to return
empty-handed, reporting back that "he weren't able to come no more,"
and, to the question, "Why not?" expressed himself in the words, "Why,
just so; he up and died; they buried him four days back." Thus did they
learn at the Bureau about the death of Akakii Akakiievich, and the very
next day a new pettifogger, considerably taller than Akakii Akakiievich,
was already sitting in his place and putting down the letters no longer in
such a straight hand, but considerably more on the slant and downhill.

But whoever could imagine that this wouldn't be all about Akakii
Akakiievich, that he was fated to live for several noisy days after his
death, as though in reward for a life that had gone by utterly unnoticed?
Yet that is how things fell out, and our poor history is taking on a fantastic
ending.

Rumors suddenly spread through Petersburg that near the Kalinkin
Bridge, and much farther out still, a dead man had started haunting of

nights, in the guise of a petty government clerk, seeking for some over-coat or other that had been purloined from him and, because of that stolen overcoat, snatching from all and sundry shoulders, without dif-ferentiating among the various ranks and titles, all sorts of overcoats: whether they had collars of catskin or beaver, whether they were quilted with cotton wool, whether they were lined with raccoon, with fox, with bear—in a word, every sort of fur and skin that man has ever thought of for covering his own hide. One of the clerks in the Bureau had seen the dead man with his own eyes and had immediately recognized in him Akakii Akakiievich. This had inspired him with such horror, how-ever, that he started running for all his legs were worth and for that reason could not make him out very well but had merely seen the other shake his finger at him from afar. From all sides came an uninterrupted flow of complaints that backs and shoulders—it wouldn't matter so much if they were merely those of Titular Councilors, but even those of Privy Councilors were affected—were exposed to the danger of catching thor-ough colds, because of this oft-repeated snatching-off of overcoats.

An order was put through to the police to capture the dead man, at any cost, dead or alive, and to punish him in the severest manner as an example to others—and they all but succeeded in this. To be precise, a policeman at a sentry box on a certain block of the Kirushkin Lane had already gotten a perfect grip on the dead man by his coat collar, at the very scene of his malefaction, while attempting to snatch off the frieze overcoat of some retired musician, who in his time had tootled a flute. Seizing the dead man by the collar, the policeman had summoned two of his colleagues by shouting and had entrusted the ghost to them to hold him, the while he himself took just a moment to reach down in his bootleg for his snuffbox, to relieve temporarily a nose that had been frostbitten six times in his life; but the snuff, probably, was of such a nature as even a dead man could not stand. Hardly had the police-man, after stopping his right nostril with a finger, succeeded in draw-ing half a handful of rapee up his left, than the dead man sneezed so heartily that he completely bespattered the eyes of all the three myrmi-dons. While they were bringing their fists up to rub their eyes, the dead man vanished without leaving as much as a trace, so that they actually did not know whether he had really been in their hands or not.

From then on the policemen developed such a phobia of dead men that they were afraid to lay hands even on living ones and merely shouted from a distance, "Hey, there, get going!" and the dead govern-ment clerk began to do his haunting even beyond the Kalinkin Bridge, inspiring not a little fear in all timid folk.

However, we have dropped entirely a certain *important person,* who, in reality, had been all but the cause of the fantastic trend taken by what is, by the bye, a perfectly true story. First of all, a sense of jus-tice compels us to say that the *certain important person,* soon after the departure of poor Akakii Akakiievich, done to a turn in the raking over

the hot coals, had felt something in the nature of compunction. He was
no stranger to compassion; many kind impulses found access to his
heart, despite the fact that his rank often stood in the way of their revealing themselves. As soon as the visiting friend had left his private
office, he actually fell into a brown study over Akakii Akakiievich. And
from that time on, almost every day, there appeared before him the
pale Akakii Akakiievich, who had not been able to stand up under an
administrative hauling over the coals. The thought concerning him dis-
quieted the certain important person to such a degree that, a week later,
he even decided to send a clerk to him to find out what the man had
wanted, and how he was, and whether it were really possible to help
him in some way. And when he was informed that Akakii Akakiievich
had died suddenly in a fever he was left actually stunned, hearkening
to the reproaches of conscience, and was out of sorts the whole day.

Wishing to distract himself to some extent and to forget the unpleasant impression this news had made upon him, he set out for an evening party to one of his friends, where he found a suitable social gathering, and, what was best of all, all the men there were of almost the
same rank, so that he absolutely could not feel constrained in any way.
This had an astonishing effect on the state of his spirits. He relaxed,
became amiable and pleasant to converse with—in a word, he passed
the time very agreeably. At supper he drank off a goblet or two of
champagne—a remedy which, as everybody knows, has not at all an ill
effect upon one's gaiety. The champagne predisposed him to certain ex-
tracurricular considerations; to be precise, he decided not to go home
yet but to drop in on a certain lady of his acquaintance, a Caroline
Ivanovna—a lady of German extraction, apparently, toward whom his
feelings and relations were friendly. It must be pointed out the important person was no longer a young man, that he was a good spouse, a
respected *paterfamilias.* He had two sons, one of whom was already
serving in a chancellery, and a pretty daughter of sixteen, with a somewhat humped yet very charming little nose, who came to kiss his hand
every day, adding, *"Bonjour,* papa," as she did so. His wife, a woman
who still had not lost her freshness and was not even in the least hard
to look at, would allow him to kiss her hand first, then, turning her own
over, kissed the hand that was holding hers.

Yet the important person, who, by the bye, was perfectly contented
with domestic tendernesses, found it respectable to have a lady friend in
another part of the city. This lady friend was not in the least fresher
or younger than his wife, but such are the enigmas that exist in this
world, and to sit in judgment upon them is none of our affair. And so
the important person came down the steps, climbed into his sleigh, and
told his driver, "To Caroline Ivanovna's!"—while he himself, after muf-
fling up rather luxuriously in his warm overcoat, remained in that pleasant state than which no better could even be thought of for a Russian—
that is, when one isn't even thinking of his own volition, but the thoughts

in the meanwhile troop into one's head by themselves, each more pleasant than the other, without giving one even the trouble of pursuing them and seeking them. Filled with agreeable feelings, he lightly recalled all the gay episodes of the evening he had spent, all his *mots* that had made the select circle go off into peals of laughter; many of them he even repeated in a low voice and found that they were still just as amusing as before, and for that reason it is not to be wondered at that even he chuckled at them heartily.

Occasionally, however, he became annoyed with the gusty wind which, suddenly escaping from God knows where and no one knows for what reason, simply cut the face, tossing tatters of snow thereat, making the collar of his overcoat belly out like a sail, or suddenly, with unnatural force, throwing it over his head and in this manner giving him ceaseless trouble in extricating himself from it.

Suddenly the important person felt that someone had seized him rather hard by his collar. Turning around, he noticed a man of no great height, in an old, much worn frock coat, and, not without horror, recognized in him Akakii Akakiievich. The petty clerk's face was wan as snow and looked utterly like the face of a dead man. But the horror of the important person passed all bounds when he saw that the mouth of the man became twisted and, horribly wafting upon him the odor of the grave, uttered the following speech: "Ah, so there you are, now, at last! At last I have collared you, now! Your overcoat is just the one I need! You didn't put yourself out any about mine, and on top of that hauled me over the coals—so now let me have yours!"

The poor important person almost passed away. No matter how firm of character he was in his chancellery and before his inferiors in general, and although after but one look merely at his manly appearance and his figure everyone said, "My, what character he has!"—in this instance, nevertheless, like quite a number of men who have the appearance of doughty knights, he experienced such terror that, not without reason, he even began to fear an attack of some physical disorder. He even hastened to throw his overcoat off his shoulders himself and cried out to the driver in a voice that was not his own. "Go home—fast as you can!"

The driver, on hearing the voice that the important person used only at critical moments and which he often accompanied by something of a far more physical nature, drew his head in between his shoulders just to be on the safe side, swung his whip, and flew off like an arrow. In just a little over six minutes the important person was already at the entrance to his own house. Pale, frightened out of his wits, and minus his overcoat, he had come home instead of to Caroline Ivanovna's, somehow made his way stumblingly to his room, and spent the night in quite considerable distress, so that the next day, during the morning tea, his daughter told him outright, "You're all pale today, papa." But papa kept silent and said not a word to anybody of what had befallen him, and where he had been, and where he had intended to go.

This adventure made a strong impression on him. He even badgered his subordinates at rarer intervals with his, "How dare you? Do you realize in whose presence you are?"—and even if he did utter these phrases he did not do so before he had first heard through to the end just what was what. But still more remarkable is the fact that from that time forth the apparition of the dead clerk ceased its visitations utterly; evidently the General's overcoat fitted him to a *t;* at least, no cases of overcoats being snatched off anybody were heard of any more, any-where. However, many energetic and solicitous people simply would not calm down and kept on saying from time to time that the dead govern-ment clerk was still haunting the remoter parts of the city.

And, sure enough, one policeman at a sentry box in Colomna had with his own eyes seen the apparition coming out of a house; but, being by nature somewhat puny, so that on one occasion an ordinary well-grown shoat, darting out of a private yard, had knocked him off his feet, to the profound amusement of the cab drivers who were standing around, from whom he had exacted a copper each for humiliating him so greatly, to buy snuff with—well, being puny, he had not dared to halt him but simply followed him in the dark until such time as the apparition sud-denly looked over its shoulder and, halting, asked him, "What are you after?" and shook a fist at him whose like for size was not to be found among the living. The policeman said, "Nothing," and at once turned back. The apparition, however, was considerably taller by now and was sporting a pair of enormous mustachios; setting its steps apparently in the direction of the Obuhov Bridge, it disappeared utterly in the dark-ness of night.

QUESTIONS

1. Why do you suppose Gogol gives such a detailed account of his clerk's name? What points are established by the humorous treatment of his family name at the end of the opening paragraph? And do you receive the impression that, because there was something odd about his "name and patronymic," he will in other respects be presented as an odd, atypical character?

2. What is the nature of the clerk's work? If the story were being recast in terms of mid-twentieth-century American life, what changes would have to be made in the clerk's mode of existence, the way he earns his living, his relations with the rest of society? Or are there no present-day equivalents to be found?

3. In the course of the story, the clerk moves through several stages of fortune, in which he stands in varying relationships to the world around him. Do there seem to you, however, to be any respects in which his relationships with society, with other human beings, are substantially unchanged throughout the story?

4. What in your view is the central theme of the story, the more or less generally applicable truth or idea which underlies the various specific events and gives them their coherence? At what point is this theme first introduced?

5. How far does the overcoat serve to reveal the qualities, content, and conditions of the clerk's life? At what point, and to what extent, does it alter his life, determine its course and outcome?

6. Assuming that the earlier phases of the clerk's life—his struggles to obtain the overcoat, for example—have an easily recognizable general applicability, is that applicability lost when the story moves on to the level of the supernatural, of fantasy, at the end? Can you keep track of the central theme all the way to the end?

7. At how many specific points in the story do you find Gogol referring, either directly or by implication, to the question of how far we can enter into the thoughts and feelings of others? What is the role of a hierarchical bureaucracy, according to Gogol's story, in helping or hindering us to understand the human needs of our fellow men?

EDGAR ALLAN POE

(1809–1849)

Poe's first few stories, one of his recent editors and critics, Edward H. Davidson, points out,[1] were written virtually as parodies or burlesques of the inane tales of horror being published in contemporary magazines and newspapers. His first-published tale, "Metzengerstein" (1832), with its feud between noble families in Hungary, its castles, its diabolical phantom steed, may remind us that the tradition of the late-eighteenth century Gothic novel, carried on by such works as Mary Shelley's *Frankenstein*, was still a tradition to which a writer turned when seeking a form and a flavor for a tale meant to entertain the reader of newspaper-fiction in the 1830's. It may well be that Poe's critics have taken this brief tale too seriously, that it was indeed aimed, as Professor Davidson suggests, only "at ridiculing the masses of horror fiction which, then as now, poured from the presses." Yet it is difficult to see it as only that, and its use of supernatural events to give a horrible embodiment to horrible human passions is not so very different from Poe's practice in his more ambitious tales.

Although many of Poe's poems and stories are among the earliest reading experiences of most Americans, he is not a writer whom we understand very well. Students of literature, accustomed to look back with a sort of fond contempt on the author of "The Raven" and "The Fall of the House of Usher," thinking that they took his measure when they last read him in school, are sometimes astonished when they discover what an important figure he was for the French Symbolists, from Baudelaire

[1] In the introduction to his *Selected Writings of Edgar Allan Poe*. Boston: Houghton Mifflin Company.

to Mallarmé and Paul Valéry. For Poe's works were written according to highly subtle, self-conscious philosophical and aesthetic principles which anticipated and confirmed those of the Symbolists. It is this whole side of his work which is overlooked by those who approach him casually as a "horror" writer, and it is a side which probably cannot be adequately represented in terms of only one or two tales.

Poe is something more than a short-story writer even when he is writing short stories, or "tales" as he called them. He is writing works which reflect and exemplify his theories about the way in which abnormal states of mind—the approach of madness, for instance, in "The Fall of the House of Usher," or a consuming obsession with the past, in "Ligeia" —are experienced by those who undergo them and may be rendered visible to those who observe them in others. Also, in creating a close, almost reciprocal correspondence between physical objects and spiritual states (for example, the way in which Roderick Usher's declining state of mind is given a direct, sympathetic representation in the decaying state of the "mansion of gloom" in which he lives, or the even more startling merging of literal and figurative at the end of "Ligeia"), Poe is using a fully developed Symbolist technique. All this is more than is bargained for by readers who turn to Poe simply as another writer of tales of horror, and indeed there is something inescapably hollow and insipid in even the best of Poe's stories when they are approached solely from this point of view. Nevertheless, he must be given his place among the initiators of the modern short story, both because he was one of the very first writers to produce a considerable body of serious work in the form, thus helping to give it standing, a place of its own in literature, and because as early as the 1840's he had spelled out the rationale of the short story as an independent art form.

Poe expressed his views on what the short story could and should be in a review of Hawthorne's *Twice-Told Tales* which he published in 1842 and again, in an altered version, in 1847. Criticism doesn't make literature happen, and no one would want to claim that the short story developed as it did simply because of some principles laid down by Poe in a magazine article. After all, the article *was* a review of a volume which contained some of Hawthorne's own finest tales, including "The Minister's Black Veil," and in Russia Gogol had published many of his tales in the 1830's. Still, in this review Poe proclaimed the essential relationship between the short-story's *brevity* and the *intensity* which that brevity made possible, provided the short-story writer was an artist who would strive for *unity of effect.*

Poe's special feeling for the short story grew out of one of his poetic principles: that to speak of "a long poem" is to utter a contradiction in terms:

A poem must intensely excite. Excitement is its province, its essentiality. Its value is in the ratio of its (elevating) excitement. But all excitement is, from a psychal necessity, transient. It cannot be sustained through a poem of great length. In the course of an hour's reading, at most, it flags, fails; and then the poem is, in effect, no longer such.

On the other hand, he goes on to say,

> A poem *too* brief . . . may produce a sharp or vivid, but never a profound or enduring impression. Without a certain continuity, without a certain duration or repetition of the cause, the soul is seldom moved to the effect. There must be the dropping of the water on the rock.

Putting these requirements together, Poe arrived at his specifications for the form of literary activity in which "the highest . . . genius could be most advantageously employed for the best display of its powers," and that is "in the composition of a rhymed poem not to exceed in length what might be perused in an hour." Next to such a poem, however, and taking precedence over other forms both of prose *and* of poetry, comes "the brief prose tale," and in describing the features and conditions of the form which in his view make it worthy of such high place, Poe is describing potentialities which have been amply fulfilled by practitioners of the modern short story.

We may feel that he has not got the novel lined up quite correctly in his sights when he complains that "as it cannot be read at one sitting, it cannot avail itself of the immense benefit of *totality*." But there is no difficulty in agreeing with his view of "the brief tale," in which "the author is enabled to carry out his full design without interruption. During the hour of perusal, the soul of the reader is at the writer's control."

The essentials of Poe's view of the advantages and requirements of the short-story form are presented in a paragraph which deserves to be quoted in full. It may not seem to say anything very startling, but actually it implies the whole program of seriousness, of artistic discipline, and of an intensity of response similar to that demanded by poetry, which has made a valid and serious art form of the modern short story.

> A skilful artist has constructed a tale. He has not fashioned his thoughts to accommodate his incidents, but having deliberately conceived a certain *single effect* to be wrought, he then invents such incidents, he then combines such events, and discusses them in such tone as may best serve him in establishing this preconceived effect. If his very first sentence tend not to the outbringing of this effect, then in his very first step has he committed a blunder. In the whole composition there should be no word written of which the tendency, direct or indirect, is not to the one pre-established design. And by such means, with such care and skill, a picture is at length painted which leaves in the mind of him who contemplates it with a kindred art, a sense of the fullest satisfaction. The idea of the tale, its thesis, has been presented unblemished, because undisturbed—an end absolutely demanded, yet, in the novel, altogether unattainable.

We need not be alarmed by the word "thesis" in the last sentence—it was removed in the version of the review published in 1847, and in any event it is clear from the passage as a whole that Poe does not see the short story as having didactic aims. What we can profitably hold in mind is his insistence on the single effect, consciously conceived and worked for with artistic strictness, and on the obligation of the reader to contemplate the finished product "with kindred art," an obligation which will be rewarded with "a sense of the fullest satisfaction." This is an exact and faithful description of one of the most distinguished and significant branches of the art of the short story as it has been practiced by such writers—each in his own way—as Chekhov, Joyce, and Hemingway.

The short story as consciously conceived, intensely wrought art, which demands from the reader the same concentration of response as is demanded by poetry: this is only *one* view of the story's essential nature. To set against it is another view, which emphasizes the anecdotal side of the form and conceives its chief interest as lying in the events described, in narrative values. Even here, however, in the more loosely organized kind of story which has a kinship with Mark Twain's "The Notorious Jumping Frog of Calaveras County" and with all yarns everywhere, Poe's insistence on unity of effect has its application. The important principle, today as when Poe wrote his review, is for the reader to approach each new story as nearly as possible in the spirit in which it was written, to be alert to the individual writer's aims, and not to read a given work against the grain by reason of looking for values in it which were never intended to be there.

LIGEIA

And the will therein lieth, which dieth not. Who knoweth the mysteries of the will, with its vigor? For God is but a great will pervading all things by nature of its intentness. Man doth not yield himself to the angels, nor unto death utterly, save only through the weakness of his feeble will.

Joseph Glanvill

I cannot, for my soul, remember how, when, or even precisely where, I first became acquainted with the lady Ligeia. Long years have since elapsed, and my memory is feeble through much suffering. Or, perhaps, I cannot *now* bring these points to mind, because, in truth, the character of my beloved, her rare learning, her singular yet placid cast of beauty, and the thrilling and enthralling eloquence of her low musical language, made their way into my heart by paces so steadily and stealthily progressive that they have been unnoticed and unknown. Yet I believe that I met her first and most frequently in some large, old, decaying city near the Rhine. Of her family—I have surely heard her speak. That it is of a remotely ancient date cannot be doubted. Ligeia! Ligeia! Buried in studies of a nature more than all else adapted to deaden impressions of the outward world, it is by that sweet word alone—by Ligeia —that I bring before mine eyes in fancy the image of her who is no more. And now, while I write, a recollection flashes upon me that I have *never known* the paternal name of her who was my friend and my betrothed, and who became the partner of my studies, and finally the wife of my bosom. Was it a playful charge on the part of my Ligeia? or was it a test of my strength of affection, that I should institute no inquiries upon this point? or was it rather a caprice of my own—a wildly romantic offering on the shrine of the most passionate devotion? I but indistinctly recall the fact itself—what wonder that I have utterly forgotten the circumstances which originated or attended it? And, indeed, if ever that spirit which is entitled *Romance*—if ever she, the wan and the misty-winged *Ashtophet* of idolatrous Egypt, presided, as they tell, over marriages ill-omened, then most surely she presided over mine.

There is one dear topic, however, on which my memory fails me not. It is the *person* of Ligeia. In stature she was tall, somewhat slender, and, in her latter days, even emaciated. I would in vain attempt to portray the majesty, the quiet ease of her demeanor, or the incomprehensible lightness and elasticity of her footfall. She came and departed as a shadow. I was never made aware of her entrance into my closed study save by the dear music of her low sweet voice, as she placed her marble hand upon my shoulder. In beauty of face no maiden ever equalled her. It was the radiance of an opium-dream—an airy and spirit-lifting vision more wildly divine than the phantasies which hovered about the slumbering souls of the daughters of Delos. Yet her features were not of that regular mould which we have been falsely taught to worship in the classical labors of the heathen. "There is no exquisite beauty," says Bacon, Lord Verulam, speaking truly of all the forms and *genera* of beauty, "without some *strangeness* in the proportion." Yet, although I saw that the features of Ligeia were not of a classic regularity—although I perceived that her loveliness was indeed "exquisite," and felt that there was much of "strangeness" pervading it, yet I have tried in vain to detect the irregularity and to trace home my own perception of "the strange." I examined the contour of the lofty and pale forehead—it was faultless—how cold indeed that word when applied to a majesty so divine!—the skin rivalling the purest ivory, the commanding extent and repose, the gentle prominence of the regions above the temples; and then the raven-black, the glossy, the luxuriant and naturally-curling tresses, setting forth the full force of the Homeric epithet, "hyacinthine!" I looked at the delicate outlines of the nose—and nowhere but in the graceful medallions of the Hebrews had I beheld a similar perfection. There were the same luxurious smoothness of surface, the same scarcely perceptible tendency to the aquiline, the same harmoniously curved nostrils speaking the free spirit. I regarded the sweet mouth. Here was indeed the triumph of all things heavenly—the magnificent turn of the short upper lip—the soft, voluptuous slumber of the under—the dimples which sported, and the color which spoke—the teeth glancing back, with a brilliancy almost startling, every ray of the holy light which fell upon them in her serene and placid yet most exultingly radiant of all smiles. I scrutinized the formation of the chin—and, here too, I found the gentleness of breadth, the softness and the majesty, the fullness and the spirituality, of the Greek—the contour which the god Apollo revealed but in a dream, to Cleomenes, the son of the Athenian. And then I peered into the large eyes of Ligeia.

For eyes we have no models in the remotely antique. It might have been, too, that in these eyes of my beloved lay the secret to which Lord Verulam alludes. They were, I must believe, far larger than the ordinary eyes of our own race. They were even fuller than the fullest of the gazelle eyes of the tribe of the valley of Nourjahad. Yet it was only at intervals—in moments of intense excitement—that this peculiarity became more than slightly noticeable in Ligeia. And at such moments was her beauty—in my heated fancy thus it appeared perhaps—the beauty of beings either above or apart from the earth—the beauty of the fabulous Houri of the Turk. The hue of the orbs was the most brilliant of black, and, far over them, hung jetty lashes of great length. The brows, slightly irregular in outline, had the same tint. The "strangeness," however, which I found in the eyes, was of a nature distinct from the formation, or the color, or the brilliancy of the features, and must, after all, be referred to the *expression*. Ah, word of no meaning! behind whose vast latitude of mere sound we intrench our ignorance of so much of the spiritual. The expression of the eyes of Ligeia! How for long hours have I pondered upon it! How have I, through the whole of a midsummer night, struggled to fathom it! What was it—that something more profound than the well of Democritus—which lay far within the pupils of my beloved? What *was* it? I was possessed with a passion to discover. Those eyes! those large, those shining, those divine orbs! they became to me twin stars of Leda, and I to them devoutest of astrologers.

There is no point, among the many incomprehensible anomalies of the science of mind, more thrillingly exciting than the fact—never, I believe, noticed in the schools—that in our endeavors to recall to memory something long forgotten, we often find ourselves *upon the very verge* of remembrance, without being able, in the end, to remember. And thus how frequently, in my intense scrutiny of Ligeia's eyes, have I felt approaching the full knowledge of their expression—felt it approaching—yet not quite be mine—and so at length entirely depart! And (strange, oh strangest mystery of all!) I found, in the commonest objects of the universe, a circle of analogies to that expression. I mean to say that, subsequently to the period when Ligeia's beauty passed into my spirit, there dwelling as in a shrine, I derived, from many existences in the material world, a sentiment such as I felt always aroused, within me, by her large and luminous orbs. Yet not the more could I define that sentiment, or analyze, or even steadily view it. I recognized it, let me repeat, sometimes in the survey of a rapidly growing vine—in the contemplation of a moth, a butterfly, a chrysalis, a stream of running water. I have felt it in the ocean; in the falling of a meteor. I have felt it in the glances of unusually aged people. And there are one or two stars in heaven—(one especially, a star of the sixth magnitude, double and changeable, to be found near the large star in Lyra) in a telescopic scrutiny of which I have been made aware of the feeling. I have been filled with it by certain sounds from stringed instruments, and not unfrequently by passages from books. Among innumerable other instances, I well remember something in a volume of Joseph Glanvill, which (perhaps from its quaintness—who shall say?) never failed to inspire me with the sentiment;—"And the will therein lieth, which dieth not. Who knoweth the mysteries of the will, with its vigor? For God is but a great will pervading all things by nature of its intentness. Man doth not yield him to the angels, nor unto death utterly, save only through the weakness of his feeble will."

Length of years and subsequent reflection, have enabled me to trace, indeed, some remote connection between this passage in the English moralist and a portion of the character of Ligeia. An *intensity* in thought, action, or speech, was possibly, in her, a result, or at least an index, of that gigantic volition which, during our long intercourse, failed to give other and more immediate evidence of its existence. Of all the women whom I have ever known, she, the outwardly calm, the ever-placid Ligeia, was the most violently a prey to the tumultuous vultures of stern passion. And of such passion I could form no estimate, save by the miraculous expansion of those eyes which at once so delighted and appalled me—by the almost magical melody, modulation, distinctness, and placidity of her very low voice—and by the fierce energy (rendered doubly effective by contrast with her manner of utterance) of the wild words which she habitually uttered.

I have spoken of the learning of Ligeia; it was immense—such as I have never known, in woman. In the classical tongues was she deeply proficient, and as far as my own acquaintance extended in regard to the modern dialects of Europe, I have never known her at fault. Indeed upon any theme of the most admired, because simply the most abstruse of the boasted erudition of the academy, have I *ever* found Ligeia at fault? How singularly—how thrillingly, this one point in the nature of my wife has forced itself, at this late period only, upon my attention! I said her knowledge was such as I have never known in woman—but where breathes the man who has traversed, and successfully, *all* the wide areas of moral, physical, and mathematical science? I saw not then what I now clearly perceive, that the acquisitions of Ligeia were gigantic, were astounding; yet I was sufficiently aware of her infinite supremacy to resign myself, with a child-like confidence, to her guidance through the chaotic world of metaphysical investigation at which I was most busily occupied during the earlier years of our marriage. With how vast a triumph—with how vivid a delight—with how much of all that is ethereal in hope—did I *feel*, as she bent over me in studies but little sought—but less known—that delicious vista by slow degrees expanding before me, down whose long, gorgeous, and all untrodden path, I might at length pass onward to the goal of a wisdom too divinely precious not to be forbidden!

How poignant, then, must have been the grief with which, after some years, I beheld my well-grounded expectations take wings to themselves and fly away! Without Ligeia I was but as a child groping benighted. Her presence, her readings alone, rendered vividly luminous the many mysteries of the transcendentalism in which we were immersed. Wanting the radiant lustre of her eyes, letters, lambent and golden, grew duller than Saturnian lead. And now those eyes shone less and less frequently upon the pages over which I pored. Ligeia grew ill. The wild eyes blazed with a too—too glorious effulgence; the pale fingers became of the transparent waxen hue of the grave; and the blue veins upon the lofty forehead swelled and sank impetuously with the tides of the most gentle emotion. I saw that she must die—and I struggled desperately in spirit with the grim Azrael. And the struggles of the passionate wife were, to my astonishment, even more energetic than my own. There had been much in her stern nature to impress me with the belief that, to her, death would have come without its terrors; but not so. Words are impotent to convey any just idea of the fierceness of resistance with which she wrestled with the Shadow. I groaned in anguish at the pitiable spectacle. I would have soothed—I would have reasoned; but, in the intensity of her wild desire for life,—for life—*but* for life—solace and reason were alike the uttermost folly. Yet not until the last instance, amid the most convulsive writhings of her fierce spirit, was shaken the external placidity of her demeanor. Her voice grew more gentle—grew more low—yet I would not wish to dwell upon the wild meaning of the quietly uttered words. My brain reeled as I hearkened entranced, to a melody more than mortal—to assumptions and aspirations which mortality had never before known.

That she loved me I should not have doubted; and I might have been easily aware that, in a bosom such as hers, love would have reigned no ordinary passion. But in death only was I fully impressed with the strength of her affection. For long hours, detaining my hand, would she pour out before me the overflowing of a heart whose more than passionate devotion amounted to idolatry. How had I deserved to be so blessed by such confessions?—how had I deserved to be so cursed with the removal of my beloved in the hour of her making them? But upon this subject I cannot bear to dilate. Let me say only, that in Ligeia's more than womanly abandonment to a love, alas! all unmerited, all unworthily bestowed, I at length recognized the principle of her longing with so wildly earnest a desire for the life which was now fleeing so rapidly away. It is this wild longing—it is this eager vehemence of desire for life—*but* for life—that I have no power to portray—no utterance capable of expressing.

At high noon of the night in which she departed, beckoning me, peremptorily, to her side, she bade me repeat certain verses composed by herself not many days before. I obeyed her.—They were these:

> Lo! 'tis a gala night
>   Within the lonesome latter years!
> An angel throng, bewinged, bedight
>   In veils, and drowned in tears,
> Sit in a theatre, to see
>   A play of hopes and fears,
> While the orchestra breathes fitfully
>   The music of the spheres.
>
> Mimes, in the form of God on high,
>   Mutter and mumble low,
> And hither and thither fly—
>   Mere puppets they, who come and go
> At bidding of vast formless things
>   That shift the scenery to and fro,
> Flapping from out their Condor wings
>   Invisible Woe!
>
> That motley drama!—oh, be sure
>   It shall not be forgot!
> With its Phantom chased forever more,
>   By a crowd that seize it not,
> Through a circle that ever returneth in
>   To the self-same spot,
> And much of Madness and more of Sin
>   And Horror the soul of the plot.
>
> But see, amid the mimic rout,
>   A crawling shape intrude!
> A blood-red thing that writhes from out
>   The scenic solitude!
> It writhes!—it writhes!—with mortal pangs
>   The mimes become its food,
> And the seraphs sob at vermin fangs
>   In human gore imbued.
>
> Out—out are the lights—out all!
>   And over each quivering form,
> The curtain, a funeral pall,
>   Comes down with the rush of a storm,
> And the angels, all pallid and wan,
>   Uprising, unveiling, affirm
> That the play is the tragedy, "Man,"
>   And its hero the Conqueror Worm.

"O God!" half shrieked Ligeia, leaping to her feet and extending her arms aloft with a spasmodic movement, as I made an end of these lines —"O God! O Divine Father!—shall these things be undeviatingly so?— shall this Conqueror be not once conquered? Are we not part and parcel in Thee? Who—who knoweth the mysteries of the will with its vigor? Man doth not yield him to the angels, *nor unto death utterly,* save only through the weakness of his feeble will."

And now, as if exhausted with emotion, she suffered her white arms to fall, and returned solemnly to her bed of death. And as she breathed her last sighs, there came mingled with them a low murmur from her lips. I bent to them my ear, and distinguished, again, the concluding words of the passage in Glanvill—"*Man doth not yield him to the angels, nor unto death utterly, save only through the weakness of his feeble will.*"

She died;—and I, crushed into the very dust with sorrow, could no longer endure the lonely desolation of my dwelling in the dim and decaying city by the Rhine. I had no lack of what the world calls wealth. Ligeia had brought me far more, very far more than ordinarily falls to the lot of mortals. After a few months, therefore, of weary and aimless wandering, I purchased, and put in some repair, an abbey, which I shall not name, in one of the wildest and least frequented portions of fair England. The gloomy and dreary grandeur of the building, the almost savage aspect of the domain, the many melancholy and time-honored memories connected with both, had much in unison with the feelings of utter abandonment which had driven me into that remote and unsocial region of the country. Yet although the external abbey, with its verdant decay hanging about it, suffered but little alteration, I gave way, with a child-like perversity, and perchance with a faint hope of alleviating my sorrows, to a display of more than regal magnificence within.—For such follies, even in childhood, I had imbibed a taste, and now they came back to me as if in the dotage of grief. Alas, I feel how much even of incipient madness might have been discovered in the gorgeous and fantastic draperies, in the solemn carvings of Egypt, in the wild cornices and furniture, in the Bedlam patterns of the carpets of tufted gold! I had become a bounden slave in the trammels of opium, and my labors and orders had taken a coloring from my dreams. But these absurdities I must not pause to detail. Let me speak only of that one chamber, ever accursed, whither, in a moment of mental alienation, I led from the altar as my bride—as the successor of the unforgotten Ligeia—the fair-haired and blue-eyed Lady Rowena Trevanion, of Tremaine.

There is no individual portion of the architecture and decoration of that bridal chamber which is not now visibly before me. Where were the souls of the haughty family of the bride, when, through thirst of gold, they permitted to pass the threshold of an apartment *so* bedecked, a maiden and a daughter so beloved? I have said that I minutely remember the details of the chamber—yet I am sadly forgetful on topics of deep moment— and here there was no system, no keeping, in the fantastic display, to

take hold upon the memory. The room lay in a high turret of the castel-
lated abbey, was pentagonal in shape, and of capacious size. Occupying
the whole southern face of the pentagon was the sole window—an immense sheet of unbroken glass from Venice—a single pane, and tinted of a
leaden hue, so that the rays of either the sun or moon, passing through it,
fell with a ghastly lustre on the objects within. Over the upper portion of
this huge window, extended the trellis-work of an aged vine, which clambered up the massy walls of the turret. The ceiling, of gloomy-looking
oak, was excessively lofty, vaulted, and elaborately fretted with the wildest and most grotesque specimens of a semi-Gothic, semi-Druidical device. From out the most central recess of this melancholy vaulting, de-
pended, by a single chain of gold with long links, a huge censer of the
same metal, Saracenic in pattern, and with many perforations so contrived
that there writhed in and out of them, as if endued with a serpent vitality,
a continual succession of parti-colored fires.

Some few ottomans and golden candelabra, of Eastern figure, were in
various stations about—and there was the couch, too—the bridal couch—
of an Indian model, and low, and sculptured of solid ebony, with a pall-
like canopy above. In each of the angles of the chamber stood on end a
gigantic sarcophagus of black granite, from the tombs of the kings over
against Luxor, with their aged lids full of immemorial sculpture. But in
the draping of the apartment lay, alas! the chief phantasy of all. The
lofty walls, gigantic in height—even unproportionably so—were hung
from summit to foot, in vast folds, with a heavy and massive-looking tapestry—tapestry of a material which was found alike as a carpet on the floor,
as a covering for the ottomans and the ebony bed, as a canopy for the
bed and as the gorgeous volutes of the curtains which partially shaded
the window. The material was the richest cloth of gold. It was spotted all
over, at irregular intervals, with arabesque figures, about a foot in diam-
eter, and wrought upon the cloth in patterns of the most jetty black. But
these figures partook of the true character of the arabesque only when
regarded from a single point of view. By a contrivance now common, and
indeed traceable to a very remote period of antiquity, they were made
changeable in aspect. To one entering the room, they bore the appearance of simple monstrosities; but upon a farther advance, this appearance
gradually departed; and step by step, as the visitor moved his station in
the chamber, he saw himself surrounded by an endless succession of the
ghastly forms which belong to the superstition of the Norman, or arise
in the guilty slumbers of the monk. The phantasmagoric effect was vastly
heightened by the artificial introduction of a strong continual current of
wind behind the draperies—giving a hideous and uneasy animation to the
whole.

In halls such as these—in a bridal chamber such as this—I passed, with
the Lady of Tremaine, the unhallowed hours of the first month of our
marriage—passed them with but little disquietude. That my wife dreaded
the fierce moodiness of my temper—that she shunned me and loved me

but little—I could not help perceiving; but it gave me rather pleasure than otherwise.I loathed her with a hatred belonging more to demon than to man. My memory flew back, (oh, with what intensity of regret!) to Ligeia, the beloved, the august, the beautiful, the entombed. I revelled in recollections of her purity, of her wisdom, of her lofty, her ethereal nature, of her passionate, her idolatrous love. Now, then, did my spirit fully and freely burn with more than all the fires of her own. In the excitement of my opium dreams (for I was habitually fettered in the shackles of the drug) I would call aloud upon her name, during the silence of the night, or among the sheltered recesses of the glens by day, as if, through the wild eagerness, the solemn passion, the consuming ardor of my longing for the departed, I could restore her to the pathways she had abandoned—ah, *could* it be forever?—upon the earth.

About the commencement of the second month of the marriage, the Lady Rowena was attacked with sudden illness, from which her recovery was slow. The fever which consumed her rendered her nights uneasy; and in her perturbed state of half-slumber, she spoke of sounds, and of motions, in and about the chamber of the turret, which I concluded had no origin save in the distemper of her fancy, or perhaps in the phantasmagoric influences of the chamber itself. She became at length convalescent—finally well. Yet but a brief period elapsed, ere a second more violent disorder again threw her upon a bed of suffering; and from this attack her frame, at all times feeble, never altogether recovered. Her illnesses were, after this epoch, of alarming character, and of more alarming recurrence, defying alike the knowledge and the great exertions of her physicians. With the increase of the chronic disease which had thus, apparently, taken too sure hold upon her constitution to be eradicated by human means, I could not fail to observe a similar increase in the nervous irritation of her temperament, and in her excitability by trivial causes of fear. She spoke again, and now more frequently and pertinaciously, of the sounds—of the slight sounds—and of the unusual motions among the tapestries, to which she had formerly alluded.

One night, near the closing in of September, she pressed this distressing subject with more than usual emphasis upon my attention. She had just awakened from an unquiet slumber, and I had been watching, with feelings half of anxiety, half of vague terror, the workings of her emaciated countenance. I sat by the side of her ebony bed, upon one of the ottomans of India. She partly arose, and spoke, in an earnest low whisper, of sounds which she *then* heard, but which I could not hear—of motions which she *then* saw, but which I could not perceive. The wind was rushing hurriedly behind the tapestries, and I wished to show her (what, let me confess it, I could not *all* believe) that those almost inarticulate breathings, and those very gentle variations of the figures upon the wall, were but the natural effects of that customary rushing of the wind. But a deadly pallor, overspreading her face, had proved to me that my exertions to reassure her would be fruitless. She appeared to be fainting, and no at-

tendants were within call. I remembered where was deposited a decan-
ter of light wine which had been ordered by her physicians, and hastened
across the chamber to procure it. But, as I stepped beneath the light of
the censer, two circumstances of a startling nature attracted my attention.
I had felt that some palpable although invisible object had passed lightly
by my person; and I saw that there lay upon the golden carpet, in the
very middle of the rich lustre thrown from the censer, a shadow—a faint,
indefinite shadow of angelic aspect—such as might be fancied for the
shadow of a shade. But I was wild with the excitement of an immoderate
dose of opium, and heeded these things but little, nor spoke of them to
Rowena. Having found the wine, I recrossed the chamber, and poured
out a goblet-ful, which I held to the lips of the fainting lady. She had
now partially recovered, however, and took the vessel herself, while I
sank upon an ottoman near me, with my eyes fastened upon her person.
It was then that I became distinctly aware of a gentle foot-fall upon the
carpet, and near the couch; and in a second thereafter, as Rowena was in
the act of raising the wine to her lips, I saw, or may have dreamed that I
saw, fall within the goblet, as if from some invisible spring in the atmosphere of the room, three or four large drops of a brilliant and ruby colored fluid. If this I saw—not so Rowena. She swallowed the wine unhesi-
tatingly, and I forbore to speak to her of a circumstance which must, after
all, I considered, have been but the suggestion of a vivid imagination,
rendered morbidly active by the terror of the lady, by the opium, and by
the hour.

Yet I cannot conceal it from my own perception that, immediately subsequent to the fall of the ruby-drops, a rapid change for the worse took
place in the disorder of my wife; so that, on the third subsequent night,
the hands of her menials prepared her for the tomb, and on the fourth, I
sat alone, with her shrouded body, in that fantastic chamber which had
received her as my bride.—Wild visions, opium-engendered, flitted, shad-
owlike, before me. I gazed with unquiet eye upon the sarcophagi in the
angles of the room, upon the varying figures of the drapery, and upon
the writhing of the parti-colored fires in the censer overhead. My eyes then
fell, as I called to mind the circumstances of a former night, to the spot
beneath the glare of the censer where I had seen the faint traces of the
shadow. It was there, however, no longer; and breathing with greater freedom, I turned my glances to the pallid and rigid figure upon the bed.
Then rushed upon me a thousand memories of Ligeia—and then came
back upon my heart, with the turbulent violence of a flood, the whole of
that unutterable woe with which I had regarded *her* thus enshrouded.
The night waned; and still, with a bosom full of bitter thoughts of the
one only and supremely beloved, I remained gazing upon the body of
Rowena.

It might have been midnight, or perhaps earlier, or later, for I had
taken no note of time, when a sob, low, gentle, but very distinct, startled
me from my revery.—I *felt* that it came from the bed of ebony—the bed

of death. I listened in an agony of superstitious terror—but there was no repetition of the sound. I strained my vision to detect any motion in the corpse—but there was not the slightest perceptible. Yet I could not have been deceived. I *had* heard the noise, however faint, and my soul was awakened within me. I resolutely and perseveringly kept my attention riveted upon the body. Many minutes elapsed before any circumstance occurred tending to throw light upon the mystery. At length it became evident that a slight, a very feeble, and barely noticeable tinge of color had flushed up within the cheeks, and along the sunken small veins of the eyelids. Through a species of unutterable horror and awe, for which the language of mortality has no sufficiently energetic expression, I felt my heart cease to beat, my limbs grow rigid where I sat. Yet a sense of duty finally operated to restore my self-possession. I could no longer doubt that we had been precipitate in our preparations—that Rowena still lived. It was necessary that some immediate exertion be made; yet the turret was altogether apart from the portion of the abbey tenanted by the servants—there were none within call—I had no means of summoning them to my aid without leaving the room for many minutes—and this I could not venture to do. I therefore struggled alone in my endeavors to call back the spirit still hovering. In a short period it was certain, how-ever, that a relapse had taken place; the color disappeared from both eye-lid and cheek, leaving a wanness even more than that of marble; the lips became doubly shrivelled and pinched up in the ghastly expression of death; a repulsive clamminess and coldness overspread rapidly the sur-face of the body; and all the usual rigorous stiffness immediately super-vened. I fell back with a shudder upon the couch from which I had been so startlingly aroused, and again gave myself up to passionate waking visions of Ligeia.

An hour thus elapsed when (could it be possible?) I was a second time aware of some vague sound issuing from the region of the bed. I listened —in extremity of horror. The sound came again—it was a sigh. Rushing to the corpse, I saw—distinctly saw—a tremor upon the lips. In a minute afterward they relaxed, disclosing a bright line of the pearly teeth. Amaze-ment now struggled in my bosom with the profound awe which had hith-erto reigned there alone. I felt that my vision grew dim, that my reason wandered; and it was only by a violent effort that I at length succeeded in nerving myself to the task which duty thus once more had pointed out. There was now a partial glow upon the forehead and upon the cheek and throat; a perceptible warmth pervaded the whole frame; there was even a slight pulsation at the heart. The lady *lived;* and with redoubled ardor I betook myself to the task of restoration. I chafed and bathed the tem-ples and the hands, and used every exertion which experience, and no little medical reading, could suggest. But in vain. Suddenly, the color fled, the pulsation ceased, the lips resumed the expression of the dead, and, in an instant afterward, the whole body took upon itself the icy chilliness, the livid hue, the intense rigidity, the sunken outline, and all the loathsome peculiarities of that which has been, for many days, a tenant of the tomb.

And again I sunk into visions of Ligeia and again, (what marvel that I shudder while I write?) *again* there reached my ears a low sob from the region of the ebony bed. But why shall I minutely detail the unspeakable horrors of that night? Why shall I pause to relate how, time after time, until near the period of the gray dawn, this hideous drama of revivification was repeated; how each terrific relapse was only into a sterner and apparently more irredeemable death; how each agony wore the aspect of a struggle with some invisible foe; and how each struggle was succeeded by I know not what of wild change in the personal appearance of the corpse? Let me hurry to a conclusion.

The greater part of the fearful night had worn away, and she who had been dead once again stirred—and now more vigorously than hitherto, although arousing from a dissolution more appalling in its utter hopelessness than any. I had long ceased to struggle or to move, and remained sitting rigidly upon the ottoman, a helpless prey to a whirl of violent emotions, of which extreme awe was perhaps the least terrible, the least consuming. The corpse, I repeat, stirred, and now more vigorously than before. The hues of life flushed up with unwonted energy into the countenance—the limbs relaxed—and, save that the eyelids were yet pressed heavily together, and that the bandages and draperies of the grave still imparted their charnel character to the figure, I might have dreamed that Rowena had indeed shaken off, utterly, the fetters of Death. But if this idea was not, even then, altogether adopted, I could at least doubt no longer, when, arising from the bed, tottering, with feeble steps, with closed eyes, and with the manner of one bewildered in a dream, the thing that was enshrouded advanced boldly and palpably into the middle of the apartment.

I trembled not—I stirred not—for a crowd of unutterable fancies connected with the air, the stature, the demeanor of the figure, rushing hurriedly through my brain, had paralyzed—had chilled me into stone. I stirred not—but gazed upon the apparition. There was a mad disorder in my thoughts—a tumult unappeasable. Could it, indeed, be the *living* Rowena who confronted me? Could it, indeed, be Rowena *at all*—the fair-haired, the blue-eyed Lady Rowena Trevanion of Tremaine? Why *why* should I doubt it? The bandage lay heavily about the mouth—but then might it not be the mouth of the breathing Lady of Tremaine? And the cheeks—there were the roses as in her noon of life—yes, these might indeed be the fair cheeks of the living Lady of Tremaine. And the chin, with its dimples, as in health, might it not be hers?—but *had she then grown taller since her malady?* What inexpressible madness seized me with that thought? One bound, and I had reached her feet! Shrinking from my touch, she let fall from her head, unloosened, the ghastly cerements which had confined it, and there streamed forth into the rushing atmosphere of the chamber huge masses of long and dishevelled hair, *it was blacker than the raven wings of midnight!* And now slowly opened *the eyes* of the figure which stood before me. "Here then, at least," I shrieked aloud, "can I never—can I never be mistaken—these are the full, and the black, and the wild eyes—of my lost love—of the Lady—of the LADY LIGEIA."

QUESTIONS

1. How, in general, does the epigraph from Glanvill epitomize the theme of the story? In what ways is it given *literal* application in the events of the story?

2. What would seem to you to be the chief differences between the way we must approach a story like "Ligeia," which presents a fantasy world governed by supernatural forces, and a realistic or naturalistic story in which the world described is substantially the world we know in our own lives? For example, how do the elaborate descriptions of Ligeia, or of the furnishings of the gloomy abbey, differ in purpose and technique from the descriptions of people and places in Joyce's "A Painful Case"?

3. How would you characterize the prose style of the story? What kinds of diction, imagery, syntax, and sentence structure are responsible for its characteristic form and flavor? What part does literary allusion play in creating the total stylistic effect? What kind of relationship does the style tend to establish between the writer and the reader?

4. What are some of the more striking details of fact, image, or expression by which Poe establishes an air of the vague and indeterminate, of the unreal and other-worldly, of the unverifiable, in the story's opening paragraph? How is this impression built up as the story continues—in the second and third paragraphs, for example?

5. How do you understand, in its meaning for the story, the connection which Poe establishes in paragraphs four and five between Ligeia's eyes and the passage from Glanvill? Does the emphasis put upon her eyes in paragraphs three, four, and five receive corresponding emphasis at a later point in the story? Where?

6. What significance do you find in the narrator's mode of decorating the apartments in which he lives with his second bride, Lady Rowena?

7. Assuming that "Ligeia" has made on a reader something like the full effect it is capable of, what kind of experience has the reader had when he returns from the realm of fantasy to the real world? Do you interpret the story as a hallucinatory vision engendered by the madness and grief of Ligeia's spouse? Or do the frequent references to the narrator's addiction to opium provide a means of explaining his vision away? Or does it seem to you that we should try to account in some other way for the bearing of this fantastic vision upon psychological reality?

THE FALL
OF THE HOUSE OF USHER

Son cœur est un luth suspendu;
Sitôt qu'on le touche il résonne.
De Béranger

During the whole of a dull, dark, and soundless day in the autumn of the year, when the clouds hung oppressively low in the heavens, I had been passing alone, on horseback, through a singularly dreary tract of country, and at length found myself, as the shades of the evening drew on, within view of the melancholy House of Usher. I know not how it was—but, with the first glimpse of the building, a sense of insufferable gloom pervaded my spirit. I say insufferable; for the feeling was unrelieved by any of that half-pleasurable, because poetic, sentiment, with which the mind usually receives even the sternest natural images of the desolate or terrible. I looked upon the scene before me—upon the mere house, and the simple landscape features of the domain—upon the bleak walls—upon the vacant eye-like windows—upon a few rank sedges—and upon a few white trunks of decayed trees—with an utter depression of soul which I can compare to no earthly sensation more properly than to the after-dream of the reveller upon opium—the bitter lapse into everyday life—the hideous dropping off of the veil. There was an iciness, a sinking, a sickening of the heart—an unredeemed dreariness of thought which no goading of the imagination could torture into aught of the sublime. What was it—I paused to think—what was it that so unnerved me in the contemplation of the House of Usher? It was a mystery all insoluble; nor could I grapple with the shadowy fancies that crowded upon me as I pondered. I was forced to fall back upon the unsatisfactory conclusion, that while, beyond doubt, there *are* combinations of very simple natural objects which have the power of thus affecting us, still the analysis of this power lies among considerations beyond our depth. It was possible, I reflected, that a mere different arrangement of the particulars of the scene, of the details of the picture, would be sufficient to modify, or perhaps to annihilate its capacity for sorrowful impression; and, acting upon this idea, I reined my horse to the precipitous brink of a black and lurid tarn that lay in unruffled lustre by the dwelling, and gazed down—but with a shudder even more thrilling than before—upon the remodelled and inverted images of the gray sedge, and the ghastly tree-stems, and the vacant and eye-like windows.

Nevertheless, in this mansion of gloom I now proposed to myself a sojourn of some weeks. Its proprietor, Roderick Usher, had been one of my boon companions in boyhood; but many years had elapsed since our last meeting. A letter, however, had lately reached me in a distant part of the country—a letter from him—which, in its wildly importunate nature, had admitted of no other than a personal reply. The MS. gave evidence of nervous agitation. The writer spoke of acute bodily illness—of a mental disorder which oppressed him—and of an earnest desire to see me, as his best, and indeed his only personal friend, with a view of attempting, by the cheerfulness of my society, some alleviation of his malady. It was the manner in which all this, and much more, was said—it was the apparent *heart* that went with his request—which allowed me no room for hesitation; and I accordingly obeyed forthwith what I still considered a very singular summons.

Although, as boys, we had been even intimate associates, yet I really knew little of my friend. His reserve had been always excessive and habitual. I was aware, however, that his very ancient family had been noted, time out of mind, for a peculiar sensibility of temperament, displaying itself, through long ages, in many works of exalted art, and manifested, of late, in repeated deeds of munificent yet unobtrusive charity, as well as in a passionate devotion to the intricacies, perhaps even more than to the orthodox and easily recognizable beauties, of musical science. I had learned, too, the very remarkable fact, that the stem of the Usher race, all time-honoured as it was, had put forth, at no period, any enduring branch; in other words, that the entire family lay in the direct line of descent, and had always, with very trifling and very temporary variation, so lain. It was this deficiency, I considered, while running over in thought the perfect keeping of the character of the premises with the accredited character of the people, and while speculating upon the possible influence which the one, in the long lapse of centuries, might have exercised upon the other—it was this deficiency, perhaps, of collateral issue, and the consequent undeviating transmission, from sire to son, of the patrimony with the name, which had, at length, so identified the two as to merge the original title of the estate in the quaint and unequivocal appellation of the "House of Usher"—an appellation which seemed to include, in the minds of the peasantry who used it, both the family and the family mansion.

I have said that the sole effect of my somewhat childish experiment—that of looking down within the tarn—had been to deepen the first singular impression. There can be no doubt that the consciousness of the rapid increase of my superstition—for why should I not so term it?—served mainly to accelerate the increase itself. Such, I have long known, is the paradoxical law of all sentiments having terror as a basis. And it might have been for this reason only, that, when I again uplifted my eyes to the house itself, from its image in the pool, there grew in my mind a strange fancy—a fancy so ridiculous, indeed, that I but mention it to show the vivid force of the sensations which oppressed me. I had so worked upon my imagination as really to believe that about the whole mansion and domain there hung an atmosphere peculiar to themselves and their immediate vicinity—an atmosphere which had no affinity with the air of heaven, but which had reeked up from the decayed trees, and the gray wall, and the silent tarn—a pestilent and mystic vapour, dull, sluggish, faintly discernible, and leaden-hued.

Shaking off from my spirit what *must* have been a dream, I scanned more narrowly the real aspect of the building. Its principal feature seemed to be that of an excessive antiquity. The discoloration of ages had been great. Minute fungi overspread the whole exterior, hanging in a fine tangled web-work from the eaves. Yet all this was apart from any extraordinary dilapidation. No portion of the masonry had fallen; and there appeared to be a wild inconsistency between its still perfect adaptation of parts, and the crumbling condition of the individual stones. In this there was much that reminded me of the specious totality of old woodwork which has rotted for long years in some neglected vault, with no disturbance from the breath of the external air. Beyond this indication of extensive decay, however, the fabric gave little token of instability. Perhaps the eye of a scrutinizing observer might have discovered a barely perceptible fissure, which, extending from the roof of the building in front, made its way down the wall in a zigzag direction, until it became lost in the sullen waters of the tarn.

Noticing these things, I rode over a short causeway to the house. A servant in waiting took my horse, and I entered the Gothic archway of the hall. A valet, of stealthy step, thence conducted me, in silence, through many dark and intricate passages in my progress to the *studio* of his master. Much that I encountered on the way contributed, I know not how, to heighten the vague sentiments of which I have already spoken. While the objects around me—while the carvings of the ceilings, the sombre tapestries of the walls, the ebon blackness of the floors, and the phantasmagoric armorial trophies which rattled as I strode, were but matters to which, or to such as which, I had been accustomed from my infancy—while I hesitated not to acknowledge how familiar was all this—I still wondered to find how unfamiliar were the fancies which ordinary images were stirring up. On one of the staircases, I met the physician of the family. His countenance, I thought, wore a mingled expression of low cunning and perplexity. He accosted me with trepidation and passed on. The valet now threw open a door and ushered me into the presence of his master.

The room in which I found myself was very large and lofty. The windows were long, narrow, and pointed, and at so vast a distance from the black oaken floor as to be altogether inaccessible from within. Feeble gleams of encrimsoned light made their way through the trellissed planes, and served to render sufficiently distinct the more prominent objects around; the eye, however, struggled in vain to reach the remoter angles of the chamber, or the recesses of the vaulted and fretted ceiling. Dark draperies hung upon the walls. The general furniture was profuse, comfortless, antique, and tattered. Many books and musical instruments lay scattered about, but failed to give any vitality to the scene. I felt that I breathed an atmosphere of sorrow. An air of stern, deep, and irredeemable gloom hung over and pervaded all.

Upon my entrance, Usher arose from a sofa on which he had been lying at full length, and greeted me with a vivacious warmth which had much in it, I at first thought, of an overdone cordiality—of the constrained effort of the *ennuyé* man of the world. A glance, however, at his countenance convinced me of his perfect sincerity. We sat down; and for some moments, while he spoke not, I gazed upon him with a feeling half of pity, half of awe. Surely, man had never before so terribly altered, in so brief a period, as had Roderick Usher! It was with difficulty that I could bring myself to admit the identity of the wan being before me with the companion of my early boyhood. Yet the character of his face had been at all times remarkable. A cadaverousness of complexion; an eye large, liquid, and luminous beyond comparison; lips somewhat thin and very pallid, but of a surpassingly beautiful curve; a nose of a delicate Hebrew model, but with a breadth of nostril unusual in similar formations; a finely moulded chin, speaking, in its want of prominence, of a want of moral energy; hair of a more than web-like softness and tenuity; these features, with an inordinate expansion above the regions of the temple, made up altogether a countenance not easily to be forgotten. And now in the mere exaggeration of the prevailing character of these features, and of the expression they were wont to convey, lay so much of change that I doubted to whom I spoke. The now ghastly pallor of the skin, and the now miraculous lustre of the eye, above all things startled and even awed me. The silken hair, too, had been suffered to grow all unheeded, and as, in its wild gossamer texture, it floated rather than fell about the face, I could not, even with effort, connect its arabesque expression with any idea of simple humanity.

In the manner of my friend I was at once struck with an incoherence—an inconsistency; and I soon found this to arise from a series of feeble and futile struggles to overcome an habitual trepidancy—an excessive nervous agitation. For something of this nature I had indeed been prepared, no less by his letter, than by reminiscences of certain boyish traits, and by conclusions deduced from his peculiar physical conformation and temperament. His action was alternately vivacious and sullen. His voice varied rapidly from a tremulous indecision (when the animal spirits seemed utterly in abeyance) to that species of energetic concision—that abrupt, weighty, unhurried, and hollow-sounding enunciation—that leaden, self-balanced, and perfectly modulated guttural utterance, which may be observed in the lost drunkard, or the irreclaimable eater of opium, during the periods of his most intense excitement.

It was thus that he spoke of the object of my visit, of his earnest desire to see me, and of the solace he expected me to afford him. He entered, at some length, into what he conceived to be the nature of his malady. It was, he said, a constitutional and a family evil, and one for which he despaired to find a remedy—a mere nervous affection, he immediately added, which would undoubtedly soon pass off. It displayed itself in a host of unnatural sensations. Some of these, as he detailed them, interested and bewildered me; although, perhaps, the terms and the general manner of their narration had their weight. He suffered much from a morbid acuteness of the senses; the most insipid food was alone endurable; he could wear only garments of certain texture; the odours of all flowers were oppressive; his eyes were tortured by even a faint light; and there were but peculiar sounds, and these from stringed instruments, which did not inspire him with horror.

To an anomalous species of terror I found him a bounden slave. "I shall perish," said he, "I *must* perish in this deplorable folly. Thus, thus, and not otherwise, shall I be lost. I dread the events of the future, not in themselves, but in their results. I shudder at the thought of any, even the most trivial, incident, which may operate upon this intolerable agitation of soul. I have, indeed, no abhorrence of danger, except in its absolute effect —in terror. In this unnerved—in this pitiable condition—I feel that the period will sooner or later arrive when I must abandon life and reason together, in some struggle with the grim phantasm, FEAR."

I learned, moreover, at intervals, and through broken and equivocal hints, another singular feature of his mental condition. He was enchained by certain superstitious impressions in regard to the dwelling which he tenanted, and whence, for many years, he had never ventured forth—in regard to an influence whose supposititious force was conveyed in terms too shadowy here to be re-stated—an influence which some peculiarities in the mere form and substance of his family mansion had, by dint of long sufferance, he said, obtained over his spirit—an effect which the *physique* of the gray wall and turrets, and of the dim tarn into which they all looked down, had, at length, brought about upon the *morale* of his existence.

He admitted, however, although with hesitation, that much of the peculiar gloom which thus afflicted him could be traced to a more natural and far more palpable origin—to the severe and long-continued illness— indeed to the evidently approaching dissolution—of a tenderly beloved sister, his sole companion for long years, his last and only relative on earth. "Her decease," he said, with a bitterness which I can never forget, "would leave him (him the hopeless and the frail) the last of the ancient race of the Ushers." While he spoke, the lady Madeline (for so was she called) passed slowly through a remote portion of the apartment, and, without having noticed my presence, disappeared. I regarded her with an utter astonishment not unmingled with dread—and yet I found it impossible to account for such feelings. A sensation of stupor oppressed me, as my eyes followed her retreating steps. When a door, at length, closed upon her, my glance sought instinctively and eagerly the countenance of the brother—but he had buried his face in his hands, and I could only perceive that a far more than ordinary wanness had overspread the emaciated fingers through which trickled many passionate tears.

The disease of the lady Madeline had long baffled the skill of her physicians. A settled apathy, a gradual wasting away of the person, and frequent although transient affections of a partially cataleptical character were the unusual diagnosis. Hitherto she had steadily borne up against the pressure of her malady, and had not betaken herself finally to bed; but on the closing in of the evening of my arrival at the house, she succumbed (as her brother told me at night with inexpressible agitation) to the prostrating power of the destroyer; and I learned that the glimpse I had obtained of her person would thus probably be the last I should obtain—that the lady, at least while living, would be seen by me no more.

For several days ensuing, her name was unmentioned by either Usher or myself: and during this period I was busied in earnest endeavours to alleviate the melancholy of my friend. We painted and read together, or I listened, as if in a dream, to the wild improvisations of his speaking guitar. And thus, as a closer and still closer intimacy admitted me more unreservedly into the recesses of his spirit, the more bitterly did I perceive the futility of all attempt at cheering a mind from which darkness, as if an inherent positive quality, poured forth upon all objects of the moral and physical universe in one unceasing radiation of gloom.

I shall ever bear about me a memory of the many solemn hours I thus spent alone with the master of the House of Usher. Yet I should fail in any attempt to convey an idea of the exact character of the studies, or of the occupations, in which he involved me, or led me the way. An excited and highly distempered ideality threw a sulphureous lustre over all. His long improvised dirges will ring forever in my ears. Among other things, I hold painfully in mind a certain singular perversion and amplification of the wild air of the last waltz of Von Weber. From the paintings over which his elaborate fancy brooded, and which grew, touch by touch, into vagueness at which I shuddered the more thrillingly, because I shuddered knowing not why;—from these paintings (vivid as their images now are before me) I would in vain endeavour to educe more than a small portion which should lie within the compass of merely written words. By the utter simplicity, by the nakedness of his designs, he arrested and overawed attention. If ever mortal painted an idea, that mortal was Roderick Usher. For me at least—in the circumstances then surrounding me —there arose out of the pure abstractions which the hypochondriac contrived to throw upon his canvas, an intensity of intolerable awe, no shadow of which I felt ever yet in the contemplation of the certainly glowing yet too concrete reveries of Fuseli.

One of the phantasmagoric conceptions of my friend, partaking not so rigidly of the spirit of abstraction, may be shadowed forth, although feebly, in words. A small picture presented the interior of an immensely long and rectangular vault or tunnel, with low walls, smooth, white, and without interruption or device. Certain accessory points of the design served well to convey the idea that this excavation lay at an exceeding depth below the surface of the earth. No outlet was observed in any portion of its vast extent, and no torch or other artificial source of light was discernible; yet a flood of intense rays rolled throughout, and bathed the whole in a ghastly and inappropriate splendour.

I have just spoken of that morbid condition of the auditory nerve which rendered all music intolerable to the sufferer, with the exception of certain effects of stringed instruments. It was, perhaps, the narrow limits to which he thus confined himself upon the guitar, which gave birth, in great measure, to the fantastic character of his performances. But the fervid *facility* of his *impromptus* could not be so accounted for. They must have been, and were, in the notes, as well as in the words of his wild fantasias (for he not unfrequently accompanied himself with rhymed verbal improvisations), the result of that intense mental collectedness and concentration to which I have previously alluded as observable only in particular moments of the highest artificial excitement. The words of one of these rhapsodies I have easily remembered. I was, perhaps, the more forcibly impressed with it, as he gave it, because, in the under or mystic current of its meaning, I fancied that I perceived, and for the first time, a full consciousness on the part of Usher, of the tottering of his lofty reason upon her throne. The verses, which were entitled "The Haunted Palace," ran very nearly, if not accurately, thus:

I

In the greenest of our valleys,
    By good angels tenanted,
Once a fair and stately palace—
    Radiant palace—reared its head.
In the monarch Thought's dominion—
    It stood there!
Never seraph spread a pinion
    Over fabric half so fair.

II

Banners yellow, glorious, golden,
    On its roof did float and flow;
(This—all this—was in the olden
    Time long ago)
And every gentle air that dallied,
    In that sweet day,
Along the ramparts plumed and pallid,
    A winged odour went away.

III

Wanderers in that happy valley
    Through two luminous windows saw
Spirits moving musically
    To a lute's well-tunèd law,
Round about a throne, where sitting
    (Porphyrogene!)
In state his glory well befitting,
    The ruler of the realm was seen.

IV

And all with pearl and ruby glowing
    Was the fair palace door,
Through which came flowing, flowing, flowing
    And sparkling evermore,
A troop of Echoes whose sweet duty
    Was but to sing,
In voices of surpassing beauty,
    The wit and wisdom of their king.

V

But evil things, in robes of sorrow,
    Assailed the monarch's high estate;
(Ah, let us mourn, for never morrow
    Shall dawn upon him, desolate!)
And, round about his home, the glory
    That blushed and bloomed
Is but a dim-remembered story
    Of the old time entombed.

VI

And travellers now within that valley,
    Through the red-litten windows see
Vast forms that move fantastically
    To a discordant melody;
While, like a rapid ghastly river,
    Through the pale door,
A hideous throng rush out forever,
    And laugh—but smile no more.

I well remember that suggestions arising from this ballad, led us into a train of thought, wherein there became manifest an opinion of Usher's which I mention not so much on account of its novelty, (for other men have thought thus,) as on account of the pertinacity with which he maintained it. This opinion, in its general form, was that of the sentience of all vegetable things. But, in his disordered fancy, the idea had assumed a more daring character, and trespassed, under certain conditions, upon the kingdom of inorganization. I lack words to express the full extent or the earnest *abandon* of his persuasion. The belief, however, was connected (as I have previously hinted) with the gray stones of the home of his forefathers. The conditions of the sentience had been here, he imagined, fulfilled in the method of collocation of these stones—in the order of their arrangement, as well as in that of the many *fungi* which overspread them, and of the decayed trees which stood around—above all, in the long undisturbed endurance of this arrangement, and in its reduplication in the still waters of the tarn. Its evidence—the evidence of the sentience —was to be seen, he said (and I here started as he spoke), in the gradual yet certain condensation of an atmosphere of their own about the waters and the walls. The result was discoverable, he added, in that silent yet importunate and terrible influence which for centuries had moulded

the destinies of his family, and which made *him* what I now saw him—
what he was. Such opinions need no comment, and I will make none.

Our books—the books which, for years, had formed no small portion
of the mental existence of the invalid—were, as might be supposed, in
strict keeping with this character of phantasm. We pored together over
such works as the Ververt et Chartreuse of Gresset; the Belphegor of
Machiavelli; the Heaven and Hell of Swedenborg; the Subterranean Voyage of Nicholas Klimm of Holberg; the Chiromancy of Robert Flud, of
Jean D'Indaginé, and of De la Chambre; the Journey into the Blue Distance of Tieck; and the City of the Sun of Campanella. One favourite volume was a small octavo edition of the *Directorium Inquisitorum,* by the
Dominican Eymeric de Gironne; and there were passages in Pomponius
Mela, about the old African Satyrs and Œgipans, over which Usher would
sit dreaming for hours. His chief delight, however, was found in the
perusal of an exceedingly rare and curious book in quarto Gothic—the
manual of a forgotten church—the *Vigilæ Mortuorum secundum Chorum
Ecclesiæ Maguntinæ.*

I could not help thinking of the wild ritual of this work, and of its
probable influence upon the hypochondriac, when, one evening, having
informed me abruptly that the lady Madeline was no more, he stated his
intention of preserving her corpse for a fortnight, (previously to its final
interment,) in one of the numerous vaults within the main walls of the
building. The worldly reason, however, assigned for this singular proceeding, was one which I did not feel at liberty to dispute. The brother
had been led to his resolution (so he told me) by consideration of the
unusual character of the malady of the deceased, of certain obtrusive and
eager inquiries on the part of her medical men, and of the remote and
exposed situation of the burial-ground of the family. I will not deny that
when I called to mind the sinister countenance of the person whom I met
upon the staircase, on the day of my arrival at the house, I had no desire
to oppose what I regarded as at best but a harmless, and by no means an
unnatural, precaution.

At the request of Usher, I personally aided him in the arrangements
for the temporary entombment. The body having been encoffined, we two
alone bore it to its rest. The vault in which we placed it (and which had
been so long unopened that our torches, half smothered in its oppressive
atmosphere, gave us little opportunity for investigation) was small, damp,
and entirely without means of admission for light; lying, at great depth,
immediately beneath that portion of the building in which was my own
sleeping apartment. It had been used, apparently, in remote feudal times,
for the worst purposes of a donjon-keep, and, in later days, as a place of
deposit for powder, or some other highly combustible substance, as a
portion of its floor, and the whole interior of a long archway through
which we reached it, were carefully sheathed with copper. The door, of
massive iron, had been, also, similarly protected. Its immense weight
caused an unusually sharp grating sound, as it moved upon its hinges.

Having deposited our mournful burden upon tressels within this region of horror, we partially turned aside the yet unscrewed lid of the coffin, and looked upon the face of the tenant. A striking similitude between the brother and sister now first arrested my attention; and Usher, divining, perhaps, my thoughts, murmured out some few words from which I learned that the deceased and himself had been twins, and that sympathies of a scarcely intelligible nature had always existed between them. Our glances, however, rested not long upon the dead—for we could not regard her unawed. The disease which had thus entombed the lady in the maturity of youth, had left, as usual in all maladies of a strictly cataleptical character, the mockery of a faint blush upon the bosom and the face, and that suspiciously lingering smile upon the lip which is so terrible in death. We replaced and screwed down the lid, and, having secured the door of iron, made our way, with toil, into the scarcely less gloomy apartments of the upper portion of the house.

And now, some days of bitter grief having elapsed, an observable change came over the features of the mental disorder of my friend. His ordinary manner had vanished. His ordinary occupations were neglected or forgotten. He roamed from chamber to chamber with hurried, unequal, and objectless step. The pallor of his countenance had assumed, if possible, a more ghastly hue—but the luminousness of his eye had utterly gone out. The once occasional huskiness of his tone was heard no more; and a tremulous quaver, as if of extreme terror, habitually characterized his utterance. There were times, indeed, when I thought his unceasingly agitated mind was labouring with some oppressive secret, to divulge which he struggled for the necessary courage. At times, again, I was obliged to resolve all into the mere inexplicable vagaries of madness, for I beheld him gazing upon vacancy for long hours, in an attitude of the profoundest attention, as if listening to some imaginary sound. It was no wonder that his condition terrified—that it infected me. I felt creeping upon me, by slow yet certain degrees, the wild influences of his own fantastic yet impressive superstitions.

It was, especially, upon retiring to bed late in the night of the seventh or eighth day after the placing of the lady Madeline within the donjon, that I experienced the full power of such feelings. Sleep came not near my couch—while the hours waned and waned away. I struggled to reason off the nervousness which had dominion over me. I endeavoured to believe that much, if not all of what I felt, was due to the bewildering influence of the gloomy furniture of the room—of the dark and tattered draperies, which, tortured into motion by the breath of a rising tempest, swayed fitfully to and fro upon the walls, and rustled uneasily about the decorations of the bed. But my efforts were fruitless. An irrepressible tremour gradually pervaded my frame; and, at length, there sat upon my very heart an incubus of utterly causeless alarm. Shaking this off with a gasp and a struggle, I uplifted myself upon the pillows, and, peering earnestly within the intense darkness of the chamber, hearkened—I know not why, except that an instinctive spirit prompted me—to certain low and indefinite sounds which came, through the pauses of the storm, at long intervals, I knew not whence. Overpowered by an intense sentiment of horror, unaccountable yet unendurable, I threw on my clothes with haste, (for I felt that I should sleep no more during the night,) and endeavoured to arouse myself from the pitiable condition into which I had fallen, by pacing rapidly to and fro through the apartment.

I had taken but few turns in this manner, when a light step on an adjoining staircase arrested my attention. I presently recognised it as that of Usher. In an instant afterward he rapped, with a gentle touch, at my door, and entered, bearing a lamp. His countenance was, as usual, cadaverously wan—but, moreover, there was a species of mad hilarity in his eyes—an evidently restrained *hysteria* in his whole demeanour. His air appalled me—but anything was preferable to the solitude which I had so long endured, and I even welcomed his presence as a relief.

"And you have not seen it?" he said abruptly, after having stared about him for some moments in silence—"you have not then seen it?—but, stay! you shall." Thus speaking, and having carefully shaded his lamp, he hurried to one of the casements, and threw it freely open to the storm.

The impetuous fury of the entering gust nearly lifted us from our feet. It was, indeed, a tempestuous yet sternly beautiful night, and one wildly singular in its terror and its beauty. A whirlwind had apparently collected its force in our vicinity; for there were frequent and violent alterations in the direction of the wind; and the exceeding density of the clouds (which hung so low as to press upon the turrets of the house) did not prevent our perceiving the life-like velocity with which they flew careering from all points against each other, without passing away into the distance. I say that even their exceeding density did not prevent our perceiving this—yet we had no glimpse of the moon or stars—nor was there any flashing forth of the lightning. But the under surfaces of the huge masses of agitated vapour, as well as all terrestrial objects immediately around us, were glowing in the unnatural light of a faintly luminous and distinctly visible gaseous exhalation which hung about and enshrouded the mansion.

"You must not—you shall not behold this!" said I, shudderingly, to Usher, as I led him, with a gentle violence, from the window to a seat. "These appearances, which bewilder you, are merely electrical phenomena not uncommon—or it may be that they have their ghastly origin in the rank miasma of the tarn. Let us close this casement;—the air is chilling and dangerous to your frame. Here is one of your favourite romances. I will read, and you shall listen;—and so we will pass away this terrible night together."

The antique volume which I had taken up was the "Mad Trist" of Sir Launcelot Canning; but I had called it a favourite of Usher's more in sad jest than in earnest; for, in truth, there is little in its uncouth and unimaginative prolixity which could have had interest for the lofty and spiritual ideality of my friend. It was, however, the only book immediately at hand; and I indulged a vague hope that the excitement which now agitated the hypochondriac, might find relief (for the history of mental disorder is full of similar anomalies) even in the extremeness of the folly which I should read. Could I have judged, indeed, by the wild overstrained air of vivacity with which he hearkened, or apparently hearkened, to the words of the tale, I might well have congratulated myself upon the success of my design.

I had arrived at that well-known portion of the story where Ethelred, the hero of the Trist, having sought in vain for peaceable admission into the dwelling of the hermit, proceeds to make good an entrance by force. Here, it will be remembered, the words of the narrative run thus:

"And Ethelred, who was by nature of a doughty heart, and who was now mighty withal, on account of the powerfulness of the wine which he had drunken, waited no longer to hold parley with the hermit, who, in sooth, was of an obstinate and maliceful turn, but, feeling the rain upon his shoulders, and fearing the rising of the tempest, uplifted his mace outright, and, with blows, made quickly room in the plankings of the door for his gauntleted hand; and now pulling therewith sturdily, he so cracked, and ripped, and tore all asunder, that the noise of the dry and hollow-sounding wood alarmed and reverberated throughout the forest."

At the termination of this sentence I started and, for a moment, paused; for it appeared to me (although I at once concluded that my excited fancy had deceived me)—it appeared to me that, from some very remote portion of the mansion, there came, indistinctly, to my ears, what might have been, in its exact similarity of character, the echo (but a stifled and dull one certainly) of the very cracking and ripping sound which Sir Launcelot had so particularly described. It was, beyond doubt, the coincidence alone which had arrested my attention; for, amid the rattling of the sashes of the casements, and the ordinary commingled noises of the still increasing storm, the sound, in itself, had nothing, surely, which should have interested or disturbed me. I continued the story:

"But the good champion Ethelred, now entering within the door, was sore enraged and amazed to perceive no signal of the maliceful hermit; but, in the stead thereof, a dragon of a scaly and prodigious demeanour, and of a fiery tongue, which sate in guard before a palace of gold, with a floor of silver; and upon the wall there hung a shield of shining brass with this legend enwritten—

Who entereth herein, a conqueror hath bin;
Who slayeth the dragon, the shield he shall win.

And Ethelred uplifted his mace, and struck upon the head of the dragon, which befell him, and gave up his pesty breath, with a shriek so horrid and harsh, and withal so piercing, that Ethelred had fain to close his ears with his hands against the dreadful noise of it, the like whereof was never before heard."

Here again I paused abruptly, and now with a feeling of wild amaze-ment—for there could be no doubt whatever that, in this instance, I did actually hear (although from what direction it proceeded I found it im-possible to say) a low and apparently distant, but harsh, protracted, and most unusual screaming or grating sound—the exact counterpart of what my fancy had already conjured up for the dragon's unnatural shriek as described by the romancer.

Oppressed, as I certainly was, upon the occurrence of the second and most extraordinary coincidence, by a thousand conflicting sensations, in which wonder and extreme terror were predominant, I still retained suf-ficient presence of mind to avoid exciting, by any observation, the sensi-tive nervousness of my companion. I was by no means certain that he had noticed the sounds in question; although, assuredly, a strange altera-tion had, during the last few minutes, taken place in his demeanour. From a position fronting my own, he had gradually brought round his chair, so as to sit with his face to the door of the chamber; and thus I could but partially perceive his features, although I saw that his lips trembled as if he were murmuring inaudibly. His head had dropped upon his breast—yet I knew that he was not asleep, from the wide and rigid opening of the eye as I caught a glance of it in profile. The motion of his body, too, was at variance with this idea—for he rocked from side to side with a gentle yet constant and uniform sway. Having rapidly taken notice of all this, I resumed the narrative of Sir Launcelot, which thus proceeded.

"And now, the champion, having escaped from the terrible fury of the dragon, bethinking himself of the brazen shield, and of the breaking up of the enchantment which was upon it, removed the carcass from out of the way before him, and approached valorously over the silver pavement of the castle to where the shield was upon the wall; which in sooth tar-ried not for his full coming, but fell down at his feet upon the silver floor, with a mighty great and terrible ringing sound."

No sooner had these syllables passed my lips, than—as if a shield of brass had indeed, at the moment, fallen heavily upon a floor of silver—I became aware of a distinct, hollow, metallic, and clangorous, yet appar-ently muffled reverberation. Completely unnerved, I leaped to my feet; but the measured rocking movement of Usher was undisturbed. I rushed to the chair in which he sat. His eyes were bent fixedly before him, and throughout his whole countenance there reigned a stony rigidity. But, as I placed my hand upon his shoulder, there came a strong shudder over his whole person; a sickly smile quivered about his lips; and I saw that he spoke in a low, hurried, and gibbering murmur, as if unconscious of my presence. Bending closely over him, I at length drank in the hideous import of his words.

"Not hear it?—yes, I hear it, and *have* heard it. Long—long—long— many minutes, many hours, many days, have I heard it—yet I dared not —oh, pity me, miserable wretch that I am!—I dared not—I *dared* not speak! *We have put her living in the tomb!* Said I not that my senses were acute? I *now* tell you that I heard her first feeble movements in the hollow coffin. I heard them—many, many days ago—yet I dared not—I *dared not speak!* And now—to-night—Ethelred—ha! ha!—the breaking of the hermit's door, and the death-cry of the dragon, and the clangour of the shield!—say, rather, the rending of her coffin, and the grating of the iron hinges of her prison, and her struggles within the coppered arch-way of the vault! Oh whither shall I fly? Will she not be here anon? Is she not hurrying to upbraid me for my haste? Have I not heard her footsteps on the stair? Do I not distinguish that heavy and horrible beating of her heart? MADMAN!"—here he sprang furiously to his feet, and shrieked out his syllables, as if in the effort he were giving up his soul— "MADMAN! I TELL YOU THAT SHE NOW STANDS WITHOUT THE DOOR!"

As if in the superhuman energy of his utterance there had been found the potency of a spell—the huge antique panels to which the speaker pointed threw slowly back, upon the instant, their ponderous and ebony jaws. It was the work of the rushing gust—but then without those doors there DID stand the lofty and enshrouded figure of the lady Madeline of Usher. There was blood upon her white robes, and the evidence of some bitter struggle upon every portion of her emaciated frame. For a moment she remained trembling and reeling to and fro upon the threshold, then, with a low moaning cry, fell heavily inward upon the person of her brother, and in her violent and now final death-agonies, bore him to the floor a corpse, and a victim to the terrors he had anticipated.

From that chamber, and from that mansion, I fled aghast. The storm was still abroad in all its wrath as I found myself crossing the old cause-way. Suddenly there shot along the path a wild light, and I turned to see whence a gleam so unusual could have issued; for the vast house and its shadows were alone behind me. The radiance was that of the full, setting, and blood-red moon, which now shone vividly through that once barely discernible fissure, of which I have before spoken as extending from the roof of the building, in a zigzag direction, to the base. While I gazed, this fissure rapidly widened—there came a fierce breath of the whirlwind— the entire orb of the satellite burst at once upon my sight—my brain reeled as I saw the mighty walls rushing asunder—there was a long tumultuous shouting sound like the voice of a thousand waters—and the deep and dank tarn at my feet closed sullenly and silently over the frag-ments of the "HOUSE OF USHER."

QUESTIONS

1. What is the difference between the point of view which Poe uses in this story and the point of view he used in "Ligeia"?

2. The two lines of verse which form the epigraph may be translated thus: "His heart is a suspended lute; one touch, and it resounds." Where in the story do you find instances of extremely sensitive responsiveness to

impulses from without? Does the epigraph seem to have as important a function in this story as the passage from Glanvill had in "Ligeia"?

3. How is Poe's over-all symbolic plan for the story foreshadowed in paragraph three?

4. In describing Roderick Usher's paintings, the narrator says: "If ever mortal painted an idea, that mortal was Roderick Usher." What does Poe seem to you to mean by "painting an idea"? Could the phrase be used to describe what Poe himself does in this story?

5. Does the "small picture" described in paragraph seventeen lend itself to symbolic interpretation? What bearing might it have on Roderick Usher's own preoccupations, as we later learn what they must have been?

6. Poe's own requirements for a short story are outlined briefly in the headnote which precedes "Ligeia," above. Does "The Fall of the House of Usher" seem to you to achieve the unity of effect which seemed to him essential? How would you describe the single, over-all effect which he strives to create in this story? How completely does the opening paragraph suggest that effect?

NATHANIEL HAWTHORNE

(1804–1864)

Like many of the other writers in the present collection, Hawthorne was both novelist and short-story writer, and although we are here interested primarily in his short stories, it is difficult to set up a hard and fast demarcation between the writer of short stories and the novelist. Most of what one would want to say about Hawthorne in a brief general statement will have application to his literary practice as a whole, not just to the specific phases of it which produced the short stories, tales, and sketches. One point may be made with confidence, however: although he is most widely known for one of his novels, *The Scarlet Letter,* and although his short stories might not by themselves have earned him his actual place as one of the very greatest figures in American literature, they are by no means a minor or incidental part of his achievement but make their own distinct contribution to its weight and quality.

The first books he published were collections of stories: *Twice-Told Tales* in 1837, followed by a second series with the same title in 1842, and by still a third collection, *Mosses from an Old Manse,* in 1846. In 1850 he published his first novel, *The Scarlet Letter,* which was also the first work to bring him any considerable success. This was followed by another novel in 1851, *The House of the Seven Gables,* a work with which most American readers are familiar, having encountered it in high school if nowhere else, and by another volume of stories, *The Snow-Image and other Twice-Told Tales* in the same year. In 1852 he published *The Blithedale Romance*, different from his other novels in that it offered realistic, almost naturalistic, criticism of a specific contemporary situation which Hawthorne had seen at first hand. And if we record that in 1860 he published under the title of *Transformation, or The Romance of Monte Beni*, the novel that was to be later and better known as *The Marble Faun*, we have listed the chief items in Hawthorne's literary production.

He had been born in Salem, Massachusetts, on July 4, 1804, and he died in Plymouth, New Hampshire, on May 19, 1864. He went to Bowdoin College, in Maine, from 1821 to 1825, where Longfellow and Franklin Pierce were fellow students. For several years after graduating from Bowdoin, he settled down to a quiet life of literary activity in his native Salem. Much of Hawthorne's life was to be rendered difficult and uncertain by the pull between his wish to devote himself to writing and the recurrent necessity of entering on a career that would enable him to make a living. Periods spent largely in writing—at the Old Manse, in Concord, for a few years after his marriage in 1842, and again later in his life at Lenox, Massachusetts—alternated with periods in which he saw the busier face of the world. Before his marriage, he had been employed at the Custom House in Boston, and later he was Collector of Customs at Salem. He lived at Brook Farm for a while, taking part in the socialist-cooperative farming venture which he described with such wry sharpness in *The Blithedale Romance*. As a result of his friendship with President Pierce, whose *Life* he wrote (1852), he held the post of U. S. Consul at Liverpool from 1853 to 1858. During the winter of 1857–58 he was in Italy, gathering in Rome and Florence the first-hand impressions which were to form the background of his only major work which does not have a New England setting, *The Marble Faun*.

Hawthorne's Italy, as he presents it in that novel, is very good— palpable, vividly and lovingly detailed, highly evocative of romance, mystery, and the constant, almost overwhelming presence of works of art. But it is fair to say that many nineteenth-century English and American writers, in love with Italy and her splendid productions, did as well. On the other hand, it is hard to think of any writer who has succeeded more completely and brilliantly in evoking the atmosphere, the ethos of a place than Hawthorne has done with New England. It is partly evocation and partly creation, for Hawthorne took the range of sights, sounds, and atmospheres which he found about him in Salem, in Concord, in Western Massachusetts, in New Hampshire, and made it the embodiment for the range of moral and spiritual perceptions and impressions which in turn produced his habitual themes.

In his critical biography of Hawthorne published in 1880, Henry James gently bewailed the thinness of resource which American life, the American scene, presented to a writer of Hawthorne's time and stamp, intent on producing romance in a country that was devoid of that commodity, as well as of all mystery, interesting gloomy wrong, or complexity of social form. But it was precisely Hawthorne's triumph to take his subject and his scene where he found them, and to compound out of the "bright, empty American air" a quintessence of feeling and significance that James's "denser, richer European spectacle" was—for Hawthorne—powerless to provide: as we know when we compare the "American" works with *The Marble Faun.*

One of Hawthorne's habitual themes—indeed, his central theme—was solitude. Not the fortuitous, external solitude of the light-house keeper or the night-watchman, but the essential solitude which a man seeks out for himself and which he will find even in the presence of those closest and dearest to him if he is driven to set himself apart in his soul from other men. This is the theme of "The Minister's Black Veil," of "Egotism, or The Bosom Serpent," and of one of Hawthorne's most nearly perfect stories, "Ethan Brand," and in its many variations—that of pride in one's skill or position or achievement, for instance—it runs through most of Hawthorne's tales. Often a given story will present a central symbol, easily recognizable, as well as the whole array or more subtly symbolic motifs and situations. But the moral question involved in the theme is not conceived in mere cold intellectuality: it is deeply and sympathetically felt, and debated in a way that shows us how deeply Hawthorne felt himself engaged in the issue. In "Ethan Brand," for example, the struggle is evenly joined. In the figure of Ethan Brand himself, we see the attraction of an exclusiveness that is bred of a certain lofty distinction of mind and soul; and in all the rag-tag-and-bobtail of the minor figures, we see humanity as it is, with all its faults, its weakness, its foolishness, and its brute ugliness. All this assortment of human types, as we know from Hawthorne's notebooks, had been directly observed in his travels and sojourns in his own New England. New England presented him with the forms, the traits, the conditions of life as it is, often thin in its appeal, uncompromising, even corrupt—but life, for all that, and as life having a categorical claim on the sympathy and fellowship of any heart made, not of marble, but of flesh and blood.

ETHAN BRAND

A Chapter from an Abortive Romance

Bartram the lime-burner, a rough, heavy-looking man, begrimed with charcoal, sat watching his kiln at nightfall, while his little son played at building houses with the scattered fragments of marble, when, on the hill-side below them, they heard a roar of laughter, not mirthful, but slow, and even solemn, like a wind shaking the boughs of the forest.

"Father, what is that?" asked the little boy, leaving his play, and pressing betwixt his father's knees.

"Oh, some drunken man, I suppose," answered the lime-burner; "some merry fellow from the bar-room in the village, who dared not laugh loud enough within doors lest he should blow the roof of the house off. So here he is, shaking his jolly sides at the foot of Graylock."

"But, father," said the child, more sensitive than the obtuse, middle-aged clown, "he does not laugh like a man that is glad. So the noise frightens me!"

"Don't be a fool, child!" cried his father, gruffly. "You will never make a man, I do believe; there is too much of your mother in you. I have known the rustling of a leaf startle you. Hark! Here comes the merry fellow now. You shall see that there is no harm in him."

Bartram and his little son, while they were talking thus, sat watching the same lime-kiln that had been the scene of Ethan Brand's solitary and meditative life, before he began his search for the Unpardonable Sin. Many years, as we have seen, had now elapsed, since that portentous night when the IDEA was first developed. The kiln, however, on the mountain-side, stood unimpaired, and was in nothing changed since he had thrown his dark thoughts into the intense glow of its furnace, and melted them, as it were, into the one thought that took possession of his life. It was a rude, round, tower-like structure about twenty feet high, heavily built of rough stones, and with a hillock of earth heaped about the larger part of its circumference; so that the blocks and fragments of marble might be drawn by cart-loads, and thrown in at the top. There was an opening at the bottom of the tower, like an oven-mouth, but large enough to admit a man in a stooping posture, and provided with a massive iron door. With the smoke and jets of flame issuing from the chinks and crevices of this door, which seemed to give admittance into the hill-side, it resembled nothing so much as the private entrance to the infernal regions, which the shepherds of the Delectable Mountains were accustomed to show to pilgrims.

There are many such lime-kilns in that tract of country, for the purpose of burning the white marble which composes a large part of the substance of the hills. Some of them, built years ago, and long deserted, with weeds growing in the vacant round of the interior, which is open to the sky, and grass and wild-flowers rooting themselves into the chinks of the stones, look already like relics of antiquity, and may yet be overspread with the lichens of centuries to come. Others, where the lime-burner still feeds his daily and night-long fire, afford points of interest to the wanderer among the hills, who seats himself on a log of wood or a fragment of marble, to hold a chat with the solitary man. It is a lonesome, and, when the character is inclined to thought, may be an intensely thoughtful occupation; as it proved in the case of Ethan Brand, who had mused to such strange purpose, in days gone by, while the fire in this very kiln was burning.

The man who now watched the fire was of a different order, and troubled himself with no thoughts save the very few that were requisite to his business. At frequent intervals, he flung back the clashing weight of the iron door, and, turning his face from the insufferable glare, thrust in huge logs of oak, or stirred the immense brands with a long pole. Within the furnace were seen the curling and riotous flames, and the burning marble, almost molten with the intensity of heat; while without, the reflection of the fire quivered on the dark intricacy of the surrounding forest, and showed in the foreground a bright and ruddy little picture of the hut, the spring beside its door, the athletic and coal-begrimed figure of the lime-burner, and the half-frightened child, shrinking into the protection of his father's shadow. And when, again, the iron door was closed, then reappeared the tender light of the half-full moon, which vainly strove to trace out the indistinct shapes of the neighboring mountains; and, in the upper sky, there was a flitting congregation of clouds, still faintly tinged with the rosy sunset, though thus far down into the valley the sunshine had vanished long and long ago.

The little boy now crept still closer to his father, as footsteps were heard ascending the hill-side, and a human form thrust aside the bushes that clustered beneath the trees.

"Halloo! who is it?" cried the lime-burner, vexed at his son's timidity, yet half infected by it. "Come forward, and show yourself, like a man, or I'll fling this chunk of marble at your head!"

"You offer me a rough welcome," said a gloomy voice, as the unknown man drew nigh. "Yet I neither claim nor desire a kinder one, even at my own fireside."

To obtain a distincter view, Bartram threw open the iron door of the kiln, whence immediately issued a gush of fierce light, that smote full upon the stranger's face and figure. To a careless eye there appeared nothing very remarkable in his aspect, which was that of a man in a coarse, brown, country-made suit of clothes, tall and thin, with the staff and heavy shoes of a wayfarer. As he advanced, he fixed his eyes—which were very bright—intently upon the brightness of the furnace, as if he beheld, or expected to behold, some object worthy of note within it.

"Good evening, stranger," said the lime-burner; "whence come you, so late in the day?"

"I come from my search," answered the wayfarer; "for, at last, it is finished."

"Drunk!—or crazy!" muttered Bartram to himself. "I shall have trouble with the fellow. The sooner I drive him away, the better."

The little boy, all in a tremble, whispered to his father, and begged him to shut the door of the kiln, so that there might not be so much light; for that there was something in the man's face which he was afraid to look at, yet could not look away from. And, indeed, even the lime-burner's dull and torpid sense began to be impressed by an indescribable something in that thin, rugged, thoughtful visage, with the grizzled hair hanging wildly about it, and those deeply sunken eyes, which gleamed like fires within the entrance of a mysterious cavern. But, as he closed the door, the stranger turned towards him, and spoke in a quiet, familiar way, that made Bartram feel as if he were a sane and sensible man, after all.

"Your task draws to an end, I see," said he. "This marble has already been burning three days. A few hours more will convert the stone to lime."

"Why, who are you?" exclaimed the lime-burner. "You seem as well acquainted with my business as I am myself."

"And well I may be," said the stranger; "for I followed the same craft many a long year, and here, too, on this very spot. But you are a new-comer in these parts. Did you never hear of Ethan Brand?"

"The man that went in search of the Unpardonable Sin?" asked Bartram, with a laugh.

"The same," answered the stranger. "He has found what he sought, and therefore he comes back again."

"What! then you are Ethan Brand himself?" cried the lime-burner, in amazement. "I am a new-comer here, as you say, and they call it eighteen years since you left the foot of Graylock. But, I can tell you, the good folks still talk about Ethan Brand, in the village yonder, and what a strange errand took him away from his lime-kiln. Well, and so you have found the Unpardonable Sin?"

"Even so!" said the stranger, calmly.

"If the question is a fair one," proceeded Bartram, "where might it be?"

Ethan Brand laid his finger on his own heart.

"Here!" replied he.

And then, without mirth in his countenance, but as if moved by an involuntary recognition of the infinite absurdity of seeking throughout the world for what was the closest of all things to himself, and looking into every heart, save his own, for what was hidden in no other breast, he broke into a laugh of scorn. It was the same slow, heavy laugh, that had almost appalled the lime-burner when it heralded the wayfarer's approach.

The solitary mountain-side was made dismal by it. Laughter, when out of place, mistimed, or bursting forth from a disordered state of feeling, may be the most terrible modulation of the human voice. The laughter of one asleep, even if it be a little child,—the madman's laugh,—the wild, screaming laugh of a born idiot,—are sounds that we sometimes tremble to hear, and would always willingly forget. Poets have imagined no utterance of fiends or hobgoblins so fearfully appropriate as a laugh. And even the obtuse lime-burner felt his nerves shaken, as this strange man looked inward at his own heart, and burst into laughter that rolled away into the night, and was indistinctly reverberated among the hills.

"Joe," said he to his little son, "scamper down to the tavern in the village, and tell the jolly fellows there that Ethan Brand has come back, and that he has found the Unpardonable Sin!"

The boy darted away on his errand, to which Ethan Brand made no objection, nor seemed hardly to notice it. He sat on a log of wood, looking steadfastly at the iron door of the kiln. When the child was out of sight, and his swift and light footsteps ceased to be heard treading first on the fallen leaves and then on the rocky mountain-path, the lime-burner began to regret his departure. He felt that the little fellow's presence had been a barrier between his guest and himself, and that he must now deal, heart to heart, with a man who, on his own confession, had committed the one only crime for which Heaven could afford no mercy. That crime, in its indistinct blackness, seemed to overshadow him, and made his memory riotous with a throng of evil shapes that asserted their kindred with the Master Sin, whatever it might be, which it was within the scope of man's corrupted nature to conceive and cherish. They were all of one family; they went to and fro between his breast and Ethan Brand's, and carried dark greetings from one to the other.

Then Bartram remembered the stories which had grown traditionary in reference to this strange man, who had come upon him like a shadow of the night, and was making himself at home in his old place, after so long absence, that the dead people, dead and buried for years, would have had more right to be at home, in any familiar spot, than he. Ethan Brand, it was said, had conversed with Satan himself in the lurid blaze of this very kiln. The legend had been matter of mirth heretofore, but looked grisly now. According to this tale, before Ethan Brand departed on his search, he had been accustomed to evoke a fiend from the hot furnace of the lime-kiln, night after night, in order to confer with him about the Unpardonable Sin; the man and the fiend each laboring to frame the image of some mode of guilt which could neither be atoned for nor forgiven. And, with the first gleam of light upon the mountain-top, the fiend crept in at the iron door, there to abide the intensest element of fire until again summoned forth to share in the dreadful task of extending man's possible guilt beyond the scope of Heaven's else infinite mercy.

While the lime-burner was struggling with the horror of these thoughts, Ethan Brand rose from the log, and flung open the door of the kiln. The action was in such accordance with the idea in Bartram's mind, that he almost expected to see the Evil One issue forth, red-hot, from the raging furnace.

"Hold! hold!" cried he, with a tremulous attempt to laugh; for he was ashamed of his fears, although they overmastered him. "Don't, for mercy's sake, bring out your Devil now!"

"Man!" sternly replied Ethan Brand, "what need have I of the Devil? I have left him behind me, on my track. It is with such half-way sinners as you that he busies himself. Fear not, because I open the door. I do but act by old custom, and am going to trim your fire, like a lime-burner, as I was once."

He stirred the vast coals, thrust in more wood, and bent forward to gaze into the hollow prison-house of the fire, regardless of the fierce glow that reddened upon his face. The lime-burner sat watching him, and half suspected this strange guest of a purpose, if not to evoke a fiend, at least to plunge into the flames, and thus vanish from the sight of man. Ethan Brand, however, drew quietly back, and closed the door of the kiln.

"I have looked," said he, "into many a human heart that was seven times hotter with sinful passions than yonder furnace is with fire. But I found not there what I sought. No, not the Unpardonable Sin!"

"What is the Unpardonable Sin?" asked the lime-burner; and then he shrank farther from his companion, trembling lest his question should be answered.

"It is a sin that grew within my own breast," replied Ethan Brand, standing erect with a pride that distinguishes all enthusiasts of his stamp. "A sin that grew nowhere else! The sin of an intellect that triumphed over the sense of brotherhood with man and reverence for God, and sacrificed everything to its own mighty claims! The only sin that deserves a recompense of immortal agony! Freely, were it to do again, would I incur the guilt. Unshrinkingly I accept the retribution!"

"The man's head is turned," muttered the lime-burner to himself. "He may be a sinner like the rest of us,—nothing more likely,—but, I'll be sworn, he is a madman too."

Nevertheless, he felt uncomfortable at his situation, alone with Ethan Brand on the wild mountain-side, and was right glad to hear the rough murmur of tongues, and the footsteps of what seemed a pretty numerous party, stumbling over the stones and rustling through the underbrush. Soon appeared the whole lazy regiment that was wont to infest the village tavern, comprehending three or four individuals who had drunk flip beside the bar-room fire through all the winters, and smoked their pipes beneath the stoop through all the summers, since Ethan Brand's departure. Laughing boisterously, and mingling all their voices together in unceremonious talk, they now burst into the moonshine and narrow streaks of firelight that illuminated the open space before the lime-kiln. Bartram set the door ajar again, flooding the spot with light, that the whole company might get a fair view of Ethan Brand, and he of them.

There, among other old acquaintances, was a once ubiquitous man, now almost extinct, but whom we were formerly sure to encounter at the hotel of every thriving village throughout the country. It was the stage-agent. The present specimen of the genus was a wilted and smoke-dried man, wrinkled and red-nosed, in a smartly cut, brown, bobtailed coat, with brass buttons, who, for a length of time unknown, had kept his desk and corner in the bar-room, and was still puffing what seemed to be the same cigar that he had lighted twenty years before. He had great fame as a dry joker, though, perhaps, less on account of any intrinsic humor than from a certain flavor of brandy-toddy and tobacco-smoke, which impregnated all his ideas and expressions, as well as his person. Another well-remembered, though strangely altered, face was that of Lawyer Giles, as people still called him in courtesy; an elderly ragamuffin, in his soiled shirtsleeves and tow-cloth trousers. This poor fellow had been an attorney, in what he called his better days, a sharp practitioner, and in great vogue among the village litigants; but flip, and sling, and toddy, and cocktails, imbibed at all hours, morning, noon, and night, had caused him to slide from intellectual to various kinds and degrees of bodily labor, till at last, to adopt his own phrase, he slid into a soap-vat. In other words, Giles was now a soap-boiler, in a small way. He had come to be but the fragment of a human being, a part of one foot having been chopped off by an axe, and an entire hand torn away by the devilish grip of a steam-engine. Yet, though the corporeal hand was gone, a spiritual member remained; for, stretching forth the stump, Giles steadfastly averred that he felt an invisible thumb and fingers with as vivid a sensation as before the real ones were amputated. A maimed and miserable wretch he was; but one, nevertheless, whom the world could not trample on, and had no right to scorn, either in this or any previous stage of his misfortunes, since he had still kept up the courage and spirit of a man, asked nothing in charity, and with his one hand—and that the left one—fought a stern battle against want and hostile circumstances.

Among the throng, too, came another personage, who with certain points of similarity to Lawyer Giles, had many more of difference. It was the village doctor; a man of some fifty years, whom, at an earlier period of his life, we introduced as paying a professional visit to Ethan Brand during the latter's supposed insanity. He was now a purple-visaged, rude, and brutal, yet half-gentlemanly figure with something wild, ruined, and desperate in his talk, and in all the details of his gesture and manners. Brandy possessed this man like an evil spirit, and made him as surly and savage as a wild beast, and as miserable as a lost soul; but there was supposed to be in him such wonderful skill, such native gifts of healing, beyond any which medical science could impart, that society caught hold of him, and would not let him sink out of its reach. So, swaying to and fro upon his horse, and grumbling thick accents at the bedside, he visited all the sick-chambers for miles about among the mountain towns, and sometimes raised a dying man, as it were, by miracle, or quite as often, no doubt, sent his patient to a grave that was dug many a year too soon. The doctor had an everlasting pipe in his mouth, and, as somebody said, in allusion to his habit of swearing, it was always alight with hell-fire.

These three worthies pressed forward, and greeted Ethan Brand each after his own fashion, earnestly inviting him to partake of the contents of a certain black bottle, in which, as they averred, he would find something far better worth seeking than the Unpardonable Sin. No mind, which has wrought itself by intense and solitary meditation into a high state of enthusiasm, can endure the kind of contact with low and vulgar modes of thought and feeling to which Ethan Brand was now subjected. It made him doubt—and, strange to say, it was a painful doubt—whether he had indeed found the Unpardonable Sin, and found it within himself. The whole question on which he had exhausted life, and more than life, looked like a delusion.

"Leave me," he said bitterly, "ye brute beasts, that have made yourselves so, shrivelling up your souls with fiery liquors! I have done with you. Years and years ago, I groped into your hearts and found nothing there for my purpose. Get ye gone!"

"Why, you uncivil scoundrel," cried the fierce doctor, "is that the way you respond to the kindness of your best friends? Then let me tell you the truth. You have no more found the Unpardonable Sin than yonder boy Joe has. You are but a crazy fellow,—I told you so twenty years ago,—neither better nor worse than a crazy fellow, and the fit companion of old Humphrey, here!"

He pointed to an old man, shabbily dressed, with long white hair, thin visage, and unsteady eyes. For some years past this aged person had been wandering about among the hills, inquiring of all travellers whom he met for his daughter. The girl, it seemed, had gone off with a company of circus-performers, and occasionally tidings of her came to the village, and fine stories were told of her glittering appearance as she rode on horseback in the ring, or performed marvellous feats on the tight-rope.

The white-haired father now approached Ethan Brand, and gazed unsteadily into his face.

"They tell me you have been all over the earth," said he, wringing his hands with earnestness. "You must have seen my daughter, for she makes a grand figure in the world, and everybody goes to see her. Did she send any word to her old father, or say when she was coming back?"

Ethan Brand's eye quailed beneath the old man's. That daughter, from whom he so earnestly desired a word of greeting, was the Esther of our tale, the very girl whom, with such cold and remorseless purpose, Ethan Brand had made the subject of a psychological experiment, and wasted, absorbed, and perhaps annihilated her soul, in the process.

"Yes," he murmured, turning away from the hoary wanderer, "it is no delusion. There is an Unpardonable Sin!"

While these things were passing, a merry scene was going forward in the area of cheerful light, beside the spring and before the door of the hut. A number of the youth of the village, young men and girls, had hurried up the hill-side, impelled by curiosity to see Ethan Brand, the hero of so many a legend familiar to their childhood. Finding nothing, however, very remarkable in his aspect,—nothing but a sunburnt wayfarer, in plain garb and dusty shoes, who sat looking into the fire as if he fancied pictures among the coals,—these young people speedily grew tired of observing him. As it happened, there was other amusement at hand. An old German Jew, travelling with a diorama on his back, was passing down the mountain-road towards the village just as the party turned aside from it, and, in hopes of eking out the profits of the day, the showman had kept them company to the lime-kiln.

"Come, old Dutchman," cried one of the young men, "let us see your pictures, if you can swear they are worth looking at!"

"Oh yes, Captain," answered the Jew,—whether as a matter of courtesy or craft, he styled everybody Captain,—"I shall show you, indeed, some very superb pictures!"

So, placing his box in a proper position, he invited the young men and girls to look through the glass orifices of the machine, and proceeded to exhibit a series of the most outrageous scratchings and daubings, as specimens of the fine arts, that ever an itinerant showman had the face to impose upon his circle of spectators. The pictures were worn out, moreover, tattered, full of cracks and wrinkles, dingy with tobacco-smoke, and otherwise in a most pitiable condition. Some purported to be cities, public edifices, and ruined castles in Europe; others represented Napoleon's battles and Nelson's sea-fights; and in the midst of these would be seen a gigantic, brown, hairy hand,—which might have been mistaken for the Hand of Destiny, though, in truth, it was only the showman's,—pointing its forefinger to various scenes of the conflict, while its owner gave historical illustrations. When, with much merriment at its abominable deficiency of merit, the exhibition was concluded, the German bade little Joe put his head into the box. Viewed through the magnifying-glasses, the boy's round, rosy visage assumed the strangest imaginable aspect of an immense Titanic child, the mouth grinning broadly, and the eyes and every other feature overflowing with fun at the joke. Suddenly, however, that merry face turned pale, and its expression changed to horror, for this easily impressed and excitable child had become sensible that the eye of Ethan Brand was fixed upon him through the glass.

"You make the little man to be afraid, Captain," said the German Jew, turning up the dark and strong outline of his visage from his stooping posture. "But look again, and, by chance, I shall cause you to see somewhat that is very fine, upon my word!"

Ethan Brand gazed into the box for an instant, and then starting back, looked fixedly at the German. What had he seen? Nothing, apparently; for a curious youth, who had peeped in almost at the same moment, beheld only a vacant space of canvas.

"I remember you now," muttered Ethan Brand to the showman.

"Ah, Captain," whispered the Jew of Nuremberg, with a dark smile, "I find it to be a heavy matter in my show-box,—this Unpardonable Sin! By my faith, Captain, it has wearied my shoulders, this long day, to carry it over the mountain."

"Peace," answered Ethan Brand, sternly, "or get thee into the furnace yonder!"

The Jew's exhibition had scarcely concluded, when a great, elderly dog —who seemed to be his own master, as no person in the company laid claim to him—saw fit to render himself the object of public notice. Hitherto, he had shown himself a very quiet, well-disposed old dog, going round from one to another, and, by way of being sociable, offering his rough head to be patted by any kindly hand that would take so much trouble. But now, all of a sudden, this grave and venerable quadruped, of his own mere motion, and without the slightest suggestion from anybody else, began to run round after his tail, which, to heighten the absurdity of the proceeding, was a great deal shorter than it should have been. Never was seen such headlong eagerness in pursuit of an object that could not possibly be attained; never was heard such a tremendous outbreak of growling, snarling, barking, and snapping,—as if one end of the ridiculous brute's body were at deadly and most unforgivable enmity with the other. Faster and faster, round about went the cur; and faster and still faster fled the unapproachable brevity of his tail; and louder and fiercer grew his yells of rage and animosity; until, utterly exhausted, and as far from the goal as ever, the foolish old dog ceased his performance as suddenly as he had begun it. The next moment he was as mild, quiet, sensible, and respectable in his deportment, as when he first scraped acquaintance with the company.

As may be supposed, the exhibition was greeted with universal laughter, clapping of hands, and shouts of encore, to which the canine performer responded by wagging all that there was to wag of his tail, but appeared totally unable to repeat his very successful effort to amuse the spectators.

Meanwhile, Ethan Brand had resumed his seat upon the log, and moved, as it might be, by a perception of some remote analogy between his own case and that of this self-pursuing cur, he broke into the awful laugh, which, more than any other token, expressed the condition of his inward being. From that moment, the merriment of the party was at an end; they stood aghast, dreading lest the inauspicious sound should be reverberated around the horizon, and that mountain would thunder it to mountain, and so the horror be prolonged upon their ears. Then, whispering one to another that it was late,—that the moon was almost down, —that the August night was growing chill,—they hurried homewards, leaving the lime-burner and little Joe to deal as they might with their unwelcome guest. Save for these three human beings, the open space on the hill-side was a solitude, set in a vast gloom of forest. Beyond that darksome verge, the firelight glimmered on the stately trunks and almost black foliage of pines, intermixed with the lighter verdure of sapling oaks, maples, and poplars, while here and there lay the gigantic corpses of dead trees, decaying on the leaf-strewn soil. And it seemed to little Joe—a timorous and imaginative child—that the silent forest was holding its breath until some fearful thing should happen.

Ethan Brand thrust more wood into the fire, and closed the door of the kiln; then looking over his shoulder at the lime-burner and his son, he bade, rather than advised, them to retire to rest.

"For myself, I cannot sleep," said he. "I have matters that it concerns me to meditate upon. I will watch the fire, as I used to do in the old time."

"And call the Devil out of the furnace to keep you company, I suppose," muttered Bartram, who had been making intimate acquaintance with the black bottle above mentioned. "But watch, if you like, and call as many devils as you like! For my part, I shall be all the better for a snooze. Come, Joe!"

As the boy followed his father into the hut, he looked back at the wayfarer, and the tears came into his eyes, for his tender spirit had an intuition of the bleak and terrible loneliness in which this man had enveloped himself.

When they had gone, Ethan Brand sat listening to the crackling of the kindled wood, and looking at the little spirits of fire that issued through the chinks of the door. These trifles, however, once so familiar, had but the slightest hold of his attention, while deep within his mind he was reviewing the gradual but marvellous change that had been wrought upon him by the search to which he had devoted himself. He remembered how the night dew had fallen upon him,—how the dark forest had whispered to him,—how the stars had gleamed upon him,—a simple and loving man, watching his fire in the years gone by, and ever musing as it burned. He remembered with what tenderness, with what love and sympathy for mankind, and what pity for human guilt and woe, he had first begun to contemplate those ideas which afterwards became the inspiration of his life; with what reverence he had then looked into the heart of man, viewing it as a temple originally divine, and, however desecrated, still to be held sacred by a brother; with what awful fear he had deprecated the success of his pursuit, and prayed that the Unpardonable Sin might never be revealed to him. Then ensued that vast intellectual development, which, in its progress, disturbed the counterpoise between his mind and heart. The Idea that possessed his life had operated as a means of education; it had gone on cultivating his powers to the highest point of which they were susceptible; it had raised him from the level of an unlettered laborer to stand on a star-lit eminence, whither the philosophers of the earth, laden with the lore of universities, might vainly strive to clamber after him. So much for the intellect! But where was the heart? That, indeed, had withered,—had contracted,—had hardened,—had perished! It had ceased to partake of the universal throb. He had lost his hold of the magnetic chain of humanity. He was no longer a brother-man, opening the chambers or the dungeons of our common nature by the key of holy sympathy, which gave him a right to share in all its secrets; he was now a cold observer, looking on mankind as the subject of his experiment, and, at length, converting man and woman to be his puppets, and pulling the wires that moved them to such degrees of crime as were demanded for his study.

Thus Ethan Brand became a fiend. He began to be so from the moment that his moral nature had ceased to keep the pace of improvement with his intellect. And now, as his highest effort and inevitable development,— as the bright and gorgeous flower, and rich, delicious fruit of his life's labor,—he had produced the Unpardonable Sin!

"What more have I to seek? what more to achieve?" said Ethan Brand to himself. "My task is done, and well done!"

Starting from the log with a certain alacrity in his gait and ascending the hillock of earth that was raised against the stone circumference of the lime-kiln, he thus reached the top of the structure. It was a space of perhaps ten feet across, from edge to edge, presenting a view of the upper surface of the immense mass of broken marble with which the kiln was heaped. All these innumerable blocks and fragments of marble were red-hot and vividly on fire, sending up great spouts of blue flame, which quivered aloft and danced madly, as within a magic circle, and sank and rose again, with continual and multitudinous activity. As the lonely man bent forward over this terrible body of fire, the blasting heat smote up against his person with a breath that, it might be supposed, would have scorched and shrivelled him up in a moment.

Ethan Brand stood erect, and raised his arms on high. The blue flames played upon his face, and imparted the wild and ghastly light which alone could have suited its expression; it was that of a fiend on the verge of plunging into his gulf of intensest torment.

"O Mother Earth," cried he, "who art no more my Mother, and into whose bosom this frame shall never be resolved! O mankind, whose brotherhood I have cast off, and trampled thy great heart beneath my feet! O stars of heaven, that shone on me of old, as if to light me onward and upward!—farewell all, and forever. Come, deadly element of Fire,—henceforth my familiar friend! Embrace me, as I do thee!"

That night the sound of a fearful peal of laughter rolled heavily through the sleep of the lime-burner and his little son; dim shapes of horror and anguish haunted their dreams, and seemed still present in the rude hovel, when they opened their eyes to the daylight.

"Up, boy, up!" cried the lime-burner, staring about him. "Thank Heaven, the night is gone, at last; and rather than pass such another, I would watch my lime-kiln, wide awake, for a twelve-month. This Ethan Brand, with his humbug of an Unpardonable Sin, has done me no such mighty favor, in taking my place!"

He issued from the hut, followed by little Joe, who kept fast hold of his father's hand. The early sunshine was already pouring its gold upon the mountain-tops, and though the valleys were still in shadow, they smiled cheerfully in the promise of the bright day that was hastening onward. The village, completely shut in by hills, which swelled away gently about it, looked as if it had rested peacefully in the hollow of the great hand of Providence. Every dwelling was distinctly visible; the little spires of the two churches pointed upwards, and caught a fore-glimmering of brightness from the sun-gilt skies upon their gilded weather-cocks. The tavern was astir, and the figure of the old, smoke-dried stage-agent, cigar in mouth, was seen beneath the stoop. Old Graylock was glorified with a golden cloud upon his head. Scattered likewise over the breasts of the surrounding mountains, there were heaps of hoary mist, in fantastic shapes, some of them far down into the valley, others high up towards the summits, and still others, of the same family of mist or cloud, hovering in the gold radiance of the upper atmosphere. Stepping from one to another of the clouds that rested on the hills, and thence to the loftier brotherhood that sailed in air, it seemed almost as if a mortal man might thus ascend into the heavenly regions. Earth was so mingled with sky that it was a daydream to look at it.

To supply that charm of the familiar and homely, which Nature so readily adopts into a scene like this, the stage-coach was rattling down the mountain-road, and the driver sounded his horn, while Echo caught up the notes, and intertwined them into a rich and varied and elaborate harmony, of which the original performer could lay claim to little share. The great hills played a concert among themselves, each contributing a strain of airy sweetness.

Little Joe's face brightened at once.

"Dear father," cried he, skipping cheerily to and fro, "that strange man is gone, and the sky and the mountains all seem glad of it!"

"Yes," growled the lime-burner, with an oath, "but he has let the fire go down, and no thanks to him if five hundred bushels of lime are not spoiled. If I catch the fellow hereabouts again, I shall feel like tossing him into the furnace!"

With his long pole in his hand, he ascended to the top of the kiln. After a moment's pause, he called to his son.

"Come up here, Joe!" said he.

So little Joe ran up the hillock, and stood by his father's side. The marble was all burnt into perfect, snow-white lime. But on its surface, in the midst of the circle,—snow-white too, and thoroughly converted into lime, lay a human skeleton, in the attitude of a person who, after long toil, lies down to long repose. Within the ribs—strange to say—was the shape of a human heart.

"Was the fellow's heart made of marble?" cried Bartram, in some perplexity at this phenomenon. "At any rate, it is burnt into what looks like special good lime; and, taking all the bones together, my kiln is half a bushel the richer for him."

So saying, the rude lime-burner lifted his pole, and, letting it fall upon the skeleton, the relics of Ethan Brand were crumbled into fragments.

QUESTIONS

1. What do you make of the sub-title, "A Chapter from an Abortive Romance"? What use does Hawthorne make of the convention that the story is a fragment from a longer work?

2. How would you characterize the prose style of the story? How does it differ, in choice of words, in construction, in the handling of dialogue, in the writer's relation to the reader, from some of the more recent stories in this book? What part does the style play in the story's total effect?

3. What use does the story make of symbolism? Of allegory? Of realism?

4. How important a role does the lime-burner's little boy have in the story? Is he an incidental character only, or does a special significance attach to him?

5. What do the stage-agent, the lawyer turned soap-boiler, and the doctor have in common with one another? Do they have anything in common with Ethan Brand?

6. What does Hawthorne mean by "the counterpoise between [a man's] mind and his heart"? By "the magnetic chain of humanity"?

7. What is the Unpardonable Sin?

GUY DE MAUPASSANT

(1850–1893)

At the moment, Guy de Maupassant is not much in vogue with readers or critics of fiction in the United States or in England, nor has he been for some time past. A few years ago Francis Steegmuller published an admirable critical biography of De Maupassant, its title, *A Lion in the Path*, provided by a statement in which Henry James—a writer who assuredly *is* in fashion, both in England and America—had arrestingly described the light in which De Maupassant appeared to him in the 1880's: "To find M. de Maupassant a lion in the path—that may seem to some people a singular proof of want of courage; but I think the obstacle will not be made light of by those who have really taken the measure of the animal."

Now, there can be no question of implying that De Maupassant is the equal of James, either in the scope or the quality of his total achievement. James outweighs him both by the magnitude of his *œuvre*, by an essential gravity of moral concern, and by utter dedication to the task of perfecting his art. Yet if we weigh the claims of the two men not on the basis of total output but solely on the basis of the short stories written by each, it is no longer certain that the advantage is all on James's side, as he himself might have been quicker than some of his latter-day admirers to recognize. James's own stories, as well as his novels, respond gratifyingly and fully to our present-day preference for works that are complex, subtly ambiguous, and richly involuted, and it is all to the good that so many readers have learned to approach them with the care and in the spirit they demand. That is not all there is to James (though it may be all that some people see in him), and there is no doubt something a little absurd in setting James and De Maupassant up as rivals and then trying to decide between them. But literary vogues are funny things, and there are at present many readers, especially many young readers, who lavish all kinds of effort on working out the final implications of "The Jolly Corner" or "The Spoils of Poynton" and fail to see that there is anything at all in "Boule de Suif." There is at least one variety of fitness in literature, particularly in French literature, that sometimes appears in the guise of perfect simplicity and limpidity.

De Maupassant crowded a vast literary productivity—over two hundred stories and six novels, to say nothing of occasional ventures into other forms—into the ten years between 1880 and 1890, and it was inevitable that a certain amount of what he wrote should fall well below his highest level. His preparation to become a writer had been long and careful. Born in 1850 at the Château de Miromesnil at Tourville-sur-Arques, in Normandy, he went to school at Yvetot and then to the Lycée at Rouen, but most of his early training he received from his mother. This lady had been a childhood friend of Flaubert, the great novelist whose name has become a synonym for literary perfectionism, and it was Flaubert who supervised De Maupassant's beginning efforts and who held him back from publication until he judged him ready. This moment came in 1880, in which year he published a book of poems that are of no special consequence and also his first story, "Boule de Suif," which appeared in a collection of six stories by six writers, including Emile Zola. "Boule de Suif," a long story of the Franco-Prussian war, is one of De Maupassant's finest works and launched him into the world of literature fully-formed, as it were.

During the previous ten years, while he had been preparing to become a writer, De Maupassant had lived mostly in Paris. At eighteen he had been employed, like the hero of "On Horseback," at the Ministère de l'Instruction Publique (Department of Education). In these positions he learned to know the life and world of the petty bureaucracy, as he already knew the larger, freer world of the Norman hunting squires and as he came to know the literary world of Paris. He went through the terrible months of the Siege of Paris in 1870–71, which figures in many of his stories, including "Two Friends." There seems always to have been present in his mind a somber strain, a dread of some unknown approaching doom, and in fact he did die in his early forties, under tragic circumstances. Yet a large part of his energy was always devoted to the vigorous pursuit of pleasure, not only during the 70's but also during the years of great literary activity. He loved boating on the Seine, he had innumerable easy love affairs: his world, when it is not the trivial and boring world of the smoking-room story or of *La Vie Parisienne*, is the world of delight in the senses and acceptance of all that they have to offer which we see reflected in the paintings of the French Impressionists, his contemporaries. In fact, in such a painting as Renoir's "Luncheon of the Boating Party" (1881), in the Phillips Collection, Washington, we have an appropriate image of what life was for De Maupassant, at any rate on its happier side.

Most of his stories are quite short, they make their points very directly, and they are apparently very simple. But they are not quite so simple as they look. De Maupassant relies more heavily on plot and on the direct presentation of a small, close-knit action than he does on analysis of motive or elaboration of his themes. He confines himself to setting in motion a small group of characters whose actions will reveal the qualities, the impulses, the desires that not only drive them but also give meaning to their lives. Sometimes these impulses, which are what they live by, come into immediate and more or less tragic conflict with the larger forces of the world outside them. Many of De Maupassant's stories seem in effect to chart the point at which the individual human being clashes directly with the forces of his environment. De Maupassant does not comment on the nature of the conflict, he confines himself to presenting the action. It is as if, in each of his better stories, he had thrown a stone into the pool of his reader's consciousness: a sharp, limited act which yet produces the soft, widening ripples of implication which go on long after the act itself has been completed. If these little tales are simple, it is with the positive simplicity of one kind of highly developed art, the kind in which all excess has been rigorously cut away, in which everything is staked on the masterly control of a few essential movements, on—the phrase is James's—"robust and vivid concision."

TWO FRIENDS

Paris was besieged, famished, and had the death rattle in her throat. Sparrows were very scarce on the roof-tops and the sewers were being depopulated. People were eating anything they could get.

As he strolled sadly along the outer boulevard one bright January morning, his hands in the pockets of his old army trousers and his stomach empty, M. Morissot, a clock-maker by profession and a man of leisure by the force of circumstances, stopped short before a fellow-idler in whom he recognized a friend. It was M. Sauvage, an acquaintance of the river's edge.

Each Sunday, before the war, Morissot had started off at dawn, a bamboo rod in his hand, a tin box hung over his shoulder. He took the train that went to Argenteuil, got off at Colombes, then walked to the island of Marante. The moment he reached this, the place of his dreams, he began to fish; he fished till night.

Each Sunday he would meet there a dumpy, jovial little man, M. Sauvage, who kept a dry-goods shop in the rue Notre-Dame de Lorette, another fanatic fisherman. They often spent half the day side by side, rod and line in hand and their feet dangling above the stream, and gradually a friendship grew up between them.

On certain days they did not talk at all. Other times, they chatted; but they understood one another perfectly without saying anything, since they had similar tastes and identical sensations.

My translation. *Ed.*

On spring mornings, about ten o'clock, when the new sun had brought out on the water the thin vapour which moves with the current, and was pouring down onto the backs of the two devoted fishermen the welcome warmth of the early season, Morissot would sometimes say to his neighbour: "Well, this is really fine, isn't it?," and M. Sauvage would reply, "I can't think of anything better." And that would be enough to establish their mutual comprehension and esteem.

In the fall, towards the close of day, when the sky enflamed by the setting sun cast on the water the shapes of its scarlet clouds, set the horizon ablaze, bathed the two friends in a light that was red as fire, and gilded the trees, which were already rust-colored and shaking with the tremors of winter, M. Sauvage would look at Morissot with a smile and say, "Quite a spectacle, isn't it?" And Morissot, marveling, but without taking his eyes off his float, would answer: "It certainly beats the boulevards, doesn't it?"

The moment they had recognized one another, they shook hands energetically, much moved at coming across one another in such different circumstances. With a sigh M. Sauvage murmured, "There certainly have been some strange goings-on." Morissot, very gloomy, moaned, "And what weather! Today is the first fine day we've had this year!"

The sky was indeed a deep blue and suffused with light.

They walked along side by side, reflective and sad. Morissot continued, "And our fishing? Something to remember, eh?"

M. Sauvage asked, "When do you suppose we'll be able to go fishing again?"

They went into a small cafe and drank an absinthe together. Then they continued their stroll along the pavements.

Morissot stopped all of a sudden: "Another absinthe, what do you say?" M. Sauvage agreed: "As you like." And they went into another wine shop.

They were quite dizzy when they came out, confused, as people are apt to be whose stomachs are full of alcohol even though they have had nothing to eat. The air was mild. A caressing breeze tickled their faces.

M. Sauvage, the warm air having put the finishing touch on his drunkenness, stopped in his tracks: "Suppose we go there now?"

"Where?"

"Why, fishing."

"But where?"

"Why, on our island. The French outposts are near Colombes. I know Colonel Dumoulin—they'll let us through without any trouble."

Morissot was trembling, so strong was his desire to go: "It's agreed. I'm with you." And they separated to pick up their fishing gear.

An hour later, they were walking along the highway side by side. Then they reached the villa occupied by the colonel. He smiled at their request and consented to their fanciful project. They started off again, equipped with a pass.

Soon they had passed through the outposts, gone through the deserted village of Colombes, and reached the edge of the little vineyards which run down towards the Seine. It was about eleven o'clock.

Opposite, the village of Argenteuil seemed completely dead. The heights of Orgemont and Sannois dominated the entire country-side. The great plain which stretches as far as Nanterre was entirely empty of life, with its bare cherry trees and its plots of gray earth.

M. Sauvage, pointing with his finger toward the heights, murmured: "The Prussians are up there!" And the two friends felt a certain paralysing disquiet in the face of this deserted landscape.

The Prussians! They had never seen any, but they had known for months that they were there, invisible and all-powerful, encircling Paris, ruining France, pillaging, murdering, bringing famine with them. And a sort of superstitious fear was added to the hatred which they felt for this unknown and victorious race.

Morissot stammered, "But suppose we run into some of them?"

M. Sauvage answered, a touch of Parisian banter coming out in spite of everything, "We'll offer them a mess of fish to fry."

But they hesitated to venture into the open country, intimidated by the silence which pressed in all around them.

Finally M. Sauvage made up his mind: "Come on, let's go! But we'll have to be careful." And they climbed down into one of the vineyards, bent double, creeping, taking advantage of the cover offered by the bushes, their eyes restless, their hearing strained.

There was a stretch of bare ground to be crossed before reaching the edge of the river. They began to run; and as soon as they had reached the bank they crouched in the dry reeds.

Morissot laid his cheek to the ground to listen for sounds of anyone walking in the vicinity. He heard nothing. They were quite alone.

They regained their self-assurance and began to fish.

Across from them the island of Marante, with no one on it, hid them from the other bank. The little building which housed the restaurant was closed up, and looked as if it had been untenanted for years.

M. Sauvage caught the first gudgeon, Morissot caught the second, and at brief intervals they would raise their rods with a tiny silvery creature twisting and turning at the end of the line: truly, a miraculous draught of fishes.

Carefully they would slip the fish into a pouch of fine-meshed net which they had lowered into the water at their feet. And they were filled with a delightful happiness, the happiness which possesses those who have regained a cherished pleasure after being long deprived of it.

The warmth of the good spring sun penetrated between their shoulder blades. Now they no longer heard anything, no longer thought of anything; the rest of the world had ceased to exist for them; they were fishing.

But suddenly there was a dull sound which seemed to come from under ground and made the earth shake. The cannon had begun to fire again.

Morissot turned his head, and above the river-bank he could see, off to the left, the high silhouette of Mont Valérien, wearing on its brow a white plume, a vapor of gunsmoke which it had just spit forth.

And immediately a second jet of smoke issued from the summit of the fortress, and a few seconds later there was the rumble of another detonation.

Then others followed, and from moment to moment the mountain would utter its deadly breath, would spew forth a milky vapor which climbed slowly into the calm sky, making a cloud above the mountain.

M. Sauvage shrugged his shoulders: "There they go again," he said.

Morissot, who was anxiously watching the feather on his float as it plunged again and again beneath the surface, was suddenly seized by the peaceful man's anger against the madmen who were fighting each other, and he grumbled, "They must be stupid to want to go killing each other like that."

M. Sauvage answered, "They're worse than animals."

And Morissot, who had just caught an *ablette*, declared: "And when you think that it will always be like that as long as there are governments!"

M. Sauvage cut him short: "The Republic wouldn't have declared war . . ."

Morissot interrupted in his turn: "With kings, you have war abroad; with the Republic, you have war at home."

And calmly they began to debate, solving the great political problems with the common sense that is proper to good-hearted men of limited horizons, and they reached agreement on one point, that they would never be free. And Mont Valérien thundered away without respite, demolishing French houses with its cannon, smashing lives, crushing human beings, putting an end to many a dream, to many an expected joy, to many a hoped-for good fortune, and opening in the hearts of wives, of daughters, of mothers, in other countries, sufferings to which no end would ever again be put.

"But that's life for you," M. Sauvage declared.

"Better say that that's death," Morissot replied, laughing as he did so.

But suddenly they shivered with fear, having heard someone walking behind them, and when they turned their heads they saw four men standing right behind them, four tall men with beards and guns, dressed like liveried servants and wearing flat military caps, with their guns aimed at them.

The two fishing rods fell from their hands and floated off down the river.

In a few seconds they had been seized, tied up, hurried off, thrown into a boat and taken over to the island.

And behind the house which they had thought abandoned, they saw that there were about twenty German soldiers.

A hairy giant, sitting astraddle a chair and sucking a large porcelain pipe, asked them in excellent French, "Well, gentlemen, and have you had good fishing?"

Then a soldier deposited at the officer's feet the net full of fish which he had taken the pains to bring with him. The Prussian smiled: "Well, now! I can see it wasn't bad at all. But now we're interested in something else. Listen to me and don't be frightened.

"From my point of view, you are two spies sent out to observe my movements. I capture you and I have you shot. You were pretending to fish, as a way of disguising your activities. Now you've fallen into my hands, so much the worse for you; *c'est la guerre.*

"But since you came out through the out-posts, you must certainly have the password to get back in. Give me that password and I'll let you off."

The two friends, deathly pale, side by side, their hands shaking with a slight nervous tremor, remained silent.

The officer continued: "No one will ever know, you will re-enter the city peacefully. The secret will disappear with you. If you refuse, it's death, and immediately. You have your choice."

They neither moved nor spoke.

The Prussian went on speaking calmly, pointing to the river as he did so: "Only think that in five minutes you will be under that water! In five minutes! You must have relatives?"

Mont Valérien was still thundering away.

The two fishermen continued to stand in silence. The German gave orders in his own language. Then he moved his chair so as not to be too close to the prisoners, and twelve men lined up at twenty paces, their rifles at order arms.

The officer spoke again: "I give you one minute, and not two seconds more."

Then he stood up abruptly, went over to the two Frenchmen, took Morissot under the arm, moved off with him a few paces, and said to him in a low voice: "Quickly now, what's the password?—your friend won't know you've told, I'll pretend to have taken pity on you."

Morissot did not answer.

Then the Prussian took M. Sauvage to one side and asked him the same question.

M. Sauvage did not answer.

They were back side by side.

And the officer gave his first command. The soldiers raised their rifles.

Then Morissot's glance chanced to fall on the netful of little fish, lying in the grass, a few paces from him.

The fish were still moving, and a ray of sunlight made them glisten. And he was suddenly overcome with weakness. Despite all he could do, tears filled his eyes.

He stammered, "Good-bye, M. Sauvage."

M. Sauvage replied, "Good-bye, M. Morissot."

They shook hands, gripped from head to foot by an uncontrollable trembling.

The officer cried, "Fire!"

The twelve shots rang out like a single shot.

M. Sauvage fell forward at once onto his face. Morissot, who was taller, swayed, pivoted, and fell across his friend, face to the sky, while blood gushed from a large hole in the breast of his jacket.

The German gave further orders.

His men dispersed, then came back with ropes and stones which they tied to the feet of the two dead men, then they carried them to the river bank.

Mont Valérien had not stopped its rumbling, and its summit was now capped with a hill of smoke.

Two soldiers took Morissot by head and feet; two others seized M. Sauvage in the same way. The bodies, balanced for a moment by the strength of the soldiers, were hurled away, described an arc, then plunged, standing erect, into the river, the stones dragging them down feet first.

The water shot up, bubbled, shuddered, then grew calm, while tiny waves moved in towards the shore.

A little blood floated on the surface.

The officer, still serene, said half-aloud: "Now the fish will have their turn."

Then he went towards the house.

And suddenly he noticed the net full of gudgeons in the grass. He picked it up, examined the fish, smiled, called: "Wilhelm!"

An orderly ran up, in a white apron. And the Prussian, throwing him the day's catch of the two men who had just been shot, gave an order: "Have these little creatures fried for me right away while they're still alive. They'll be delicious."

Then he went on smoking his pipe.

QUESTIONS

1. What is the background of historical events against which the story takes place?

2. What points of comparison can you find between the relationship of historical events to private lives in this story and in Shirley Ann Grau's "Joshua"? Do the two stories present similar themes, or different ones?

3. De Maupassant is sometimes thought of as a writer whose stories depend more heavily on plot-interest than on any other single element of story-telling. How would you describe the plot of this story, that is, the closed circle of causal relationships of one event to another? How large a part does the plot play in the story's total range of effect?

4. Does "Two Friends" have all the elements which in your view constitute a complete short story, or are certain elements missing? If so, which ones? Do you wish that the story had been more fully developed at any point?

ON HORSEBACK

The poor couple were living with difficulty and discomfort on the husband's small wages. Since their marriage there had been two children, and the awkwardness of the first days had settled into one of those humble states of wretchedness, veiled and ashamed, the wretchedness of a noble family which wants to maintain its rank in spite of everything.

Hector de Gribelin had been brought up in the country, in the paternal manor house, by an elderly teaching priest. The family was not rich, but they managed to scrape along from day to day and to keep up appearances.

Then, when he was twenty, they had found a position for him, and he had gone to work at the Navy Department, as a clerk, at a salary of fifteen hundred francs. On this reef he had been wrecked, as all are wrecked who have not been given an early training for the harsh battle of life, who see existence and its problems through a cloud, who know nothing of how to live life and resist its pressures, in whom no special aptitudes or particular abilities have been developed from childhood, in whom no sharp energy for the struggle has been aroused, all those in whose hands no weapon, no tool has ever been placed.

His first three years in the office were sheer horror.

He had discovered a few friends of his family, old people who were behind the times and no more prosperous than he, who lived in the sad, genteel streets of the Faubourg St. Germain, and of them he had made his circle of acquaintances.

Strangers to modern life, at once humble and proud, these needy aristocrats lived in the upper stories of sleepy old houses. The tenants of these dwellings, from top to bottom, were titled gentry, but money seemed just as scarce on the second floor as on the sixth.

Their everlasting prejudices, their preoccupation with rank, their concern with not falling from their position haunted these families which had once been brilliant and were now ruined by human inertia. In this circle Hector de Gribelin met a girl who, like him, was of noble birth and poor, and married her.

They had two children in the first four years of their marriage.

For another four years this household, harassed by poverty, had no pleasures other than their Sunday strolls along the Champs-Élysées and a few evenings at the theatre, one or two each winter, when some fellow-employee had given them a pair of complimentary tickets.

But now, just as it was beginning to be spring, the clerk was entrusted with some extra work by his boss, and he received an extraordinary bonus of three hundred francs.

My translation. *Ed.*

When he brought this money home, he said to his wife: "My dear Henriette, we ought to give ourselves a treat, perhaps a little excursion for the children."

And after a lengthy discussion, it was decided that they would go have lunch somewhere in the country.

"For heaven's sake," Hector exclaimed, "one time won't ruin us; we'll hire a break for you, the children, and the maid, and I'll rent a horse at the riding school. It will do me good."

And for the entire week they talked of nothing but their plans for the outing.

Each evening, when he got home from the office, Hector would seize his older son, place him astraddle his knee, and while he bounced him up and down with all his might would say: "That's how papa's going to gallop on the outing next Sunday."

And all day long the little boy would straddle the chairs and drag them around the room, crying: "I'm papa on the horsie!"

And even the maid looked at her master with a marvelling eye, as she thought of how he would accompany the carriage on horse-back; and during every meal she would listen to him as he talked of horsemanship, or recounted his exploits of earlier days at his father's. Oh, he'd been trained the right way, and once he felt the animal beneath him he was afraid of nothing, but nothing!

Rubbing his hands he would say to his wife: "If they could give me a rather difficult mount, I'd be delighted. You'll see how I ride; and if you like, we'll come back by way of the Champs-Élysées when everyone's returning from the Bois. I tell you we'll make quite an impression, I wouldn't mind meeting someone from the Ministry. That's just the sort of thing that makes the higher-ups have some respect for you."

On the appointed day, the carriage and the riding-horse arrived at the door at the same time. He went down immediately to examine his mount. He had had under-straps sewn to his trousers and was carrying a riding-whip bought the day before.

He raised the horse's four legs one at a time and felt them over carefully, felt the neck, the flanks, the hocks, probed the loins with a finger, opened the horse's mouth, looked at its teeth, announced its age, and, when the family had come down, delivered a sort of brief lecture, both theoretical and practical, on horses in general and on this one in particular—an excellent horse, he had decided.

When everybody had been satisfactorily placed in the carriage, he checked the stirrups; then, raising himself by one stirrup, came down somewhat heavily on the horse, who started to dance about under his weight and came close to unseating his rider.

Hector, agitated, tried to calm him: "Come now, easy does it, my friend, easy does it."

Then when the beast had recovered its tranquillity and the rider had regained his aplomb, the latter asked: "Are we ready?"

All voices replied: "Yes."

Then, he gave the word of command: "En route!"

And the procession started off.

The eyes of every spectator were upon him. He trotted in the English style, rising exaggeratedly in the saddle. No sooner had he fallen back into the saddle than he would leap up out of it again as if to hurl himself into space. Often he seemed about to fall forward onto the horse's mane, and he kept his eyes fixed straight ahead, his face contorted, and his cheeks pale.

His wife, holding one of the children on her knees, and the maid who was holding the other one, kept exclaiming over and over again: "Look at papa, look at papa!"

And the two little ones, intoxicated with the motion, with their happiness, and with the bright air, uttered continual sharp cries. The horse, frightened by all this noise, finally began to gallop, and the horseman, in his efforts to stop him, lost his hat. The coachman had to get down off his seat to retrieve this headpiece, and Hector, when he had received it from the coachman's hands, addressed his wife from a certain distance: "Keep the children from shouting like that, you'll have him running away with me!"

They ate their lunch on the grass, in the Bois du Vésinet, picknicking on the boxes of provisions they had brought with them.

Although the coachman took care of all three horses, Hector got up every two minutes to see if his wanted anything, and he stroked its neck, giving it bread, little cakes, and lumps of sugar.

He declared: "He's got a terrific pace. He even shook me up a little just at first, but you saw how quickly I managed him—he saw that I was his master. He won't try anything from now on."

As had been decided, they went back to town by way of the Champs-Élysées.

The wide avenue was swarming with carriages. And on the sidewalks the strollers were so numerous that it was as if two long black ribbons had been unrolled from the Arc de Triomphe to the Place de la Concorde. A shower of sunlight was falling on all this crowd, glistening off the carriage-varnish, the harness metal, the door handles.

This mass of people, of vehicles, and of horses seemed to be kept in constant agitation by a mad desire for movement, by an intoxication with life. And the Obelisk, in the distance, stood erect in a golden haze.

Hector's horse, once past the Arc de Triomphe, was suddenly seized with new ardor and set off at a spanking pace towards the stable, through the carriages moving wheel to wheel, despite all his rider's efforts at moderation.

By now the carriage had been left far behind, and suddenly, when horse and rider were in front of the Palace of Industry, the animal, seeing a clear field opening up, veered to the right and began to gallop.

An old woman in an apron was calmly proceeding across the road; she was exactly in Hector's path, and he was charging towards her at full speed. Incapable of controlling his mount, he began to shout with all his might: "Holà! Hey! Look out there!"

She may have been deaf, because she kept peacefully on her way until the moment when, knocked aside by the chest of the horse, who had come at her like an express train, she rolled ten paces farther, her skirts in the air, after somersaulting three times on her head.

Voices cried: "Stop him!"

Hector, beside himself, clung to the horse's mane, all the while yelling, "Help! Help!"

A sudden terrible shock sent him like a cannon ball over the ears of his charger and into the arms of a police sergeant who had planted himself in his way.

In a second a furious crowd had formed around him, vociferous and gesticulating. One old gentleman especially, an old gentleman wearing a large round medal and great white moustaches, seemed utterly exasperated. He kept saying: "*Sacrebleu*, when you're as clumsy as that you stay home. You don't come out into the streets to kill people when you don't know how to handle a horse."

But now four men appeared, carrying the old woman. She seemed to be dead, with her face yellow and her bonnet on sideways, and gray with dust.

"Take this woman to a dispensary," the old gentleman ordered, "and let us go to the police station."

Hector started off, between the two policemen. A third led his horse. A crowd followed; and suddenly the break came in sight. His wife hurled herself out of it, the maid lost her head, the children were squalling. Hector explained that he would be back, that he had knocked down a woman, that there was nothing to worry about. And his family, distracted with worry, left him.

At the police station the explanation was brief, he gave his name, Hector de Gribelin, employed at the Navy Department, and then they waited for news of the injured woman. A policeman who had been sent to get information returned. She had regained consciousness, but she said she had dreadful internal pains. She was a house-keeper, sixty-five years old, named Mme. Simon.

When he knew that she had not died, Hector regained hope and promised to take care of the expense of getting her well. Then he ran to the dispensary.

A crowd was standing in front of the door; the old woman, slumped down in an arm-chair, was moaning, her hands motionless, her face dazed. Two doctors were still looking her over. No bones were broken, but they were afraid there was an internal injury.

Hector spoke to her: "Are you suffering a great deal?"

"Oh, yes!"

"Where exactly?"

"It's as if there were a fire in my stomach."

One of the doctors came over to Hector: "Are you the one who caused the accident, monsieur?"

"Yes, monsieur."

"This woman ought to be sent to a convalescent home. I know one where they'd keep her for six francs a day. Shall I take care of it for you?"

Hector, delighted, thanked the doctor and went home quite easy in his mind.

His wife was waiting for him in tears: he calmed her, saying: "It's nothing at all, this Simon woman is already better, in three days she'll never know there's been anything wrong with her. I've sent her to a rest home. It's nothing at all."

It's nothing at all!

When he left the office the next day he went to see how Mme. Simon was getting along. He found her eating a bowl of thick broth, with an air of considerable satisfaction.

"Well?" he asked.

She answered, "Oh, my poor dear sir, there's no change! I feel as if I'm just about done for. I'm not a bit better!"

The doctor said they would have to wait for a few days, to see if there were any complications.

Hector waited three days, then he went back. The old woman—her complexion clear, her eyes bright—began to moan as soon as she saw him: "I can't move at all, my poor dear sir, not at all! I'm stuck for the rest of my days!"

A chill ran through Hector's bones. He asked to see the doctor. The doctor threw up his hands: "What can you do, monsieur, I'm sure I don't know. She moans if we try to lift her. If we even try to move her chair she utters the most blood-curdling shrieks. I have to believe what she tells me, monsieur; I'm not inside her myself. As long as I haven't actually seen her walking, I have no right to suppose that she's lying."

The old woman was listening, motionless, her eyes crafty.

Eight days passed, then fifteen days, then a month. Mme. Simon didn't leave her chair. She ate from morning to night, put on weight, chatted gaily with the other patients, seemed to accept her immobility as if it were a rest well earned by her fifty years of going up and down stairs, of turning mattresses, of carrying coal from one floor to another, of brushing and sweeping.

Hector, in dismay, went to see her every day; each day he found her peaceful and serene, and still declaring, "I can't move at all, my poor dear sir, not at all."

Each evening Mme. de Gribelin would ask, consumed with worry, "And Mme. Simon?"

And each time he would reply in hopeless dejection: "No change, absolutely none!"

They dismissed the maid, whose wages were now too heavy an expense for them. They scrimped and did without more and more things, until every pleasure they had ever had was gone.

Then Hector called in four important doctors who held a consultation over the old woman. She let them examine her, probe her, prod her all over, watching them all the time with a shrewd eye.

"We must make her walk," one of them said.

"But," she cried, "I can't move at all, my good sirs, not at all!"

Then they took hold of her, lifted her up, pulled her along for a few steps; but she slid out of their grasp and collapsed on the floor uttering such dreadful cries that they carried her back to her chair with infinite care.

They gave a somewhat reserved opinion, concluding nevertheless that it was impossible for her to work.

And when Hector took the news home to his wife she collapsed on to a chair, stammering: "It would be better to have her come here, it wouldn't be so expensive."

He started up: "Here, with us? How can you think of such a thing?"

But she answered, resigned to everything now, and with tears in her eyes, "What can I do, my friend, it isn't my fault! . . ."

QUESTIONS

1. How would you summarize the plot of "On Horseback"? In establishing its meaning and working out its total effect, does this story depend more or less centrally on plot than "Two Friends" does?

2. What seems to you to be the theme of the story? Do you find this theme explicitly stated at any point, or must it be deduced from the pattern of relationships established by the incidents themselves?

3. How far does the outcome of the story depend on character and how far on circumstances, accident, or coincidence? What are the traits of character which are chiefly operative in the story?

4. How would you describe the author's attitude towards the characters whose lives he portrays in the story?

HENRY JAMES

(1843–1916)

"Four Meetings" represents Henry James at the beginning of his long career as a writer of fiction. For fifty years the central and constant purpose of his life was writing, the exploitation of the word, and of the techniques and resources of fiction, as a means of fixing the impressions he received from life, of describing the unceasing battle between human right and human wrong. Although toward the end of his life he became a British subject, he was in all essentials an American writer. Born in New York's Washington Square, brought up (when the family was not travelling or living in Europe) in New York and Albany, he was endowed with thoroughly American modes of conscience, and although much of the life he observed was European—or at least took place in Europe—he looked at it with American eyes. He had been taken to Europe for the first time before he was two years old, and he was there often, and for extended periods, throughout his childhood and youth. In his early thirties, moved primarily by considerations of finding a place to live that would be as favorable as possible for his art and for the life of the imagination, he decided to make his permanent home in Europe—in England, as it happened.

One of his earliest interests as a novelist and story-writer was "The International Situation," that is, the whole complex of shocks—delightful and otherwise—conflicts, and inter-relationships that arose when Americans were confronted with Europe and Europeans. After the Civil War, Americans were going to Europe in ever larger numbers, and to James there were infinitely interesting dramatic possibilities in the impact made on his fellow citizens by a world for which nothing in America had prepared them. He saw the Americans of his early novels and stories as venturing into a world that was considerably richer than the one they left behind them in all kinds of complexities: in the varieties of the picturesque which it presented, in the splendor of its artistic heritage, in the length of its history, in the developed state of its social forms. He also saw, hidden beneath the interest of European life and the arabesques of its social complexity, a wiliness and even a downright wickedness in whose toils his innocent Americans were speedily and infallibly enmeshed. But it should be noticed that, except for the unconvincingly melodramatic French noble family in *The American,* James's most heartless and thorough-paced exploiters of the innocent are to be found among his Europeanized Americans. In this respect, the artist-cousin of "Four Meetings," who has decided that the cultivation of his artistic sensibility is an end that justifies any means, has, for all his crudeness and vulgarity, certain traits in common with the elegantly cultivated and diabolically cruel Gilbert Osmond of *The Portrait of a Lady* (1881), the great and intensely exciting novel which may be seen as the climax of this first phase of James's development.

James was to return to the International Situation in the three masterpieces, all written in the first decade of the present century, which are his crowning achievement: *The Wings of the Dove, The Ambassadors,* and *The Golden Bowl.* Yet it should be noticed, both in these late novels and in the early works which make use of this particular subject matter, that the International Situation is never the whole subject, exploited entirely for its own sake. It sets the stage, determines the background, provides the two main ranges of characters, and sets up the issues and events which will occupy the foreground. But the essential issues, the themes which give the novels and stories their deeper meaning and their heavier weight of importance, lie elsewhere.

"Four Meetings" is fully representative of James's later development in these respects, too. It may be said, without too great over-simplification, that at no matter what point we approach his work, we shall sooner or later encounter two underlying assumptions. First, there is his life-long belief in the value, the interest to be derived from the imaginative observation of the aesthetic surface of life. In a moving passage of his autobiographical volume *A Small Boy and Others,* he describes a characteristic childhood experience: stopping on his way home from school, in the New York of the 1850's, to peer through the iron fence of a brownstone house in the front yard of which was to be seen an assortment of "browsing and pecking creatures"—a small cow or two, a peacock and guinea-hens—all ordinary enough, no doubt, but holding a note of the wonderful and the romantic for his "town-bred" imagination. And looking back, more than fifty years later, he saw prefigured in the small boy "dawdling and gaping" on his way home from school the very image of what was to be the guiding interest of so much of his later life, both in New York for a while and then in the great cities of Europe. "Just to be somewhere," as he put it, "—almost anywhere would do—and somehow receive an impression, perceive a relation, experience a vibration"—that was to be the abiding satisfaction of his whole life. And in "Four Meetings," the little schoolteacher from North Verona is as firm as James himself in the belief that it can be a matter of deeply satisfying interest to discriminate the shades, the individual notes of color and life that differentiate Europe, even the tiny portion of it that it is granted to her to see, from her native New England.

A second assumption concerns the right of the individual to decide what he will do with his life. "We see our lives from our own point of view," Isabel Archer declares in *The Portrait of a Lady,* "that is the privilege of the weakest and humblest of us." But James saw that the path through the free life, so endlessly full of interest for those endowed with imagination and insight, was heavily beset with perils for the innocent. Again and again in his novels and stories, the pilgrim is waylaid by those who mean to trick him and exploit him for their own purposes. The trap is often baited with the prospect of a full initiation into the life of "impressions," "relations," and "vibrations," and the attraction of the victim is usually, quite simply, his money—more often, her money. The novel or the story does not end with the springing of the trap, however. It is the fate of many of James's personages to face the bitter knowledge that they have been duped, that a relationship which had seemed to offer the opportunity to serve the highest values of beauty, tradition, interest, and sometimes love, has in reality been only a mask for sordid trickery. And the right of the individual to lead his own life carries with it the obligation to abide by a decision once taken, even when it has turned out badly, for freedom is nothing without integrity, without virtue. Thus Isabel Archer follows out the moral curve of her destiny and returns to her bitter, hateful life with Gilbert Osmond, and the school-teacher of "Four Meetings," more passive and possessing less positive moral force, remains the humble servant of her shabby, exotic guest, meanwhile hoping "to see something of this dear old Europe yet."

FOUR MEETINGS

I saw her but four times, though I remember them vividly; she made her impression on me. I thought her very pretty and very interesting—a touching specimen of a type with which I had had other and perhaps less charming associations. I'm sorry to hear of her death, and yet when I think of it why *should* I be? The last time I saw her she was certainly not—! But it will be of interest to take our meetings in order.

I

The first was in the country, at a small tea-party, one snowy night some seventeen years ago. My friend Latouche, going to spend Christmas with his mother, had insisted on my company, and the good lady had given in our honour the entertainment of which I speak. To me it was really full of savour—it had all the right marks: I had never been in the depths of New England at that season. It had been snowing all day and the drifts were knee-high. I wondered how the ladies had made their way to the house; but I inferred that just those general rigours rendered any assembly offering the attraction of two gentlemen from New York worth a desperate effort.

Mrs. Latouche in the course of the evening asked me if I "didn't want to" show the photographs to some of the young ladies. The photographs were in a couple of great portfolios, and had been brought home by her son, who, like myself, was lately returned from Europe. I looked round and was struck with the fact that most of the young ladies were provided with an object of interest more absorbing than the most vivid sun-picture. But there was a person alone near the mantel-shelf who looked round the room with a small vague smile, a discreet, a disguised yearning, which seemed somehow at odds with her isolation. I looked at her a moment and then chose. "I should like to show them to that young lady."

"Oh yes," said Mrs. Latouche, "she's just the person. She doesn't care for flirting—I'll speak to her." I replied that if she didn't care for flirting she wasn't perhaps just the person; but Mrs. Latouche had already, with a few steps, appealed to her participation. "She's delighted," my hostess came back to report; "and she's just the person—so quiet and so bright." And she told me the young lady was by name Miss Caroline Spencer—with which she introduced me.

Miss Caroline Spencer was not quite a beauty, but was none the less, in her small odd way, formed to please. Close upon thirty, by every presumption, she was made almost like a little girl and had the complexion of a child. She had also the prettiest head, on which her hair was arranged as nearly as possible like the hair of a Greek bust, though indeed it was to be doubted if she had ever seen a Greek bust. She was "artistic," I suspected, so far as the polar influences of North Verona could allow for such yearnings or could minister to them. Her eyes were perhaps just too round and too inveterately surprised, but her lips had a certain mild decision and her teeth, when she showed them, were charming. About her neck she wore what ladies call, I believe, a "ruche" fastened with a very small pin of pink coral, and in her hand she carried a fan made of plaited straw and adorned with pink ribbon. She wore a scanty black silk dress. She spoke with slow soft neatness, even without smiles showing the prettiness of her teeth, and she seemed extremely pleased, in fact quite fluttered, at the prospect of my demonstrations. These went forward very smoothly after I had moved the portfolios out of their corner and placed a couple of chairs near a lamp. The photographs were usually things I knew—large views of Switzerland, Italy and Spain, landscapes, reproductions of famous buildings, pictures and statues. I said what I could for them, and my companions, looking at them as I held them up, sat perfectly still, her straw fan raised to her under-lip and gently, yet, as I could feel, almost excitedly, rubbing it. Occasionally, as I laid one of the pictures down, she said without confidence, which would have been too much: "Have you seen that place?" I usually answered that I had seen it several times—I had been a great traveller, though I was somehow particularly admonished not to swagger—and then I felt her look at me askance for a moment with her pretty eyes. I had asked her at the outset whether she had been to Europe; to this she had answered "No, no, no"—almost as much below her breath as if the image of such an event scarce, for solemnity, brooked phrasing. But after that, though she never took her eyes off the pictures, she said so little that I feared she was at last bored. Accordingly when we had finished one portfolio I offered, if she desired it, to desist. I rather guessed the exhibition really held her, but her reticence puzzled me and I wanted to make her speak. I turned round to judge better and then saw a faint flush in each of her cheeks. She kept waving her little fan to and fro. Instead of looking at me she fixed her eyes on the remainder of the collection, which leaned, in its receptacle, against the table.

"Won't you show me that?" she quavered, drawing the long breath of a person launched and afloat but conscious of rocking a little.

"With pleasure," I answered, "if you're really not tired."

"Oh I'm not tired a bit. I'm just fascinated." With which as I took up the other portfolio she laid her hand on it, rubbing it softly. "And have you been here too?"

On my opening the portfolio it appeared I had indeed been there. One of the first photographs was a large view of the Castle of Chillon by the Lake of Geneva. "Here," I said, "I've been many a time. Isn't it beautiful?" And I pointed to the perfect reflexion of the rugged rocks and pointed towers in the clear still water. She didn't say "Oh enchanting!" and push it away to see the next picture. She looked a while and then asked if it weren't where Bonnivard, about whom Byron wrote, had been confined. I assented, trying to quote Byron's verses, but not quite bringing it off.

She fanned herself a moment and then repeated the lines correctly, in a soft flat voice but with charming conviction. By the time she had finished, she was nevertheless blushing. I complimented her and assured her she was perfectly equipped for visiting Switzerland and Italy. She looked at me askance again, to see if I might be serious, and I added that if she wished to recognise Byron's descriptions she must go abroad speedily— Europe was getting sadly dis-Byronised. "How soon must I go?" she thereupon enquired.

"Oh I'll give you ten years."

"Well, I guess I can go in *that* time," she answered as if measuring her words.

"Then you'll enjoy it immensely," I said; "you'll find it of the highest interest." Just then I came upon a photograph of some nook in a foreign city which I had been very fond of and which recalled tender memories. I discoursed (as I supposed) with considerable spirit; my companion sat listening breathless.

"Have you been *very* long over there?" she asked some time after I had ceased.

"Well, it mounts up, put all the times together."

"And have you travelled everywhere?"

"I've travelled a good deal. I'm very fond of it and happily have been able."

Again she turned on me her slow shy scrutiny. "Do you know the foreign languages?"

"After a fashion."

"Is it hard to speak them?"

"I don't imagine you'd find it so," I gallantly answered.

"Oh I shouldn't want to speak—I should only want to listen." Then on a pause she added: "They say the French theatre's so beautiful."

"Ah the best in the world."

"Did you go there very often?"

"When I was first in Paris I went every night."

"Every night!" And she opened her clear eyes very wide. "That to me is"—and her expression hovered—"as if you tell me a fairy-tale." A few minutes later she put to me: "And which country do you prefer?"

"There's one I love beyond any. I think you'd do the same."

Her gaze rested as on a dim revelation and then she breathed "Italy?"

"Italy," I answered softly too; and for a moment we communed over it. She looked as pretty as if instead of showing her photographs I had been making love to her. To increase the resemblance she turned off blushing. It made a pause which she broke at last by saying: "That's the place which—in particular—I thought of going to."

"Oh that's the place—that's the place!" I laughed.

She looked at two or three more views in silence. "They say it's not very dear."

"As some other countries? Well, one gets back there one's money. That's not the least of the charms."

"But it's *all* very expensive, isn't it?"

"Europe, you mean?"

"Going there and travelling. That has been the trouble. I've very little money. I teach, you know," said Miss Caroline Spencer.

"Oh of course one must have money," I allowed; "but one can manage with a moderate amount judiciously spent."

"I think I should manage. I've saved and saved up, and I'm always adding a little to it. It's all for that." She paused a moment, and then went on with suppressed eagerness, as if telling me the story were a rare, but possibly an impure satisfaction. "You see it hasn't been only the money—it has been everything. Everything has acted against it. I've waited and waited. It has been my castle in the air. I'm almost afraid to talk about it. Two or three times it has come a little nearer, and then I've talked about it and it has melted away. I've talked about it too much," she said hypocritically—for I saw such talk was now a small tremulous ecstasy. "There's a lady who's a great friend of mine—she doesn't want to go, but I'm always at her about it. I think I must tire her dreadfully. She told me just the other day she didn't know what would become of me. She guessed I'd go crazy if I didn't sail, and yet certainly I'd go crazy if I did."

"Well," I laughed, "you haven't sailed up to now—so I suppose you *are* crazy."

She took everything with the same seriousness. "Well, I guess I must be. It seems as if I couldn't think of anything else—and I don't require photographs to work me up! I'm always right *on* it. It kills any interest in things nearer home—things I ought to attend to. That's a kind of craziness."

"Well then the cure for it's just to go," I smiled—"I mean the cure for this kind. Of course you may have the other kind worse," I added—"the kind you get over there."

"Well, I've a faith that I'll go *some* time all right!" she quite elatedly cried. "I've a relative right there on the spot," she went on, "and I guess he'll know how to control me." I expressed the hope that he would, and I forget whether we turned over more photographs; but when I asked her if she had always lived just where I found her, "Oh no sir," she quite eagerly replied; "I've spent twenty-two months and a half in Boston." I met it with the inevitable joke that in this case foreign lands might prove a disappointment to her, but I quite failed to alarm her. "I know more about them than you might think"—her earnestness resisted even that. "I mean by reading—for I've really read considerable. In fact I guess I've prepared my mind about as much as you *can*—in advance. I've not only read Byron—I've read histories and guide-books and articles and lots of things. I know I shall rave about everything."

" 'Everything' is saying much, but I understand your case," I returned. "You've the great American disease, and you've got it 'bad'—the appetite, morbid and monstrous, for colour and form, for the picturesque and the romantic at any price. I don't know whether we come into the world with it—with the germs implanted and antecedent to experience; rather perhaps we catch it early, almost before developed consciousness—we *feel*, as we look about, that we're going (to save our souls, or at least our senses) to be thrown back on it hard. We're like travellers in the desert— deprived of water and subject to the terrible mirage, the torment of illusion, of the thirst-fever. They hear the plash of fountains, they see green gardens and orchards that are hundreds of miles away. So we with *our* thirst—except that with us it's *more* wonderful: we have before us the beautiful old things we've never seen at all, and when we do at last see them—if we're lucky!—we simply recognise them. What experience does is merely to confirm and consecrate our confident dream."

She listened with her rounded eyes. "The way you express it it's too lovely, and I'm sure it will be just like that. I've dreamt of everything— I'll know it all!"

"I'm afraid," I pretended for harmless comedy, "that you've wasted a great deal of time."

"Oh yes, that has been my great wickedness!" The people about us had begun to scatter; they were taking their leave. She got up and put out her hand to me, timidly, but as if quite shining and throbbing.

"I'm going back there—one *has* to," I said as I shook hands with her. "I shall look out for you."

Yes, she fairly glittered with her fever of excited faith. "Well, I'll tell you if I'm disappointed." And she left me, fluttering all expressively her little straw fan.

II

A few months after this I crossed the sea eastward again and some three years elapsed. I had been living in Paris and, toward the end of October, went from that city to the Havre, to meet a pair of relatives who had written me they were about to arrive there. On reaching the Havre I found the steamer already docked—I was two or three hours late. I repaired directly to the hotel where my travellers were duly established. My sister had gone to bed, exhausted and disabled by her voyage; she was the unsteadiest of sailors and her sufferings on this occasion had been extreme. She desired for the moment undisturbed rest and was able to see me but five minutes—long enough for us to agree to stop over, restoratively, till the morrow. My brother-in-law, anxious about his wife, was unwilling to leave her room; but she insisted on my taking him a walk for aid to recovery of his spirits and his land-legs.

The early autumn day was warm and charming, and our stroll through the bright-coloured busy streets of the old French seaport beguiling cnough. We walked along the sunny noisy quays and then turned into a wide pleasant street which lay half in sun and half in shade—a French provincial street that resembled an old water-colour drawing: tall grey steep-roofed red-gabled many-storied houses; green shutters on windows and old scroll-work above them; flower-pots in balconies and white-capped women in doorways. We walked in the shade; all this stretched away on the sunny side of the vista and made a picture. We looked at it as we passed along; then suddenly my companion stopped—pressing my arm and staring. I followed his gaze and saw that we had paused just before reaching a café where, under an awning, several tables and chairs were disposed upon the pavement. The windows were open behind; half a dozen plants in tubs were ranged beside the door; the pavement was besprinkled with clean bran. It was a dear little quiet old-world café; inside, in the comparative dusk, I saw a stout handsome woman, who had pink ribbons in her cap, perched up with a mirror behind her back and smiling at some one placed out of sight. This, to be exact, I noted afterwards; what I first observed was a lady seated alone, outside, at one of the little marble-topped tables. My brother-in-law had stopped to look at her. Something had been put before her, but she only leaned back, motionless and with her hands folded, looking down the street and away from us. I saw her but in diminished profile; nevertheless I was sure I knew on the spot that we must already have met.

"The little lady of the steamer!" my companion cried.

"Was she on your steamer?" I asked with interest.

"From morning till night. She was never sick. She used to sit perpetually at the side of the vessel with her hands crossed that way, looking at the eastward horizon."

"And are you going to speak to her?"

"I don't know her. I never made acquaintance with her. I wasn't in form to make up to ladies. But I used to watch her and—I don't know why—to be interested in her. She's a dear little Yankee woman. I've an idea she's a school-mistress taking a holiday—for which her scholars have made up a purse."

She had now turned her face a little more into profile, looking at the steep grey house-fronts opposite. On this I decided. "I shall speak to her myself."

"I wouldn't—she's very shy," said my brother-in-law.

"My dear fellow, I know her. I once showed her photographs at a tea-party." With which I went up to her, making her, as she turned to look at me, leave me in no doubt of her identity. Miss Caroline Spencer had achieved her dream. But she was less quick to recognise me and showed a slight bewilderment. I pushed a chair to the table and sat down. "Well," I said, "I hope you're not disappointed!"

She stared, blushing a little—then gave a small jump and placed me. "It was you who showed me the photographs—at North Verona."

"Yes, it was I. This happens very charmingly, for isn't it quite proper for me to give you a formal reception here—the official welcome? I talked to you so much about Europe."

"You didn't say too much. I'm so intensely happy!" she declared.

Very happy indeed she looked. There was no sign of her being older; she was as gravely, decently, demurely pretty as before. If she had struck me then as a thin-stemmed, mild-hued flower of Puritanism it may be imagined whether in her present situation this clear bloom was less appealing. Beside her an old gentleman was drinking absinthe; behind her the *dame de comptoir* in the pink ribbons called "Alcibiade, Alcibiade!" to the long-aproned waiter. I explained to Miss Spencer that the gentleman with me had lately been her shipmate, and my brother-in-law came up and was introduced to her. But she looked at him as if she had never so much as seen him, and I remembered he had told me her eyes were always fixed on the eastward horizon. She had evidently not noticed him, and, still timidly smiling, made no attempt whatever to pretend the contrary. I stayed with her on the little terrace of the café while he went back to the hotel and to his wife. I remarked to my friend that this meeting of ours at the first hour of her landing partook, among all chances, of the miraculous, but that I was delighted to be there and receive her first impressions.

"Oh I can't tell you," she said—"I feel so much in a dream. I've been sitting here an hour and I don't want to move. Everything's so delicious and romantic. I don't know whether the coffee has gone to my head—it's *so* unlike the coffee of my dead past."

"Really," I made answer, "if you're so pleased with this poor prosaic Havre you'll have no admiration left for better things. Don't spend your appreciation all the first day—remember it's your intellectual letter of credit. Remember all the beautiful places and things that are waiting for you. Remember that lovely Italy we talked about."

"I'm not afraid of running short," she said gaily, still looking at the opposite houses. "I could sit here all day—just saying to myself that here I am at last. It's so dark and strange—so old and different."

"By the way then," I asked, "how come you to be encamped in this odd place? Haven't you gone to one of the inns?" For I was half-amused, half-alarmed at the good conscience with which this delicately pretty woman had stationed herself in conspicuous isolation on the edge of the sidewalk.

"My cousin brought me here and—a little while ago—left me," she returned. "You know I told you I had a relation over here. He's still here—a real cousin. Well," she pursued with unclouded candour, "he met me at the steamer this morning."

It was absurd—and the case moreover none of my business; but I felt somehow disconcerted. "It was hardly worth his while to meet you if he was to desert you so soon."

"Oh he has only left me for half an hour," said Caroline Spencer. "He has gone to get my money."

I continued to wonder. "Where *is* your money?"

She appeared seldom to laugh, but she laughed for the joy of this. "It makes me feel very fine to tell you! It's in circular notes."

"And where are your circular notes?"

"In my cousin's pocket."

This statement was uttered with such clearness of candour that—I can hardly say why—it gave me a sensible chill. I couldn't at all at the moment have justified my lapse from ease, for I knew nothing of Miss Spencer's cousin. Since he stood in that relation to her—dear respectable little person—the presumption was in his favour. But I found myself wincing at the thought that half an hour after her landing her scanty funds should have passed into his hands. "Is he to travel with you?" I asked.

"Only as far as Paris. He's an art-student in Paris—I've always thought that so splendid. I wrote to him that I was coming, but I never expected him to come off to the ship. I supposed he'd only just meet me at the train in Paris. It's very kind of him. But he *is*," said Caroline Spencer, "very kind—and very bright."

I felt at once a strange eagerness to see this bright kind cousin who was an art-student. "He's gone to the banker's?" I enquired.

"Yes, to the banker's. He took me to an hotel—such a queer quaint cunning little place, with a court in the middle and a gallery all round, and a lovely landlady in such a beautifully fluted cap and such a perfectly fitting dress! After a while we came out to walk to the banker's, for I hadn't any French money. But I was very dizzy from the motion of the vessel and I thought I had better sit down. He found this place for me here—then he went off to the banker's himself. I'm to wait here till he comes back."

Her story was wholly lucid and my impression perfectly wanton, but it passed through my mind that the gentleman would never come back. I settled myself in a chair beside my friend and determined to await the event. She was lost in the vision and the imagination of everything near us and about us—she observed, she recognised and admired, with a touching intensity. She noticed everything that was brought before us by the movement of the street—the peculiarities of costume, the shapes of vehicles, the big Norman horses, the fat priests, the shaven poodles. We talked of these things, and there was something charming in her freshness of perception and the way her book-nourished fancy sallied forth for the revel.

"And when your cousin comes back what are you going to do?" I went on.

For this she had, a little oddly, to think. "We don't quite know."

"When do you go to Paris? If you go by the four o'clock train I may have the pleasure of making the journey with you."

"I don't think we shall do that." So far she was prepared. "My cousin thinks I had better stay here a few days."

"Oh!" said I—and for five minutes had nothing to add. I was wondering what our absentee was, in vulgar parlance, "up to." I looked up and down the street, but saw nothing that looked like a bright and kind American art-student. At last I took the liberty of observing that the Havre was hardly a place to choose as one of the aesthetic stations of a European tour. It was a place of convenience, nothing more; a place of transit, through which transit should be rapid. I recommended her to go to Paris by the afternoon train and meanwhile to amuse herself by driving to the ancient fortress at the mouth of the harbour—that remarkable circular structure which bore the name of Francis the First and figured a sort of small Castle of Saint Angelo. (I might really have foreknown that it was to be demolished.)

She listened with much interest—then for a moment looked grave. "My cousin told me that when he returned he should have something particular to say to me, and that we could do nothing or decide nothing till I should have heard it. But I'll make him tell me right off, and then we'll go to the ancient fortress. Francis the First, did you say? Why, that's lovely. There's no hurry to get to Paris; there's plenty of time."

She smiled with her softly severe little lips as she spoke those last words, yet, looking at her with a purpose, I made out in her eyes, I thought, a tiny gleam of apprehension. "Don't tell me," I said, "that this wretched man's going to give you bad news!"

She coloured as if convicted of a hidden perversity, but she was soaring too high to drop. "Well, I guess it's a *little* bad, but I don't believe it's *very* bad. At any rate I must listen to it."

I usurped an unscrupulous authority. "Look here; you didn't come to Europe to listen—you came to *see!*" But now I was sure her cousin would come back; since he had something disagreeable to say to her he'd infallibly turn up. We sat a while longer and I asked her about her plans of travel. She had them on her fingers' ends and told over the names as solemnly as a daughter of another faith might have told over the beads of a rosary: from Paris to Dijon and to Avignon, from Avignon to Marseilles and the Cornice road; thence to Genoa, to Spezia, to Pisa, to Florence, to Rome. It apparently had never occurred to her that there could be the least incommodity in her travelling alone; and since she was unprovided with a companion I of course civilly abstained from disturbing her sense of security.

At last her cousin came back. I saw him turn toward us out of a side-street, and from the moment my eyes rested on him I knew he could but be the bright, if not the kind, American art-student. He wore a slouch hat and a rusty black velvet jacket, such as I had often encountered in the Rue Bonaparte. His shirt-collar displayed a stretch of throat that at a distance wasn't strikingly statuesque. He was tall and lean, he had red hair and freckles. These items I had time to take in while he approached the café, staring at me with natural surprise from under his romantic brim. When he came up to us I immediately introduced myself as an old acquaintance of Miss Spencer's, a character she serenely permitted me to claim. He looked at me hard with a pair of small sharp eyes, then he gave me a solemn wave, in the "European" fashion, of his rather rusty sombrero.

"You weren't on the ship?" he asked.

"No, I wasn't on the ship. I've been in Europe these several years."

He bowed once more, portentously, and motioned me to be seated again. I sat down, but only for the purpose of observing him an instant— I saw it was time I should return to my sister. Miss Spencer's European protector was, by my measure, a very queer quantity. Nature hadn't shaped him for a Raphaelesque or Byronic attire, and his velvet doublet and exhibited though not columnar throat weren't in harmony with his facial attributes. His hair was cropped close to his head; his ears were large and ill-adjusted to the same. He had a lackadaisical carriage and a sentimental droop which were peculiarly at variance with his keen con-scious strange-coloured eyes—of a brown that was almost red. Perhaps I was prejudiced, but I thought his eyes too shifty. He said nothing for some time; he leaned his hands on his stick and looked up and down the street. Then at last, slowly lifting the stick and pointing with it, "That's a very nice bit," he dropped with a certain flatness. He had his head to one side—he narrowed his ugly lids. I followed the direction of his stick; the object it indicated was a red cloth hung out of an old window. "Nice bit of colour," he continued; and without moving his head transferred his half-closed gaze to me. "Composes well. Fine old tone. Make a nice thing." He spoke in a charmless vulgar voice.

"I see you've a great deal of eye," I replied. "Your cousin tells me you're studying art." He looked at me in the same way, without an-swering, and I went on with deliberate urbanity: "I suppose you're at the studio of one of those great men." Still on this he continued to fix me, and then he named one of the greatest of that day; which led me to ask him if he liked his master.

"Do you understand French?" he returned.

"Some kinds."

He kept his little eyes on me; with which he remarked: "Je suis fou de la peinture!"

"Oh I understand that kind!" I replied. Our companion laid her hand on his arm with a small pleased and fluttered movement; it was delight-ful to be among people who were on such easy terms with foreign tongues. I got up to take leave and asked her where, in Paris, I might have the honour of waiting on her. To what hotel would she go?

She turned to her cousin enquiringly and he favoured me again with his little languid leer. "Do you know the Hôtel des Princes?"

"I know where it is."

"Well, that's the shop."

"I congratulate you," I said to Miss Spencer. "I believe it's the best inn in the world; but, in case I should still have a moment to call on you here, where are you lodged?"

"Oh it's such a pretty name," she returned gleefully. "À la Belle Normande."

"I guess I know my way round!" her kinsman threw in; and as I left them he gave me with his swaggering head-cover a great flourish that was like the wave of a banner over a conquered field.

III

My relative, as it proved, was not sufficiently restored to leave the place by the afternoon train; so that as the autumn dusk began to fall I found myself at liberty to call at the establishment named to me by my friends. I must confess that I had spent much of the interval in wondering what the disagreeable thing was that the less attractive of these had been telling the other. The *auberge* of the Belle Normande proved an hostelry in a shady by-street, where it gave me satisfaction to think Miss Spencer must have encountered local colour in abundance. There was a crooked little court, where much of the hospitality of the house was carried on; there was a staircase climbing to bedrooms on the outer side of the wall; there was a small trickling fountain with a stucco statuette set in the midst of it; there was a little boy in a white cap and apron cleaning copper vessels at a conspicuous kitchen door; there was a chattering landlady, neatly laced, arranging apricots and grapes into an artistic pyramid upon a pink plate. I looked about, and on a green bench outside of an open door labelled Salle-à-Manger, I distinguished Caroline Spencer. No sooner had I looked at her than I was sure something had happened since the morning. Supported by the back of her bench, with her hands clasped in her lap, she kept her eyes on the other side of the court, where the landlady manipulated the apricots.

But I saw that, poor dear, she wasn't thinking of apricots or even of landladies. She was staring absently, thoughtfully; on a nearer view I could have certified she had been crying. I had seated myself beside her before she saw me; then, when she had done so, she simply turned round without surprise and showed me her sad face. Something very bad indeed had happened; she was completely changed, and I immediately charged her with it. "Your cousin has been giving you bad news. You've had a horrid time."

For a moment she said nothing, and I supposed her afraid to speak lest her tears should again rise. Then it came to me that even in the few hours since my leaving her she had shed them all—which made her now intensely, stoically composed. "My poor cousin has been having one," she replied at last. "He has had great worries. His news was bad." Then after a dismally conscious wait: "He was in dreadful want of money."

"In want of yours, you mean?"

"Of any he could get—honourably of course. Mine *is* all—well, that's available."

Ah it was as if I had been sure from the first! "And he has taken it from you?"

Again she hung fire, but her face meanwhile was pleading. "I gave him what I had."

I recall the accent of those words as the most angelic human sound I had ever listened to—which is exactly why I jumped up almost with a sense of personal outrage. "Gracious goodness, madam, do you call that his getting it 'honourably'?"

I had gone too far—she coloured to her eyes. "We won't speak of it."

"We *must* speak of it," I declared as I dropped beside her again. "I'm your friend—upon my word I'm your protector; it seems to me you need one. What's the matter with this extraordinary person?"

She was perfectly able to say. "He's just badly in debt."

"No doubt he is! But what's the special propriety of your—in such tearing haste!—paying for that?"

"Well, he has told me all his story. I *feel* for him so much."

"So do I, if you come to that! But I hope," I roundly added, "he'll give you straight back your money."

As to this she was prompt. "Certainly he will—as soon as ever he can."

"And when the deuce will that be?"

Her lucidity maintained itself. "When he has finished his great picture."

It took me full in the face. "My dear young lady, damn his great picture! Where is this voracious man?"

It was as if she must let me feel a moment that I did push her!—though indeed, as appeared, he was just where he'd naturally be. "He's having his dinner."

I turned about and looked through the open door into the salle-à-manger. There, sure enough, alone at the end of a long table, was the object of my friend's compassion—the bright, the kind young art-student. He was dining too attentively to notice me at first, but in the act of setting down a well-emptied wine-glass he caught sight of my air of observation. He paused in his repast and, with his head on one side and his meagre jaws slowly moving, fixedly returned my gaze. Then the landlady came brushing lightly by with her pyramid of apricots.

"And that nice little plate of fruit is for him?" I wailed.

Miss Spencer glanced at it tenderly. "They seem to arrange everything so nicely!" she simply sighed.

I felt helpless and irritated. "Come now, really," I said; "do you think it right, do you think it decent, that that long strong fellow should collar your funds?" She looked away from me—I was evidently giving her pain. The case was hopeless; the long strong fellow had "interested" her.

"Pardon me if I speak of him so unceremoniously," I said. "But you're really too generous, and he hasn't, clearly, the rudiments of delicacy. He made his debts himself—he ought to pay them himself."

"He has been foolish," she obstinately said—"of course I know that. He has told me everything. We had a long talk this morning—the poor fellow threw himself on my charity. He has signed notes to a large amount."

"The more fool he!"

"He's in real distress—and it's not only himself. It's his poor young wife."

"Ah, he has a poor young wife?"

"I didn't know—but he made a clean breast of it. He married two years since—secretly."

"Why secretly?"

My informant took precautions as if she feared listeners. Then with low impressiveness: "She was a Countess!"

"Are you very sure of that?"

"She has written me the most beautiful letter."

"Asking you—whom she has never seen—for money?"

"Asking me for confidence and sympathy"—Miss Spencer spoke now with spirit. "She has been cruelly treated by her family—in consequence of what she has done for him. My cousin has told me every particular, and she appeals to me in her own lovely way in the letter, which I've here in my pocket. It's such a wonderful old-world romance," said my prodigious friend. "She was a beautiful young widow—her first husband was a Count, tremendously high-born, but really most wicked, with whom she hadn't been happy and whose death had left her ruined after he had deceived her in all sorts of ways. My poor cousin, meeting her in that situation and perhaps a little too recklessly pitying her and charmed with her, found her, don't you see?"——Caroline's appeal on this head was amazing!—"but too ready to trust a better man after all she had been through. Only when her 'people,' as he says—and I do like the word!—understood she *would* have him, poor gifted young American art-student though he simply was, because she just adored him, her great-aunt, the old Marquise, from whom she had expectations of wealth which she could yet sacrifice for her love, utterly cast her off and wouldn't so much as speak to her, much less to *him*, in their dreadful haughtiness and pride. They *can* be haughty over here, it seems," she ineffably developed—"there's no mistake about that! It's like something in some famous old book. The family, my cousin's wife's," she by this time almost complacently wound up, "are of the oldest Provençal noblesse."

I listened half-bewildered. The poor woman positively found it so interesting to be swindled by a flower of that stock—if stock or flower or solitary grain of truth was really concerned in the matter—as practically to have lost the sense of what the forfeiture of her hoard meant for her. "My dear young lady," I groaned, "you don't want to be stripped of every dollar for such a rigmarole!"

She asserted, at this, her dignity—much as a small pink shorn lamb might have done. "It isn't a rigmarole, and I shan't be stripped. I shan't live any worse than I *have* lived, don't you see? And I'll come back before long to stay with them. The Countess—he still gives her, he says, her title, as they do to noble widows, that is to 'dowagers,' don't you know? in England—insists on a visit from me *some* time. So I guess for *that* I can start afresh—and meanwhile I'll have recovered my money."

It was all too heart-breaking. "You're going home then at once?"

I felt the faint tremor of voice she heroically tried to stifle. "I've nothing left for a tour."

"You gave it *all* up?"

"I've kept enough to take me back."

I uttered, I think, a positive howl, and at this juncture the hero of the situation, the happy proprietor of my little friend's sacred savings and of the infatuated *grande dame* just sketched for me, reappeared with the clear consciousness of a repast bravely earned and consistently enjoyed. He stood on the threshold an instant, extracting the stone from a plump apricot he had fondly retained; then he put the apricot into his mouth and, while he let it gratefully dissolve there, stood looking at us with his long legs apart and his hands thrust into the pockets of his velvet coat. My companion got up, giving him a thin glance that I caught in its passage and which expressed at once resignation and fascination— the last dregs of her sacrifice and with it an anguish of upliftedness. Ugly vulgar pretentious dishonest as I thought him, and destitute of every grace of plausibility, he had yet appealed successfully to her eager and tender imagination. I was deeply disgusted, but I had no warrant to interfere, and at any rate felt that it would be vain. He waved his hand meanwhile with a breadth of appreciation. "Nice old court. Nice mellow old place. Nice crooked old staircase. Several pretty things."

Decidedly I couldn't stand it, and without responding I gave my hand to my friend. She looked at me an instant with her little white face and rounded eyes, and as she showed her pretty teeth I suppose she meant to smile. "Don't be sorry for me," she sublimely pleaded; "I'm very sure I shall see something of this dear old Europe yet."

I refused however to take literal leave of her—I should find a moment to come back next morning. Her awful kinsman, who had put on his sombrero again, flourished it off at me by way of a bow—on which I hurried away.

On the morrow early I did return, and in the court of the inn met the landlady, more loosely laced than in the evening. On my asking for Miss Spencer, "*Partie,* monsieur," the good woman said. "She went away last night at ten o'clock, with her—her—not her husband, eh?—in fine her Monsieur. They went down to the American ship." I turned off—I felt the tears in my eyes. The poor girl had been some thirteen hours in Europe.

IV

I myself, more fortunate, continued to sacrifice to opportunity as I myself met it. During this period—of some five years—I lost my friend Latouche, who died of a malarious fever during a tour in the Levant.

One of the first things I did on my return to America was to go up to North Verona on a consolatory visit to his poor mother. I found her in deep affliction and sat with her the whole of the morning that followed my arrival—I had come in late at night—listening to her tearful descant and singing the praises of my friend. We talked of nothing else, and our conversation ended only with the arrival of a quick little woman who drove herself up to the door in a "carry-all" and whom I saw toss the reins to the horse's back with the briskness of a startled sleeper throwing off the bedclothes. She jumped out of the carry-all and she jumped into the room. She proved to be the minister's wife and the great town-gossip, and she had evidently, in the latter capacity, a choice morsel to communicate. I was as sure of this as I was that poor Mrs. Latouche was not absolutely too bereaved to listen to her. It seemed to me discreet to retire, and I described myself as anxious for a walk before dinner.

"And by the way," I added, "if you'll tell me where my old friend Miss Spencer lives, I think I'll call on her."

The minister's wife immediately responded. Miss Spencer lived in the fourth house beyond the Baptist church; the Baptist church was the one on the right, with that queer green thing over the door; they called it a portico, but it looked more like an old-fashioned bedstead swung in the air. "Yes, do look up poor Caroline," Mrs. Latouche further enjoined. "It will refresh her to see a strange face."

"I should think she had had enough of strange faces!" cried the minister's wife.

"To see, I mean, a charming visitor"—Mrs. Latouche amended her phrase.

"I should think she had had enough of charming visitors!" her companion returned. "But *you* don't mean to stay ten years," she added with significant eyes on me.

"Has she a visitor of that sort?" I asked in my ignorance.

"You'll make out the sort!" said the minister's wife. "She's easily seen; she generally sits in the front yard. Only take care what you say to her, and be very sure you're polite."

"Ah she's so sensitive?"

The minister's wife jumped up and dropped me a curtsey—a most sarcastic curtsey. "That's what she is, if you please. 'Madame la Comtesse!'"

And pronouncing these titular words with the most scathing accent, the little woman seemed fairly to laugh in the face of the lady they designated. I stood staring, wondering, remembering.

"Oh I shall be very polite!" I cried; and, grasping my hat and stick, I went on my way.

I found Miss Spencer's residence without difficulty. The Baptist church was easily identified, and the small dwelling near it, of a rusty white, with a large central chimney-stack and a Virginia creeper, seemed naturally and properly the abode of a withdrawn old maid with a taste for striking effects inexpensively obtained. As I approached I slackened my pace, for I had heard that some one was always sitting in the front yard, and I wished to reconnoitre. I looked cautiously over the low white fence that separated the small garden-space from the unpaved street, but I descried nothing in the shape of a Comtesse. A small straight path led up to the crooked door-step, on either side of which was a little grass-plot fringed with currant-bushes. In the middle of the grass, right and left, was a large quince-tree, full of antiquity and contortions, and beneath one of the quince-trees were placed a small table and a couple of light chairs. On the table lay a piece of unfinished embroidery and two or three books in bright-coloured paper covers. I went in at the gate and paused halfway along the path, scanning the place for some further token of its occupant, before whom—I could hardly have said why—I hesitated abruptly to present myself. Then I saw the poor little house to be of the shabbiest and felt a sudden doubt of my right to penetrate, since curiosity had been my motive and curiosity here failed of confidence. While I demurred a figure appeared in the open doorway and stood there looking at me. I immediately recognised Miss Spencer, but she faced me as if we had never met. Gently, but gravely and timidly, I advanced to the door-step, where I spoke with an attempt at friendly banter.

"I waited for you over there to come back, but you never came."

"Waited where, sir?" she quavered, her innocent eyes rounding themselves as of old. She was much older; she looked tired and wasted.

"Well," I said, "I waited at the old French port."

She stared harder, then recognised me, smiling, flushing, clasping her two hands together. "I remember you now—I remember that day." But she stood there, neither coming out nor asking me to come in. She was embarrassed.

I too felt a little awkward while I poked at the path with my stick. "I kept looking out for you year after year."

"You mean in Europe?" she ruefully breathed.

"In Europe of course! Here apparently you're easy enough to find."

She leaned her hand against the unpainted door-post and her head fell a little to one side. She looked at me thus without speaking, and I caught the expression visible in women's eyes when tears are rising. Suddenly she stepped out on the cracked slab of stone before her threshold and closed the door. Then her strained smile prevailed and I saw her teeth were as pretty as ever. But there had been tears too. "Have you been there ever since?" she lowered her voice to ask.

"Until three weeks ago. And you—you never came back?"

Still shining at me as she could, she put her hand behind her and re-opened the door. "I'm not very polite," she said. "Won't you come in?"

"I'm afraid I incommode you."

"Oh no!"—she wouldn't hear of it now. And she pushed back the door with a sign that I should enter.

I followed her in. She led the way to a small room on the left of the narrow hall, which I supposed to be her parlour, though it was at the back of the house, and we passed the closed door of another apartment which apparently enjoyed a view of the quince-trees. This one looked out upon a small wood-shed and two clucking hens. But I thought it pretty until I saw its elegance to be of the most frugal kind; after which, presently, I thought it prettier still, for I had never seen faded chintz and old mezzotint engravings, framed in varnished autumn leaves, disposed with so touching a grace. Miss Spencer sat down on a very small section of the sofa, her hands tightly clasped in her lap. She looked ten years older, and I needn't now have felt called to insist on the facts of her person. But I still thought them interesting, and at any rate I was moved by them. She was peculiarly agitated. I tried to appear not to notice it; but suddenly, in the most inconsequent fashion—it was an irresistible echo of our concentrated passage in the old French port—I said to her: "I do incommode you. Again you're in distress."

She raised her two hands to her face and for a moment kept it buried in them. Then taking them away, "It's because you remind me," she said.

"I remind you, you mean, of that miserable day at the Havre?"

She wonderfully shook her head. "It wasn't miserable. It was delightful."

Ah was it? my manner of receiving this must have commented. "I never was so shocked as when, on going back to your inn the next morning, I found you had wretchedly retreated."

She waited an instant, after which she said: "Please let us not speak of that."

"Did you come straight back here?" I nevertheless went on.

"I was back here just thirty days after my first start."

"And here you've remained ever since?"

"Every minute of the time."

I took it in; I didn't know what to say, and what I presently said had almost the sound of mockery. "When then are you going to make that tour?" It might be practically aggressive; but there was something that irritated me in her depths of resignation, and I wished to extort from her some expression of impatience.

She attached her eyes a moment to a small sun-spot on the carpet; then she got up and lowered the window-blind a little to obliterate it. I waited, watching her with interest—as if she had still something more to give me. Well, presently, in answer to my last question, she gave it. "Never!"

"I hope at least your cousin repaid you that money," I said.

At this again she looked away from me. "I don't care for it now."

"You don't care for your money?"

"For ever going to Europe."

"Do you mean you wouldn't go if you could?"

"I can't—I can't," said Caroline Spencer. "It's all over. Everything's different. I never think of it."

"The scoundrel never repaid you then!" I cried.

"Please, please—!" she began.

But she had stopped—she was looking toward the door. There had been a rustle and a sound of steps in the hall.

I also looked toward the door, which was open and now admitted another person—a lady who paused just within the threshold. Behind her came a young man. The lady looked at me with a good deal of fixedness—long enough for me to rise to a vivid impression of herself. Then she turned to Caroline Spencer and, with a smile and a strong foreign accent, "*Pardon, ma chère!* I didn't know you had company," she said. "The gentleman came in so quietly." With which she again gave me the benefit of her attention. She was very strange, yet I was at once sure I had seen her before. Afterwards I rather put it that I had only seen ladies remarkably like her. But I had seen them very far away from North Verona, and it was the oddest of all things to meet one of them in that frame. To what quite other scene did the sight of her transport me? To some dusky landing before a shabby Parisian *quatrième*— to an open door revealing a greasy antechamber and to Madame leaning over the banisters while she holds a faded wrapper together and bawls down to the portress to bring up her coffee. My friend's guest was a very large lady, of middle age, with a plump dead-white face and hair drawn back *à la chinoise*. She had a small penetrating eye and what is called in French *le sourire agréable*. She wore an old pink cashmere dressing-gown covered with white embroideries, and, like the figure in my momentary vision, she confined it in front with a bare and rounded arm and a plump and deeply-dimpled hand.

"It's only to spick about my café," she said to her hostess with her *sourire agréable*. "I should like it served in the garden under the leetle tree."

The young man behind her had now stepped into the room, where he also stood revealed, though with rather less of a challenge. He was a gentleman of few inches but a vague importance, perhaps the leading man of the world of North Verona. He had a small pointed nose and a small pointed chin; also, as I observed, the most diminutive feet and a manner of no point at all. He looked at me foolishly and with his mouth open.

"You shall have your coffee," said Miss Spencer as if an army of cooks had been engaged in the preparation of it.

"*C'est bien!*" said her massive inmate. "Find your bouk"—and this personage turned to the gaping youth.

He gaped now at each quarter of the room. "My grammar, d'ye mean?"

The large lady however could but face her friend's visitor while persistently engaged with a certain laxity in the flow of her wrapper. "Find your bouk," she more absently repeated.

"My poetry, d'ye mean?" said the young man, who also couldn't take his eyes off me.

"Never mind your bouk"—his companion reconsidered. "Today we'll just talk. We'll make some conversation. But we mustn't interrupt Mademoiselle's. Come, come"—and she moved off a step. "Under the leetle tree," she added for the benefit of Mademoiselle. After which she gave me a thin salutation, jerked a measured "Monsieur!" and swept away again with her swain following.

I looked at Miss Spencer, whose eyes never moved from the carpet, and I spoke, I fear, without grace. "Who in the world's that?"

"The Comtesse—that *was:* my *cousine* as they call it in French."

"And who's the young man?"

"The Countess's pupil, Mr. Mixter." This description of the tie uniting the two persons who had just quitted us must certainly have upset my gravity; for I recall the marked increase of my friend's own as she continued to explain. "She gives lessons in French and music, the simpler sorts—"

"The simpler sorts of French?" I fear I broke in.

But she was still impenetrable, and in fact had now an intonation that put me vulgarly in the wrong. "She has had the worst reverses—with no one to look to. She's prepared for any exertion—and she takes her misfortunes with gaiety."

"Ah well," I returned—no doubt a little ruefully, "that's all I myself am pretending to do. If she's determined to be a burden to nobody, nothing could be more right and proper."

My hostess looked vaguely, though I thought quite wearily enough, about: she met this proposition in no other way. "I must go and get the coffee," she simply said.

"Has the lady many pupils?" I none the less persisted.

"She has only Mr. Mixter. She gives him all her time." It might have set me off again, but something in my whole impression of my friend's sensibility urged me to keep strictly decent. "He pays very well," she at all events inscrutably went on. "He's not very bright—as a pupil; but he's very rich and he's very kind. He has a buggy—with a back, and he takes the Countess to drive."

"For good long spells I hope," I couldn't help interjecting—even at the cost of her so taking it that she had still to avoid my eyes. "Well, the country's beautiful for miles," I went on. And then as she was turning away: "You're going for the Countess's coffee?"

"If you'll excuse me a few moments."

"Is there no one else to do it?"

She seemed to wonder who there should be. "I keep no servants."

"Then can't I help?" After which, as she but looked at me, I bettered it. "Can't she wait on herself?"

Miss Spencer had a slow headshake—as if that too had been a strange idea. "She isn't used to *manual* labour."

The discrimination was a treat, but I cultivated decorum. "I see—and you *are.*" But at the same time I couldn't abjure curiosity. "Before you go, at any rate, please tell me this: who *is* this wonderful lady?"

"I told you just who in France—that extraordinary day. She's the wife of my cousin, whom you saw there."

"The lady disowned by her family in consequence of her marriage?"

"Yes; they've never seen her again. They've completely broken with her."

"And where's her husband?"

"My poor cousin's dead."

I pulled up, but only a moment. "And where's your money?"

The poor thing flinched—I kept her on the rack. "I don't know," she woefully said.

I scarce know what it didn't prompt me to—but I went step by step. "On her husband's death this lady at once came to you?"

It was as if she had had too often to describe it. "Yes, she arrived one day."

"How long ago?"

"Two years and four months."

"And has been here ever since?"

"Ever since."

I took it all in. "And how does she like it?"

"Well, not *very* much," said Miss Spencer divinely.

That too I took in. "And how do *you*—?"

She laid her face in her two hands an instant as she had done ten minutes before. Then, quickly, she went to get the Countess's coffee.

Left alone in the little parlour I found myself divided between the perfection of my disgust and a contrary wish to see, to learn more. At the end of a few minutes the young man in attendance on the lady in question reappeared as for a fresh gape at me. He was inordinately grave—to be dressed in such parti-coloured flannels; and he produced with no great confidence on his own side the message with which he had been charged. "She wants to know if you won't come right out."

"Who wants to know?"

"The Countess. That French lady."

"She has asked you to bring me?"

"Yes sir," said the young man feebly—for I may claim to have surpassed him in stature and weight.

I went out with him, and we found his instructress seated under one of the small quince-trees in front of the house; where she was engaged in drawing a fine needle with a very fat hand through a piece of embroidery not remarkable for freshness. She pointed graciously to the chair beside her and I sat down. Mr. Mixter glanced about him and then accommodated himself on the grass at her feet; whence he gazed upward more gapingly than ever and as if convinced that between us something wonderful would now occur.

"I'm sure you spick French," said the Countess, whose eyes were singularly protuberant as she played over me her agreeable smile.

"I do, madam—*tant bien que mal*," I replied, I fear, more dryly.

"Ah *voilà!*" she cried as with delight. "I knew it as soon as I looked at you. You've been in my poor dear country."

"A considerable time."

"You love it then, *mon pays de France?*"

"Oh it's an old affection." But I wasn't exuberant.

"And you know Paris well?"

"Yes, *sans me vanter,* madam, I think I really do." And with a certain conscious purpose I let my eyes meet her own.

She presently, hereupon, moved her own and glanced down at Mr. Mixter. "What are we talking about?" she demanded of her attentive pupil.

He pulled his knees up, plucked at the grass, stared, blushed a little. "You're talking French," said Mr. Mixter.

"*La belle découverte!*" mocked the Countess. "It's going on ten months," she explained to me, "since I took him in hand. Don't put yourself out not to say he's *la bêtise même,*" she added in fine style. "He won't in the least understand you."

A moment's consideration of Mr. Mixter, awkwardly sporting at our feet, quite assured me that he wouldn't. "I hope your other pupils do you more honour," I then remarked to my entertainer.

"I have no others. They don't know what French—or what anything else—is in this place; they don't want to know. You may therefore imagine the pleasure it is to me to meet a person who speaks it like yourself." I could but reply that my own pleasure wasn't less, and she continued to draw the stitches through her embroidery with an elegant curl of her little finger. Every few moments she put her eyes, near-sightedly, closer to her work—this as if for elegance too. She inspired me with no more confidence than her late husband, if husband he was, had done, years before, on the occasion with which this one so detestably matched: she was coarse, common, affected, dishonest—no more a Countess than I was a Caliph. She had an assurance—based clearly on experience; but this couldn't have been the experience of "race." Whatever it was indeed it did now, in a yearning fashion, flare out of her. "Talk to me of Paris, *mon beau Paris* that I'd give my eyes to see. The very name of it *me fait languir.* How long since you were there?"

"A couple of months ago."

"*Vous avez de la chance!* Tell me something about it. What were they doing? Oh for an hour of the Boulevard!"

"They were doing about what they're always doing—amusing themselves a good deal."

"At the theatres, *hein?*" sighed the Countess. "At the cafés-concerts? *sous ce beau ciel*—at the little tables before the doors? *Quelle existence!* You know I'm a Parisienne, monsieur," she added, "to my finger-tips."

"Miss Spencer was mistaken then," I ventured to return, "in telling me you're a Provençale."

She stared a moment, then put her nose to her embroidery, which struck me as having acquired even while we sat a dingier and more desultory air. "Ah I'm a Provençale by birth, but a Parisienne by—inclination." After which she pursued: "And by the saddest events of my life—as well as by some of the happiest, *hélas!*"

"In other words by a varied experience!" I now at last smiled.

She questioned me over it with her hard little salient eyes. "Oh experience!—I could talk of that, no doubt, if I wished. *On en a de toutes les sortes*—and I never dreamed that mine, for example, would ever have *this* in store for me." And she indicated with her large bare elbow and with a jerk of her head all surrounding objects; the little white house, the pair of quince-trees, the rickety paling, even the rapt Mr. Mixter.

I took them all bravely in. "Ah if you mean you're decidedly in exile—!"

"You may imagine what it is. These two years of my *épreuve—elles m'en ont données, des heures, des heures!* One gets used to things"—and she raised her shoulders to the highest shrug ever accomplished at North Verona; "so that I sometimes think I've got used to this. But there are some things that are always beginning again. For example my coffee."

I so far again lent myself. "Do you always have coffee at this hour?"

Her eyebrows went up as high as her shoulders had done. "At what hour would you propose to me to have it? I must have my little cup after breakfast."

"Ah you breakfast at this hour?"

"At mid-day—*comme cela se fait.* Here they breakfast at a quarter past seven. That 'quarter past' is charming!"

"But you were telling me about your coffee," I observed sympathetically.

"My *cousine* can't believe in it; she can't understand it. *C'est une fille charmante,* but that little cup of black coffee with a drop of 'fine,' served at this hour—they exceed her comprehension. So I have to break the ice each day, and it takes the coffee the time you see to arrive. And when it does arrive, monsieur—! If I don't press it on *you*—though monsieur here sometimes joins me!—it's because you've drunk it on the Boulevard."

I resented extremely so critical a view of my poor friend's exertions, but I said nothing at all—the only way to be sure of my civility. I dropped my eyes on Mr. Mixter, who, sitting cross-legged and nursing his knees, watched my companion's foreign graces with an interest that familiarity had apparently done little to restrict. She became aware, naturally, of my mystified view of him and faced the question with all her boldness. "He adores me, you know," she murmured with her nose again in her tapestry—"he dreams of becoming *mon amoureux.* Yes, *il me fait une cour acharnée*—such as you see him. That's what we've come to. He has read some French novel—it took him six months. But ever since that he has thought himself a hero and me—such as I am, monsieur— *je ne sais quelle dévergondée!*"

Mr. Mixter may have inferred that he was to that extent the object of our reference; but of the manner in which he was handled he must have had small suspicion—preoccupied as he was, as to my companion, with the ecstasy of contemplation. Our hostess moreover at this moment came out of the house, bearing a coffee-pot and three cups on a neat little tray. I took from her eyes, as she approached us, a brief but intense appeal—the mute expression, as I felt, conveyed in the hardest little look she had yet addressed me, of her longing to know what, as a man of the world in general and of the French world in particular, I thought of these allied forces now so encamped on the stricken field of her life. I could only "act" however, as they said at North Verona, quite impenetrably—only make no answering sign. I couldn't intimate, much less could I frankly utter, my inward sense of the Countess's probable past, with its measure of her virtue, value and accomplishments, and of the limits of the consideration to which she could properly pretend. I couldn't give my friend a hint of how I myself personally "saw" her interesting pensioner—whether as the runaway wife of a too-jealous hairdresser or of a too-morose pastry-cook, say; whether as a very small bourgeoise, in fine, who had vitiated her case beyond patching up, or even as some character, of the nomadic sort, less edifying still. I couldn't let in, by the jog of a shutter, as it were, a hard informing ray and then, washing my hands of the business, turn my back for ever. I could on the contrary but save the situation, my own at least, for the moment, by pulling myself together with a master hand and appearing to ignore everything but that the dreadful person between us *was* a "grande dame." This effort was possible indeed but as a retreat in good order and with all the forms of courtesy. If I couldn't speak, still less could I stay, and I think I must, in spite of everything, have turned black with disgust to see Caroline Spencer stand there like a waiting-maid. I therefore won't answer for the shade of success that may have attended my saying to the Countess, on my feet and as to leave her: "You expect to remain some time in these *parages?*"

What passed between us, as from face to face, while she looked up at me, *that* at least our companion may have caught, that at least may have sown, for the after-time, some seed of revelation. The Countess repeated her terrible shrug. "Who knows? I don't see my way—! It isn't an existence, but when one's in misery—! *Chère belle*," she added as an appeal to Miss Spencer, "you've gone and forgotten the *'fine'!*"

I detained that lady as, after considering a moment in silence the small array, she was about to turn off in quest of this article. I held out my hand in silence—I had to go. Her wan set little face, severely mild and with the question of a moment before now quite cold in it, spoke of extreme fatigue, but also of something else strange and conceived—whether a desperate patience still, or at last some other desperation, being more than I can say. What was clearest on the whole was that she was glad I was going. Mr. Mixter had risen to his feet and was pouring

out the Countess's coffee. As I went back past the Baptist church I
could feel how right my poor friend had been in her conviction at the
other, the still intenser, the now historic crisis, that she should still see
something of that dear old Europe.

QUESTIONS

1. Does James's diagnosis of "the great American disease" (section I,
sixth paragraph from the end), made in the 1870's, have applicability
today, or has the situation changed to such an extent that Americans no
longer look to Europe for the values and satisfactions he describes?

2. In terms of what specific places, and of what detailed glimpses of
life, does James present Europe in this story? What are some of the details
which highlight his presentation of American life and the American
scene?

3. Which persons represent America, and what phases of American life
does each serve to bring out? Which ones represent Europe? Where do
(a) the artist-cousin and (b) the narrator stand in this regard?

4. In his total presentation, does James weight the balance in favor of
Europe or of America?

5. Does James wish us to feel that Miss Spencer has "the right idea" of
Europe? All the way through the story, or only at the beginning, or only
at the end? By the end of the story, what principal elements has her
experience of Europe consisted in?

6. How do you understand the motives which determine the narrator's
behavior towards the "Countess" in the final scene?

ANTON CHEKHOV

(1860–1904)

Chekhov was born at Taganrog, in the Ukraine, in January, 1860. His
father had moved his family to Moscow in 1876 because of the failure
of his business, Anton staying behind until, in 1879, he passed his ma-
triculation examinations for the study of medicine. He took his degree
at Moscow in 1884 but did not actually practice medicine for long (he
returned to it during the emergency produced by the cholera epidemic
of 1892-93). In the early 1890's he acquired a small estate at Melichovo,
near Moscow, and carried on a program of aid for the peasants of the
surrounding district. He was not able to settle into this life for very long,
since it had become evident during this same decade that he was tuber-
cular and must seek a warmer climate. In search of health he went at var-

ious times to the Crimea, especially Yalta, to Nice and Biarritz, and to German spas.

He had begun to write while he was still a medical student, helping to support the family by sketches published in the Moscow humorous magazines and written to their uninspiring prescription. In 1885 he began to gain entrée into periodicals that would publish more serious work, and he gradually gained the favorable attention of the literary world centering in St. Petersburg and of the reading public. He published his first volumes of short stories in the mid-eighties, and continued to publish successive volumes until 1900. In 1898 his play *The Seagull* had been successfully performed by the Moscow Art Theater under Stanislavsky, after having been a failure earlier in St. Petersburg, and thus began the connection with this great theater which was to prove so momentous for theatrical history in the present century. During the few years that remained to him, Chekhov wrote for the Moscow Art Theater (in 1901 he married one of its actresses, Olga Knipper) three of the most powerful, haunting, and original plays the modern theater has known: *Uncle Vanya* (1900), *The Three Sisters* (1901), and *The Cherry Orchard* (1903). He died at Badenweiler, in the Black Forest (Germany) on July 2, 1904.

Something has already been said in the Introduction to the present collection of stories about Chekhov's commanding position in the development of the modern short story. Readers whose experience, at the time they first encounter Chekhov, has been mostly with the kind of story which puts a heavy emphasis on plot, on a surprise ending, will probably find that Chekhov's stories take a certain amount of getting used to. At first, these readers may be inclined to dismiss a story like "The Beauties" as being scarcely more than a sketch, or at best something they may call, with lukewarm approbation, a "mood story." This is all right—it is true that "The Beauties" works very skillfully with moods that are not often captured so well—as long as the phrase isn't allowed to imply that the story is somehow incomplete, empty of the fullest interest. It will certainly seem so if we read through it hastily, expecting that it will go together with a click at the end when some surprising new element is introduced, some coincidence that will link the two incidents. There is no click, no surprise, no coincidence on the level of event. The two instances *are* linked, however, by what they have in common. Each points out that there is often a certain sadness intermixed with the pleasure of seeing youthful beauty, especially the beauty of a person whose life is remote from that of the observer. This mood of intermingled pleasure and sadness is created for us with remarkable power and subtlety, and the question of *why* such a mood arises, what there is in the conditions of life that should make it so, is allowed to linger in our minds after we have put the story down.

The writer who produces a surprise ending also wants to leave something lingering in our minds, but if the surprise has been led up to and produced simply for its own sake the something which lingers will be not merely shallow but even frustrating, because it has no relation with anything beyond itself, no relation with the conditions of life as they habitually operate. In this story, on the contrary, Chekhov has offered us two instances of the way a certain range of feelings is excited by a certain kind of event, of observation, and in doing so has called to our attention data that may be new to us about the way things are, about the conditions of life. The way things are: that is Chekhov's subject. Not the way we would like things to be, neatly arranged and uniformly favorable, happy, promising, with joy in one compartment and sorrow in another, with the sublime here and the ridiculous there and no connection between them, but with all the elements inextricably mixed so that it is hard to say at a given moment whether what we are feeling is joy or sorrow, hard to know whether we ought to focus on the beauty or the squalor of a scene, of a moment.

"The Beauties" dates from 1888, "In the Ravine," which is justly one of Chekhov's most celebrated stories, from 1900. It is the story of a whole village, focussed in the lives of a few individuals, a few eccentricities, a few moments, including the good moments when, what with the concertina and the moonlight, "Ukleevo no longer seemed a wretched hole." On the surface, it seems as if the events in these lives, the connections from one of them to another, are being recounted almost haphazardly. But beneath the surface, beyond Chekhov's deep taciturnity which forbids him to offer direct comment on the events he displays before us, there exists a pattern of bitter criticism of the social injustice, the exploitation, and the hardship of pre-Revolutionary Russia. Chekhov presents a most searching picture of the life of his time, with specific applicability to the conditions he saw prevailing all about him. It is precisely because he is so minutely faithful in his portrayal of the institutions, habits, and surfaces of his own particular time and place that his stories and plays have continued to have deep and compelling things to say about life and human nature at points far distant, both in space and time, from Chekhov's Russia.

THE BEAUTIES

1

I remember, when I was a high-school boy in the fifth or sixth class, I was driving with my grandfather from the village of Bolshoe Kryepkoe in the Don region to Rostov-on-the-Don. It was a sultry, languidly dreary day of August. Our eyes were glued together, and our mouths were parched from the heat and the dry burning wind which drove clouds of dust to meet us; one did not want to look or speak or think, and when our drowsy driver, a Little Russian called Karpo, swung his whip at the

TRANSLATED by Constance Garnett. Reprinted by permission of the Macmillan Co.

horses and lashed me on my cap, I did not protest or utter a sound, but only, rousing myself from half-slumber, gazed mildly and dejectedly into the distance to see whether there was a village visible through the dust. We stopped to feed the horses in a big Armenian village at a rich Armenian's whom my grandfather knew. Never in my life have I seen a greater caricature than that Armenian. Imagine a little shaven head with thick overhanging eyebrows, a beak of a nose, long grey moustaches, and a wide mouth with a long cherry-wood chibouk sticking out of it. This little head was clumsily attached to a lean hunchback carcase attired in a fantastic garb, a short red jacket, and full bright blue trousers. This figure walked straddling its legs and shuffling with its slippers, spoke without taking the chibouk out of its mouth, and behaved with truly Armenian dignity, not smiling, but staring with wide-open eyes and trying to take as little notice as possible of its guests.

There was neither wind nor dust in the Armenian's rooms, but it was just as unpleasant, stifling, and dreary as in the steppe and on the road. I remember, dusty and exhausted by the heat, I sat in the corner on a green box. The unpainted wooden walls, the furniture, and the floors coloured with yellow ochre, smelt of dry wood baked by the sun. Wherever I looked there were flies and flies and flies. . . . Grandfather and the Armenian were talking about grazing, about manure, and about oats. . . . I knew that they would be a good hour getting the samovar; that grandfather would be not less than an hour drinking his tea, and then would lie down to sleep for two or three hours; that I should waste a quarter of the day waiting, after which there would be again the heat, the dust, the jolting cart. I heard the muttering of the two voices, and it began to seem to me that I had been seeing the Armenian, the cupboard with the crockery, the flies, the windows with the burning sun beating on them, for ages and ages, and should only cease to see them in the far-off future, and I was seized with hatred for the steppe, the sun, the flies. . . .

A Little Russian peasant woman in a kerchief brought in a tray of tea-things, then the samovar. The Armenian went slowly out into the passage and shouted: "Mashya, come and pour out tea! Where are you, Mashya?"

Hurried footsteps were heard, and there came into the room a girl of sixteen in a simple cotton dress and a white kerchief. As she washed the crockery and poured out the tea, she was standing with her back to me, and all I could see was that she was of a slender figure, barefooted, and that her little bare heels were covered by long trousers.

The Armenian invited me to have tea. Sitting down to the table, I glanced at the girl, who was handing me a glass of tea, and felt all at once as though a wind were blowing over my soul and blowing away all the impressions of the day with their dust and dreariness. I saw the bewitching features of the most beautiful face I have ever met in real life or in my dreams. Before me stood a beauty, and I recognized that at the first glance as I should have recognized lightning.

I am ready to swear that Masha—or, as her father called her, Mashya—was a real beauty, but I don't know how to prove it. It sometimes happens that clouds are huddled together in disorder on the horizon, and the sun hiding behind them colours them and the sky with tints of every possible shade—crimson, orange, gold, lilac, muddy pink; one cloud is like a monk, another like a fish, a third like a Turk in a turban. The glow of sunset enveloping a third of the sky gleams on the cross on the church, flashes on the windows of the manor house, is reflected in the river and the puddles, quivers on the trees; far, far away against the background of the sunset, a flock of wild ducks is flying homewards. . . . And the boy herding the cows, and the surveyor driving in his chaise over the dam, and the gentleman out for a walk, all gaze at the sunset, and every one of them thinks it terribly beautiful, but no one knows or can say in what its beauty lies.

I was not the only one to think the Armenian girl beautiful. My grandfather, an old man of seventy, gruff and indifferent to women and the beauties of nature, looked caressingly at Masha for a full minute, and asked:

"Is that your daughter, Avert Nazaritch?"

"Yes, she is my daughter," answered the Armenian.

"A fine young lady," said my grandfather approvingly.

An artist would have called the Armenian girl's beauty classical and severe; it was just that beauty the contemplation of which—God knows why!—inspires in one the conviction that one is seeing correct features; that hair, eyes, nose, mouth, neck, bosom, and every movement of the young body all go together in one complete harmonious accord in which nature has not blundered over the smallest line. You fancy for some reason that the ideally beautiful woman must have such a nose as Masha's, straight and slightly aquiline, just such great dark eyes, such long lashes, such a languid glance; you fancy that her black curly hair and eyebrows go with the soft white tint of her brow and cheeks as the green reeds go with the quiet stream. Masha's white neck and her youthful bosom were not fully developed, but you fancy the sculptor would need a great creative genius to mould them. You gaze, and little by little the desire comes over you to say to Masha something extraordinarily pleasant, sincere, beautiful, as beautiful as she herself was.

At first I felt hurt and abashed that Masha took no notice of me, but was all the time looking down; it seemed to me as though a peculiar atmosphere, proud and happy, separated her from me and jealously screened her from my eyes.

"That's because I am covered with dust," I thought, "am sunburnt, and am still a boy."

But little by little I forgot myself, and gave myself up entirely to the consciousness of beauty. I thought no more now of the dreary steppe, of the dust, no longer heard the buzzing of the flies, no longer tasted the tea, and felt nothing except that a beautiful girl was standing only the other side of the table.

I felt this beauty rather strangely. It was not desire, nor ecstasy, nor enjoyment that Masha excited in me, but a painful though pleasant sadness. It was a sadness vague and undefined as a dream. For some reason I felt sorry for myself, for my grandfather and for the Armenian, even for the girl herself, and I had a feeling as though we all four had lost something important and essential to life which we should never find again. My grandfather, too, grew melancholy; he talked no more about manure or about oats, but sat silent, looking pensively at Masha.

After tea my grandfather lay down for a nap while I went out of the house into the porch. The house, like all the houses in the Armenian village, stood in the full sun; there was not a tree, not an awning, no shade. The Armenian's great courtyard, overgrown with goosefoot and wild mallows, was lively and full of gaiety in spite of the great heat. Threshing was going on behind one of the low hurdles which intersected the big yard here and there. Round a post stuck into the middle of the threshing-floor ran a dozen horses harnessed side by side, so that they formed one long radius. A Little Russian in a long waistcoat and full trousers was walking beside them, cracking a whip and shouting in a tone that sounded as though he were jeering at the horses and showing off his power over them.

"A—a—a, you damned brutes! . . . A—a—a, plague take you! Are you frightened?"

The horses, sorrel, white, and piebald, not understanding why they were made to run round in one place and to crush the wheat straw, ran unwillingly, as though with effort, swinging their tails with an offended air. The wind raised up perfect clouds of golden chaff from under their hoofs and carried it away far beyond the hurdle. Near the tall fresh stacks peasant women were swarming with rakes, and carts were moving, and beyond the stacks in another yard another dozen similar horses were running round a post, and a similar Little Russian was cracking his whip and jeering at the horses.

The steps on which I was sitting were hot; on the thin rails and here and there on the window-frames sap was oozing out of the wood from the heat; red ladybirds were huddling together in the streaks of shadow under the steps and under the shutters. The sun was baking me on my head, on my chest, and on my back, but I did not notice it, and was conscious only of the thud of bare feet on the uneven floor in the passage and in the rooms behind me. After clearing away the tea-things, Masha ran down the steps, fluttering the air as she passed, and like a bird flew into a little grimy outhouse—I suppose the kitchen—from which came the smell of roast mutton and the sound of angry talk in Armenian. She vanished into the dark doorway, and in her place there appeared on the threshold an old bent, red-faced Armenian woman wearing green trousers. The old woman was angry and was scolding someone. Soon afterwards Masha appeared in the doorway, flushed with the heat of the kitchen and carrying a big black loaf on her shoulder; swaying gracefully under the weight of the bread, she ran across the yard to the thresh-ing-floor, darted over the hurdle, and, wrapt in a cloud of golden chaff, vanished behind the carts. The Little Russian who was driving the horses lowered his whip, sank into silence, and gazed for a minute in the direc-tion of the carts. Then when the Armenian girl darted again by the horses and leaped over the hurdle, he followed her with his eyes, and shouted to the horses in a tone as though he were greatly disappointed:

"Plague take you, unclean devils!"

And all the while I was unceasingly hearing her bare feet, and seeing how she walked across the yard with a grave, preoccupied face. She ran now down the steps, swishing the air about me, now into the kitchen, now to the threshing-floor, now through the gate, and I could hardly turn my head quickly enough to watch her.

And the oftener she fluttered by me with her beauty, the more acute became my sadness. I felt sorry both for her and for myself and for the Little Russian, who mournfully watched her every time she ran through the cloud of chaff to the carts. Whether it was envy of her beauty, or that I was regretting that the girl was not mine, and never would be, or that I was a stranger to her; or whether I vaguely felt that her rare beauty was accidental, unnecessary, and, like everything on earth, of short duration; or whether, perhaps, my sadness was that peculiar feeling which is excited in man by the contemplation of real beauty, God only knows.

The three hours of waiting passed unnoticed. It seemed to me that I had not had time to look properly at Masha when Karpo drove up to the river, bathed the horse, and began to put it in the shafts. The wet horse snorted with pleasure and kicked his hoofs against the shafts. Karpo shouted to it: "Ba-ack!" My grandfather woke up. Masha opened the creaking gates for us, we got into the chaise and drove out of the yard. We drove in silence as though we were angry with one another.

When, two or three hours later, Rostov and Nahitchevan appeared in the distance, Karpo, who had been silent the whole time, looked round quickly, and said:

"A fine wench, that at the Armenian's."

And he lashed his horses.

2

Another time, after I had become a student, I was travelling by rail to the south. It was May. At one of the stations, I believe it was between Byelgorod and Harkov, I got out of the train to walk about the platform.

The shades of evening were already lying on the station garden, on the platform, and on the fields; the station screened off the sunset, but on the topmost clouds of smoke from the engine, which were tinged with rosy light, one could see the sun had not yet quite vanished.

As I walked up and down the platform I noticed that the greater num-ber of the passengers were standing or walking near a second-class compartment, and that they looked as though some celebrated person were in that compartment. Among the curious whom I met near this compartment I saw, however, an artillery officer who had been my fellow-traveller, an intelligent, cordial, and sympathetic fellow—as people mostly are whom we meet on our travels by chance and with whom we are not long acquainted.

"What are you looking at there?" I asked.

He made no answer, but only indicated with his eyes a feminine figure. It was a young girl of seventeen or eighteen, wearing a Russian dress, with her head bare and a little shawl flung carelessly on one shoulder; not a passenger, but I suppose a sister or daughter of the station-master. She was standing near the carriage window, talking to an elderly woman who was in the train. Before I had time to realize what I was seeing, I was suddenly overwhelmed by the feeling I had once experienced in the Armenian village.

The girl was remarkably beautiful, and that was unmistakable to me and to those who were looking at her as I was.

If one is to describe her appearance feature by feature, as the practice is, the only really lovely thing was her thick wavy fair hair, which hung loose with a black ribbon tied round her head; all the other features were either irregular or very ordinary. Either from a peculiar form of coquettishness, or from short-sightedness, her eyes were scewed up, her nose had an undecided tilt, her mouth was small, her profile was feebly and insipidly drawn, her shoulders were narrow and undeveloped for her age—and yet the girl made the impression of being really beautiful, and looking at her, I was able to feel convinced that the Russian face does not need strict regularity in order to be lovely; what is more, that if instead of her turn-up nose the girl had been given a different one, correct and plastically irreproachable like the Armenian girl's, I fancy her face would have lost all its charm from the change.

Standing at the window talking, the girl, shrugging at the evening damp, continually looking round at us, at one moment put her arms akimbo, at the next raised her hands to her head to straighten her hair, talked, laughed, while her face at one moment wore an expression of wonder, the next of horror, and I don't remember a moment when her face and body were at rest. The whole secret and magic of her beauty lay just in these tiny, infinitely elegant movements, in her smile, in the play of her face, in her rapid glances at us, in the combination of the subtle grace of her movements with her youth, her freshness, the purity of her soul that sounded in her laugh and voice, and with the weakness we love so much in children, in birds, in fawns, and in young trees.

It was that butterfly's beauty so in keeping with waltzing, darting about the garden, laughter and gaiety, and incongruous with serious thought, grief, and repose; and it seemed as though a gust of wind blowing over the platform, or a fall of rain, would be enough to wither the fragile body and scatter the capricious beauty like the pollen of a flower.

"So—o! . . ." the officer muttered with a sigh when, after the second bell, we went back to our compartment.

And what that "So—o" meant I will not undertake to decide.

Perhaps he was sad, and did not want to go away from the beauty and the spring evening into the stuffy train; or perhaps he, like me, was unaccountably sorry for the beauty, for himself, and for me, and for all the passengers, who were listlessly and reluctantly sauntering back to their compartments. As we passed the station window, at which a pale, red-haired telegraphist with upstanding curls and a faded, broad-cheeked face was sitting beside his apparatus, the officer heaved a sigh and said:

"I bet that telegraphist is in love with that pretty girl. To live out in the wilds under one roof with that ethereal creature and not fall in love is beyond the power of man. And what a calamity, my friend! what an ironical fate, to be stooping, unkempt, grey, a decent fellow and not a fool, and to be in love with that pretty, stupid little girl who would never take a scrap of notice of you! Or worse still: imagine that telegraphist is in love, and at the same time married, and that his wife is as stooping, as unkempt, and as decent a person as himself."

On the platform between our carriage and the next the guard was standing with his elbows on the railing, looking in the direction of the beautiful girl, and his battered, wrinkled, unpleasantly beefy face, exhausted by sleepless nights and the jolting of the train, wore a look of tenderness and of the deepest sadness, as though in that girl he saw happiness, his own youth, soberness, purity, wife, children; as though he were repenting and feeling in his whole being that that girl was not his, and that for him, with his premature old age, his uncouthness, and his beefy face, the ordinary happiness of a man and a passenger was as far away as heaven. . . .

The third bell rang, the whistles sounded, and the train slowly moved off. First the guard, the station-master, then the garden, the beautiful girl with her exquisitely sly smile, passed before our windows. . . .

Putting my head out and looking back, I saw how, looking after the train, she walked along the platform by the window where the telegraph clerk was sitting, smoothed her hair, and ran into the garden. The station no longer screened off the sunset, the plain lay open before us, but the sun had already set and the smoke lay in black clouds over the green, velvety young corn. It was melancholy in the spring air, and in the darkening sky, and in the railway carriage.

The familiar figure of the guard came into the carriage, and he began lighting the candles.

QUESTIONS

1. In each of the two incidents, the narrator describes carefully and explicitly what seemed to him to be the reasons for the mixture of pleasure and sadness which the sudden appearance of the beautiful young girl made upon him. Does it seem to you that he explains his feelings completely, or is there something left for a reader to wonder about after he has finished the story?

2. Could each of the incidents effectively stand alone? Does Chekhov achieve anything more than the *addition* of one incident to another by putting them together? Is it possible that by presenting two parallel incidents, observed at different periods of the narrator's life, a meaning is built up that would not be entirely visible in either of the incidents taken separately?

3. In how many respects do the two incidents parallel one another?

4. What is the function of setting in this story?

IN THE RAVINE

1

The village of Ukleevo lay in a ravine so that only the belfry and the chimneys of the printed cotton factories could be seen from the highroad and the railway-station. When visitors asked what village this was, they were told:

"That's the village where the deacon ate all the caviare at the funeral."

It had happened at the dinner at the funeral of Kostukov that the old deacon saw among the savouries some large-grained caviare and began eating it greedily; people nudged him, tugged at his arm, but he seemed petrified with enjoyment: felt nothing, and only went on eating. He ate up all the caviare, and there were four pounds in the jar. And years had passed since then, the deacon had long been dead, but the caviare was still remembered. Whether life was so poor here or people had not been clever enough to notice anything but that unimportant incident that had occurred ten years before, anyway the people had nothing else to tell about the village Ukleevo.

The village was never free from fever, and there was boggy mud there even in the summer, especially under the fences over which hung old willow-trees that gave deep shade. Here there was always a smell from the factory refuse and the acetic acid which was used in the finishing of the cotton print.

The three cotton factories and the tanyard were not in the village itself but a little way off. They were small factories, and not more than four hundred workmen were employed in all of them. The tanyard often made the water in the little river stink; the refuse contaminated the meadows, the peasants' cattle suffered from Siberian plague, and orders were given that the factory should be closed. It was considered to be closed,

TRANSLATED by Constance Garnett. Reprinted by permission of the Macmillan Co.

but went on working in secret with the connivance of the local police officer and the district doctor, who was paid ten rubles a month by the owner. In the whole village there were only two decent houses built of brick with iron roofs; one of them was the local court, in the other, a two-storeyed house just opposite the church, there lived a shopkeeper from Epifan called Grigory Petrovitch Tsybukin.

Grigory kept a grocer's shop, but that was only for appearance' sake: in reality he sold vodka, cattle, hides, grain, and pigs; he traded in anything that came to hand, and when, for instance, magpies were wanted abroad for ladies' hats, he made some thirty kopecks on every pair of birds; he bought timber for felling, lent money at interest, and altogether was a sharp old man, full of resources.

He had two sons. The elder, Anisim, was in the police in the detective department and was rarely at home. The younger, Stepan, had gone in for trade and helped his father: but no great help was expected from him as he was weak in health and deaf; his wife Aksinya, a handsome woman with a good figure, who wore a hat and carried a parasol on holidays, got up early and went to bed late, and ran about all day long, picking up her skirts and jingling her keys, going from the granary to the cellar and from there to the shop, and old Tsybukin looked at her good-humouredly while his eyes glowed, and at such moments he regretted she had not been married to his elder son instead of to the younger one, who was deaf, and who evidently knew very little about female beauty.

The old man had always an inclination for family life, and he loved his family more than anything on earth, especially his elder son, the detective, and his daughter-in-law. Aksinya had no sooner married the deaf son than she began to display an extraordinary gift for business, and knew who could be allowed to run up a bill and who could not: she kept the keys and would not trust them even to her husband; she kept the accounts by means of the reckoning beads, looked at the horses' teeth like a peasant, and was always laughing or shouting; and whatever she did or said the old man was simply delighted and muttered:

"Well done, daughter-in-law! You are a smart wench!"

He was a widower, but a year after his son's marriage he could not resist getting married himself. A girl was found for him, living twenty miles from Ukleevo, called Varvara Nikolaevna, no longer quite young, but good-looking, comely, and belonging to a decent family. As soon as she was installed into the upper-storey room everything in the house seemed to brighten up as though new glass had been put into all the windows. The lamps gleamed before the ikons, the tables were covered with snow-white cloths, flowers with red buds made their appearance in the windows and in the front garden, and at dinner, instead of eating from a single bowl, each person had a separate plate set for him. Varvara Nikolaevna had a pleasant, friendly smile, and it seemed as though the whole house were smiling, too. Beggars and pilgrims, male and female, began to come into the yard, a thing which had never happened in the past; the plaintive sing-song voices of the Ukleevo peasant women and the apologetic coughs of weak, seedy-looking men, who had been dismissed from the factory for drunkenness, were heard under the windows. Varvara helped them with money, with bread, with old clothes, and afterwards, when she felt more at home, began taking things out of the shop. One day the deaf man saw her take four ounces of tea and that disturbed him.

"Here, mother's taken four ounces of tea," he informed his father afterwards; "where is that to be entered?"

The old man made no reply but stood still and thought a moment, moving his eyebrows, and then went upstairs to his wife.

"Varvarushka, if you want anything out of the shop," he said affectionately, "take it, my dear. Take it and welcome; don't hesitate."

And the next day the deaf man, running across the yard, called to her: "If there is anything you want, mother, take it."

There was something new, something gay and lighthearted in her giving of alms, just as there was in the lamps before the ikons and in the red flowers. When at Carnival or at the church festival, which lasted for three days, they sold the peasants tainted salt meat, smelling so strong it was hard to stand near the tub of it, and took scythes, caps, and their wives' kerchiefs in pledge from the drunken men; when the factory hands stupefied with bad vodka lay rolling in the mud, and sin seemed to hover thick like a fog in the air, then it was a relief to think that up there in the house there was a gentle, neatly dressed woman who had nothing to do with salt meat or vodka; her charity had in those burdensome, murky days the effect of a safety-valve in a machine.

The days in Tsybukin's house were spent in business cares. Before the sun had risen in the morning Aksinya was panting and puffing as she washed in the outer room, and the samovar was boiling in the kitchen with a hum that boded no good. Old Grigory Petrovitch, dressed in a long black coat, cotton breeches and shiny top-boots, looking a dapper little figure, walked about the rooms, tapping with his little heels like the father-in-law in a well-known song. The shop was opened. When it was daylight a racing droshky was brought up to the front door and the old man got jauntily on to it, pulling his big cap down to his ears; and, looking at him, no one would have said he was fifty-six. His wife and daughter-in-law saw him off, and at such times when he had on a good, clean coat, and had in the droshky a huge black horse that had cost three hundred rubles, the old man did not like the peasants to come up to him with their complaints and petitions; he hated the peasants and disdained them, and if he saw some peasants waiting at the gate, he would shout angrily:

"Why are you standing there? Go further off."

Or if it were a beggar, he would say:

"God will provide!"

He used to drive off on business; his wife, in a dark dress and a black apron, tidied the rooms or helped in the kitchen. Aksinya attended to the shop, and from the yard could be heard the clink of bottles and of money, her laughter and loud talk, and the anger of customers whom she had offended; and at the same time it could be seen that the secret sale of vodka was already going on in the shop. The deaf man sat in the shop, too, or walked about the street bareheaded, with his hands in his pockets looking absent-mindedly now at the huts, now at the sky overhead. Six times a day they had tea; four times a day they sat down to meals; and in the evening they counted over their takings, put them down, went to bed, and slept soundly.

All the three cotton factories in Ukleevo and the houses of the factory owners—Hrymin Seniors, Hrymin Juniors, and Kostukov—were on a telephone. The telephone was laid on in the local court, too, but it soon ceased to work as bugs and beetles bred there. The elder of the rural district had had little education and wrote every word in the official documents in capitals. But when the telephone was spoiled he said:

"Yes, now we shall be badly off without a telephone."

The Hrymin Seniors were continually at law with the Juniors, and sometimes the Juniors quarrelled among themselves and began going to law, and their factory did not work for a month or two till they were reconciled again, and this was an entertainment for the people of Ukleevo, as there was a great deal of talk and gossip on the occasion of each quarrel. On holidays Kostukov and the Juniors used to get up races, used to dash about Ukleevo and run over calves. Aksinya, rustling her starched petticoats, used to promenade in a low-necked dress up and down the street near her shop; the Juniors used to snatch her up and carry her off as though by force. Then old Tsybukin would drive out to show his new horse and take Varvara with him.

In the evening, after the races, when people were going to bed, an expensive concertina was played in the Juniors' yard and, if it were a moonlight night, those sounds sent a thrill of delight to the heart, and Ukleevo no longer seemed a wretched hole.

2

The elder son Anisim came home very rarely, only on great holidays, but he often sent by a returning villager presents and letters written in very good writing by some other hand, always on a sheet of foolscap in the form of a petition. The letters were full of expressions that Anisim never made use of in conversation: "Dear papa and mamma, I send you a pound of flower tea for the satisfaction of your physical needs."

At the bottom of every letter was scratched, as though with a broken pen: "Anisim Tsybukin," and again in the same excellent hand: "Agent."

The letters were read aloud several times, and the old father, touched, red with emotion, would say:

"Here he did not care to stay at home, he has gone in for an intellectual line. Well, let him! Every man to his own job!"

It happened just before Carnival there was a heavy storm of rain mixed with hail; the old man and Varvara went to the window to look at it, and lo and behold! Anisim drove up in a sledge from the station. He was quite unexpected. He came indoors, looking anxious and troubled about something, and he remained the same all the time; there was something free and easy in his manner. He was in no haste to go away, it seemed as though he had been dismissed from the service. Varvara was pleased at his arrival; she looked at him with a sly expression, sighed, and shook her head.

"How is this, my friends?" she said. "Tut, tut, the lad's in his twenty-eighth year, and he is still leading a gay bachelor life; tut, tut, tut. . . ."

From the other room her soft, even speech sounded like tut, tut, tut. She began whispering with her husband and Aksinya, and their faces wore the same sly and mysterious expression as though they were conspirators.

It was decided to marry Anisim.

"Oh, tut, tut . . . the younger brother has been married long ago," said Varvara, "and you are still without a helpmate like a cock at a fair. What is the meaning of it? Tut, tut, you will be married, please God, then as you choose—you will go into the service and your wife will remain here at home to help us. There is no order in your life, young man, and I see you have forgotten how to live properly. Tut, tut, it's the same trouble with all you townspeople."

When the Tsybukins married, the most handsome girls were chosen as brides for them as rich men. For Anisim, too, they found a handsome one. He was himself of an uninteresting and inconspicuous appearance; of a feeble, sickly build and short stature; he had full, puffy cheeks which looked as though he were blowing them out; his eyes looked with a keen, unblinking stare; his beard was red and scanty, and when he was thinking he always put it into his mouth and bit it; moreover he often drank too much, and that was noticeable from his face and his walk. But when he was informed that they had found a very beautiful bride for him, he said:

"Oh well, I am not a fright myself. All of us Tsybukins are handsome, I may say."

The village of Torguevo was near the town. Half of it had lately been incorporated into the town, the other half remained a village. In the first —the town half—there was a widow living in her own little house; she had a sister living with her who was quite poor and went out to work by the day, and this sister had a daughter called Lipa, a girl who went out to work, too. People in Torguevo were already talking about Lipa's good looks, but her terrible poverty put everyone off; people opined that some widower or elderly man would marry her regardless of her poverty, or would perhaps take her to himself without marriage, and that her mother would get enough to eat living with her. Varvara heard about Lipa from the matchmakers, and she drove over to Torguevo.

Then a visit of inspection was arranged at the aunt's, with lunch and wine all in due order, and Lipa wore a new pink dress made on purpose for this occasion, and a crimson ribbon like a flame gleamed in her hair. She was pale-faced, thin, and frail, with soft, delicate features sunburnt from working in the open air; a shy, mournful smile always hovered about her face, and there was a child-like look in her eyes, trustful and curious.

She was young, quite a little girl, her bosom still scarcely perceptible, but she could be married because she had reached the legal age. She really was beautiful, and the only thing that might be thought unattractive was her big masculine hands which hung idle now like two big claws.

"There is no dowry—and we don't think much of that," said Tsybukin to the aunt. "We took a wife from a poor family for our son Stepan, too, and now we can't say too much for her. In house and in business alike she has hands of gold."

Lipa stood in the doorway and looked as though she would say: "Do with me as you will, I trust you," while her mother Praskovya the workwoman hid herself in the kitchen numb with shyness. At one time in her youth a merchant whose floors she was scrubbing stamped at her in a rage; she went chill with terror and there always was a feeling of fear at the bottom of her heart. When she was frightened her arms and legs trembled and her cheeks twitched. Sitting in the kitchen she tried to hear what the visitors were saying, and she kept crossing herself, pressing her fingers to her forehead, and gazing at the ikons. Anisim, slightly drunk, opened the door into the kitchen and said in a free-and-easy way:

"Why are you sitting in here, precious mamma? We are dull without you."

And Praskovya, overcome with timidity, pressing her hands to her lean, wasted bosom, said:

"Oh, not at all. . . . It's very kind of you."

After the visit of inspection the wedding-day was fixed. Then Anisim walked about the rooms at home whistling, or suddenly thinking of something, would fall to brooding and would look at the floor fixedly, silently, as though he would probe to the depths of the earth. He expressed neither pleasure that he was to be married, married so soon, on Low Sunday, nor a desire to see his bride, but simply went on whistling. And it was evident he was only getting married because his father and stepmother wished him to, and because it was the custom in the village to marry the son in order to have a woman to help in the house. When he went away he seemed in no haste, and behaved altogether not as he had done on previous visits—was particularly free and easy, and talked inappropriately.

3

In the village Shikalovo lived two dressmakers, sisters, belonging to the Flagellant sect. The new clothes for the wedding were ordered from them, and they often came to try them on, and stayed a long while drinking tea. They were making Varvara a brown dress with black lace and bugles on it, and Aksinya a light green dress with a yellow front, with a train. When the dressmakers had finished their work Tsybukin paid them not in money but in goods from the shop, and they went away depressed carrying parcels of tallow candles and tins of sardines which they did not in the least need, and when they got out of the village into the open country they sat down on a hillock and cried.

Anisim arrived three days before the wedding, rigged out in new clothes from top to toe. He had dazzling india-rubber goloshes, and instead of a cravat wore a red cord with little balls on it, and over his shoulder he had hung an overcoat, also new, without putting his arms into the sleeves.

After crossing himself sedately before the ikon, he greeted his father and gave him ten silver rubles and ten half-rubles; to Varvara he gave as much, and to Aksinya twenty quarter-rubles. The chief charm of the present lay in the fact that all the coins, as though carefully matched, were new and glittered in the sun. Trying to seem grave and sedate he pursed up his face and puffed out his cheeks, and he smelt of spirits. Probably he had visited the refreshment bar at every station. And again there was a free-and-easiness about the man—something superfluous and out of place. Then Anisim had lunch and drank tea with the old man, and Varvara turned the new coins over in her hands and enquired about villagers who had gone to live in the town.

"They are all right, thank God, they get on quite well," said Anisim. "Only something has happened to Ivan Yegorov: his old wife Sofya Nikiforovna is dead. From consumption. They ordered the memorial dinner for the peace of her soul at the confectioner's at two and a half rubles a head. And there was real wine. Those who were peasants from our village—they paid two and a half rubles for them, too. They ate nothing, as though a peasant would understand sauce!"

"Two and a half," said his father, shaking his head.

"Well, it's not like the country there, you go into a restaurant to have a snack of something, you ask for one thing and another, others join till there is a party of us, one has a drink—and before you know where you are it is daylight and you've three or four rubles each to pay. And when one is with Samorodov he likes to have coffee with brandy in it after everything, and brandy is sixty kopecks for a little glass."

"And he is making it all up," said the old man enthusiastically; "he is making it all up, lying!"

"I am always with Samorodov now. It is Samorodov who writes my letters to you. He writes splendidly. And if I were to tell you, mamma," Anisim went on gaily, addressing Varvara, "the sort of fellow that Samorodov is, you would not believe me. We call him Muhtar because he is black like an Armenian. I can see through him, I know all his affairs like the five fingers of my hand, and he feels that, and he always follows me about, we are regular inseparables. He seems not to like it in a way, but he

can't get on without me. Where I go he goes. I have a correct, trust-
worthy eye, mamma. One sees a peasant selling a shirt in the market-
place. 'Stay, that shirt's stolen.' And really it turns out it is so: the shirt
was a stolen one."

"What do you tell from?" asked Varvara.

"Not from anything, I have just an eye for it. I know nothing about the
shirt, only for some reason I seem drawn to it: it's stolen, and that's all I
can say. Among us detectives it's come to their saying, 'Oh, Anisim has
gone to shoot snipe!' That means looking for stolen goods. Yes. . . . Anybody can steal, but it is another thing to keep! The earth is wide, but
there is nowhere to hide stolen goods."

"In our village a ram and two ewes were carried off last week," said
Varvara, and she heaved a sigh, "and there is no one to try and find
them. . . . Oh, tut, tut. . . ."

"Well, I might have a try. I don't mind."

The day of the wedding arrived. It was a cool but bright, cheerful
April day. People were driving about Ukleevo from early morning with
pairs or teams of three horses decked with many-coloured ribbons on
their yokes and manes, with a jingle of bells. The rooks, disturbed by
this activity, were cawing noisily in the willows, and the starlings sang
their loudest unceasingly as though rejoicing that there was a wedding
at the Tsybukins'.

Indoors the tables were already covered with long fish, smoked hams,
stuffed fowls, boxes of sprats, pickled savouries of various sorts, and a
number of bottles of vodka and wine; there was a smell of smoked sau-
sage and of sour tinned lobster. Old Tsybukin walked about near the
tables, tapping with his heels and sharpening the knives against each
other. They kept calling Varvara and asking for things, and she was constantly with a distracted face running breathlessly into the kitchen, where
the man cook from Kostukov's and the woman cook from Hrymin Juniors'
had been at work since early morning. Aksinya, with her hair curled, in
her stays without her dress on, in new creaky boots, flew about the yard
like a whirlwind showing glimpses of her bare knees and bosom.

It was noisy, there was a sound of scolding and oaths; passers-by
stopped at the wide-open gates, and in everything there was a feeling
that something extraordinary was happening.

"They have gone for the bride!"

The bells began jingling and died away far beyond the village. . . .
Between two and three o'clock people ran up: again there was a jingling
of bells: they were bringing the bride! The church was full, the candelabra
were lighted, the choir were singing from music books as old Tsybukin
had wished it. The glare of the lights and the bright coloured dresses
dazzled Lipa; she felt as though the singers with their loud voices were
hitting her on the head with a hammer. Her boots and the stays, which
she had put on for the first time in her life, pinched her, and her face
looked as though she had only just come to herself after fainting; she

gazed about without understanding. Anisim, in his black coat with a red cord instead of a tie, stared at the same spot lost in thought, and when the singers shouted loudly he hurriedly crossed himself. He felt touched and disposed to weep. This church was familiar to him from earliest childhood; at one time his dead mother used to bring him here to take the sacrament; at one time he used to sing in the choir; every ikon he remembered so well, every corner. Here he was being married, he had to take a wife for the sake of doing the proper thing, but he was not thinking of that now, he had forgotten his wedding completely. Tears dimmed his eyes so that he could not see the ikons, he felt heavy at heart; he prayed and besought God that the misfortunes that threatened him, that were ready to burst upon him to-morrow, if not to-day, might somehow pass him by as storm-clouds in time of drought pass over the village without yielding one drop of rain. And so many sins were heaped up in the past, so many sins, all getting away from them or setting them right was so beyond hope that it seemed incongruous even to ask forgiveness. But he did ask forgiveness, and even gave a loud sob, but no one took any notice of that, since they all supposed he had had a drop too much.

There was a sound of a fretful childish wail:

"Take me away, mamma darling!"

"Quiet there!" cried the priest.

When they returned from the church people ran after them; there were crowds, too, round the shop, round the gates, and in the yard under the windows. The peasant women came in to sing songs of congratulation to them. The young couple had scarcely crossed the threshold when the singers, who were already standing in the outer room with their music books, broke into a loud chant at the top of their voices; a band ordered expressly from the town began playing. Foaming Don wine was brought in tall wineglasses, and Elizarov, a carpenter who did jobs by contract, a tall, gaunt old man with eyebrows so bushy that his eyes could scarcely be seen, said, addressing the happy pair:

"Anisim and you, my child, love one another, live in God's way, little children, and the Heavenly Mother will not abandon you."

He leaned his face on the old father's shoulder and gave a sob.

"Grigory Petrovitch, let us weep, let us weep with joy!" he said in a thin voice, and then at once burst out laughing in a loud bass guffaw. "Ho-ho-ho! This is a fine daughter-in-law for you too! Everything is in its place in her; all runs smoothly, no creaking, the mechanism works well, lots of screws in it."

He was a native of the Yegoryevsky district, but had worked in the factories in Ukleevo and the neighbourhood from his youth up, and had made it his home. He had been a familiar figure for years as old and gaunt and lanky as now, and for years he had been nicknamed "Crutch." Perhaps because he had been for forty years occupied in repairing the factory machinery he judged everybody and everything by its soundness or its need of repair. And before sitting down to the table he tried several chairs to see whether they were solid, and he touched the smoked fish also.

After the Don wine, they all sat down to the table. The visitors talked, moving their chairs. The singers were singing in the outer room. The band was playing, and at the same time the peasant women in the yard were singing their songs all in chorus—and there was an awful, wild medley of sounds which made one giddy.

Crutch turned round in his chair and prodded his neighbours with his elbows, prevented people from talking, and laughed and cried alternately. "Little children, little children, little children," he muttered rapidly. "Aksinya, my dear, Varvara darling, we will live all in peace and harmony, my dear little axes. . . ."

He drank little and was now only drunk from one glass of English bitters. The revolting bitters, made from nobody knows what, intoxicated everyone who drank it as though it had stunned them. Their tongues began to falter.

The local clergy, the clerks from the factories with their wives, the tradesmen and tavern-keepers from the other villages were present. The clerk and the elder of the rural district who had served together for fourteen years, and who had during all that time never signed a single document for anybody nor let a single person out of the local court without deceiving or insulting him, were sitting now side by side, both fat and well-fed, and it seemed as though they were so saturated in injustice and falsehood that even the skin of their faces was somehow peculiar, fraudulent. The clerk's wife, a thin woman with a squint, had brought all her children with her, and like a bird of prey looked aslant at the plates and snatched anything she could get hold of to put in her own or her children's pockets.

Lipa sat as though turned to stone, still with the same expression as in church. Anisim had not said a single word to her since he had made her acquaintance, so that he did not yet know the sound of her voice; and now, sitting beside her, he remained mute and went on drinking bitters, and when he got drunk he began talking to the aunt who was sitting opposite:

"I have a friend called Samorodov. A peculiar man. He is by rank an honorary citizen, and he can talk. But I know him through and through, auntie, and he feels it. Pray join me in drinking to the health of Samorodov, auntie!"

Varvara, worn out and distracted, walked round the table pressing the guests to eat, and was evidently pleased that there were so many dishes and that everything was so lavish—no one could disparage them now. The sun set, but the dinner went on: the guests were beyond knowing what they were eating or drinking, it was impossible to distinguish what was said, and only from time to time when the band subsided some peasant woman could be heard shouting:

"They have sucked the blood out of us, the Herods; a pest on them!"

In the evening they danced to the band. The Hrymin Juniors came, bringing their wine, and one of them, when dancing a quadrille, held a bottle in each hand and a wineglass in his mouth, and that made everyone laugh. In the middle of the quadrille they suddenly crooked their knees and danced in a squatting position; Aksinya in green flew by like a flash, stirring up a wind with her train. Someone trod on her flounce and Crutch shouted:

"Aie, they have torn off the panel! Children!"

Aksinya had naïve grey eyes which rarely blinked, and a naïve smile played continually on her face. And in those unblinking eyes, and in that little head on the long neck, and in her slenderness there was something snake-like; all in green but for the yellow on her bosom, she looked with a smile on her face as a viper looks out of the young rye in the spring at the passers-by, stretching itself and lifting its head. The Hrymins were free in their behaviour to her, and it was very noticeable that she was on intimate terms with the elder of them. But her deaf husband saw nothing, he did not look at her; he sat with his legs crossed and ate nuts, cracking them so loudly that it sounded like pistol shots.

But, behold, old Tsybukin himself walked into the middle of the room and waved his handkerchief as a sign that he, too, wanted to dance the Russian dance, and all over the house and from the crowd in the yard rose a roar of approbation:

"*He's* going to dance! *He* himself!"

Varvara danced, but the old man only waved his handkerchief and kicked up his heels, but the people in the yard, propped against one another, peeping in at the windows, were in raptures, and for the moment forgave him everything—his wealth and the wrongs he had done them.

"Well done, Grigory Petrovitch!" was heard in the crowd. "That's right, do your best! You can still play your part! Ha-ha!"

It was kept up till late, till two o'clock in the morning. Anisim, staggering, went to take leave of the singers and bandsmen, and gave each of them a new half-ruble. His father, who was not staggering but still seemed to be standing on one leg, saw his guests off, and said to each of them:

"The wedding has cost two thousand."

As the party was breaking up, someone took the Shikalovo innkeeper's good coat instead of his own old one, and Anisim suddenly flew into a rage and began shouting:

"Stop, I'll find it at once; I know who stole it, stop."

He ran out into the street and pursued someone. He was caught, brought back home and shoved, drunken, red with anger, and wet, into the room where the aunt was undressing Lipa, and was locked in.

4

Five days had passed. Anisim, who was preparing to go, went upstairs to say good-bye to Varvara. All the lamps were burning before the ikons, there was a smell of incense, while she sat at the window knitting a stocking of red wool.

"You have not stayed with us long," she said. "You've been dull, I dare say. Oh, tut, tut. . . . We live comfortably; we have plenty of everything. We celebrated your wedding properly, in good style; your father says it came to two thousand. In fact we live like merchants, only it's dreary. We treat the people very badly. My heart aches, my dear; how we treat them, my goodness! Whether we exchange a horse or buy something or hire a labourer—it's cheating in everything. Cheating and cheating. The Lenten oil in the shop is bitter, rancid, the people have pitch that is better. But surely, tell me, pray, couldn't we sell good oil?"

"Every man to his job, mamma."

"But you know we all have to die? Oy, oy, really you ought to talk to your father . . . !"

"Why, you should talk to him yourself."

"Well, well, I did put in my word, but he said just what you do: 'Every man to his own job.' Do you suppose in the next world they'll consider what job you have been put to? God's judgment is just."

"Of course no one will consider," said Anisim, and he heaved a sigh. "There is no God, anyway, you know, mamma, so what considering can there be?"

Varvara looked at him with surprise, burst out laughing, and clasped her hands. Perhaps because she was so genuinely surprised at his words and looked at him as though he were a queer person, he was confused.

"Perhaps there is a God, only there is no faith. When I was being married I was not myself. Just as you may take an egg from under a hen and there is a chicken chirping in it, so my conscience was beginning to chirp in me, and while I was being married I thought all the time there was a God! But when I left the church it was nothing. And indeed, how can I tell whether there is a God or not? We are not taught right from childhood, and while the babe is still at his mother's breast he is only taught 'every man to his own job.' Father does not believe in God, either. You were saying that Guntorev had some sheep stolen. . . . I have found them; it was a peasant at Shikalovo stole them; he stole them, but father's got the fleeces . . . so that's all his faith amounts to."

Anisim winked and wagged his head.

"The elder does not believe in God, either," he went on. "And the clerk and the deacon, too. And as for their going to church and keeping the fasts, that is simply to prevent people talking ill of them, and in case it really may be true that there will be a Day of Judgment. Nowadays people say that the end of the world has come because people have grown weaker, do not honour their parents, and so on. All that is nonsense. My idea, mamma, is that all our trouble is because there is so little conscience in people. I see through things, mamma, and I understand. If a man has a stolen shirt I see it. A man sits in a tavern and you fancy he is drinking tea and no more, but to me the tea is neither here nor there; I see further, he has no conscience. You can go about the whole day and not meet one man with a conscience. And the whole reason is that they don't know whether there is a God or not. . . . Well, good-bye, mamma, keep alive and well, don't remember evil against me."

Anisim bowed down at Varvara's feet.

"I thank you for everything, mamma," he said. "You are a great gain to our family. You are a very lady-like woman, and I am very pleased with you."

Much moved, Anisim went out, but returned again and said:

"Samorodov has got me mixed up in something: I shall either make my fortune or come to grief. If anything happens, then you must comfort my father, mamma."

"Oh nonsense, don't you worry, tut, tut, tut . . . God is merciful. And Anisim, you should be affectionate to your wife, instead of giving each other sulky looks as you do; you might smile at least."

"Yes, she is rather a queer one," said Anisim, and he gave a sigh. "She does not understand anything, she never speaks. She is very young, let her grow up."

A tall, sleek white stallion was already standing at the front door, harnessed to the chaise.

Old Tsybukin jumped in jauntily with a run and took the reins. Anisim kissed Varvara, Aksinya, and his brother. On the steps Lipa, too, was standing; she was standing motionless, looking away, and it seemed as though she had not come to see him off but just by chance for some unknown reason. Anisim went up to her and just touched her cheek with his lips.

"Good-bye," he said.

And without looking at him she gave a strange smile; her face began to quiver, and everyone for some reason felt sorry for her. Anisim, too, leaped into the chaise with a bound and put his arms jauntily akimbo, for he considered himself a good-looking fellow.

When they drove up out of the ravine Anisim kept looking back towards the village. It was a warm, bright day. The cattle were being driven out for the first time, and the peasant girls and women were walking by the herd in their holiday dresses. The dun-coloured bull bellowed, glad to be free, and pawed the ground with his forefeet. On all sides, above and below, the larks were singing. Anisim looked round at the elegant white church—it had only lately been white-washed—and he thought how he had been praying in it five days before; he looked round at the school with its green roof, at the little river in which he used once to bathe and catch fish, and there was a stir of joy in his heart, and he wished that walls might rise up from the ground and prevent him from going further, and that he might be left with nothing but the past.

At the station they went to the refreshment-room and drank a glass of sherry each. His father felt in his pocket for his purse to pay.

"I will stand treat," said Anisim. The old man, touched and delighted, slapped him on the shoulder, and winked to the waiter as much as to say, "See what a fine son I have got."

"You ought to stay at home in the business, Anisim," he said; "you would be worth any price to me! I would shower gold on you from head to foot, my son."

"It can't be done, papa."

The sherry was sour and smelt of sealing-wax, but they had another glass.

When old Tsybukin returned home from the station, for the first moment he did not recognize his younger daughter-in-law. As soon as her husband had driven out of the yard, Lipa was transformed and suddenly brightened up. Wearing a threadbare old petticoat, with her feet bare and her sleeves tucked up to the shoulders, she was scrubbing the stairs in the entry and singing in a silvery little voice, and when she brought out a big tub of dirty water and looked up at the sun with her child-like smile it seemed as though she, too, were a lark.

An old labourer who was passing by the door shook his head and cleared his throat.

"Yes, indeed, your daughters-in-law, Grigory Petrovitch, are a blessing from God," he said. "Not women, but treasures!"

5

On Friday, the 8th of July, Elizarov, nicknamed Crutch, and Lipa were returning from the village of Kazanskoe, where they had been to a service on the occasion of a church holiday in honour of the Holy Mother of Kazan. A good distance after them walked Lipa's mother Praskovya, who always fell behind, as she was ill and short of breath. It was drawing towards evening.

"A-a-a . . ." said Crutch, wondering as he listened to Lipa. "A-a! . . . We-ell!"

"I am very fond of jam, Ilya Makaritch," said Lipa. "I sit down in my little corner and drink tea and eat jam. Or I drink it with Varvara Niko-laevna, and she tells some story full of feeling. We have a lot of jam— four jars. 'Have some, Lipa; eat as much as you like.' "

"A-a-a, four jars!"

"They live very well. We have white bread with our tea; and meat, too, as much as one wants. They live very well, only I am frightened with them, Ilya Makaritch. Oh, oh, how frightened I am!"

"Why are you frightened, child?" asked Crutch, and he looked back to see how far Praskovya was behind.

"To begin with, when the wedding had been celebrated I was afraid of Anisim Grigoritch. Anisim Grigoritch did nothing, he didn't ill-treat me, only when he comes near me a cold shiver runs all over me, through all my bones. And I did not sleep one night, I trembled all over and kept praying to God. And now I am afraid of Aksinya, Ilya Makaritch. It's not that she does anything, she is always laughing, but sometimes she glances at the window, and her eyes are so fierce and there is a gleam of green in them—like the eyes of the sheep in the shed. The Hrymin Juniors are leading her astray: 'Your old man,' they tell her, 'has a bit of land at Butyokino, a hundred and twenty acres,' they say, 'and there is sand and water there, so you, Aksinya,' they say, 'build a brickyard there and we will go shares in it.' Bricks now are twenty rubles the thousand, it's a profitable business. Yesterday at dinner Aksinya said to my father-in-law: 'I want to build a brickyard at Butyokino; I'm going into business on my own account.' She laughed as she said it. And Grigory Petro-vitch's face darkened, one could see he did not like it. 'As long as I live,' he said, 'the family must not break up, we must go on altogether.' She gave a look and gritted her teeth. . . . Fritters were served, she would not eat them."

"A-a-a! . . ." Crutch was surprised.

"And tell me, if you please, when does she sleep?" said Lipa. "She sleeps for half an hour, then jumps up and keeps walking and walking about to see whether the peasants have not set fire to something, have not stolen something. . . . I am frightened with her, Ilya Makaritch. And the Hrymin Juniors did not go to bed after the wedding, but drove to the town to go to law with each other; and folks do say it is all on account of Aksinya. Two of the brothers have promised to build her a brickyard, but the third is offended, and the factory has been at a stand-still for a month, and my uncle Prohor is without work and goes about from house to house getting crusts. 'Hadn't you better go working on the land or sawing up wood, meanwhile, uncle?' I tell him; 'why disgrace yourself?' 'I've got out of the way of it,' he says; 'I don't know how to do any sort of peasant's work now, Lipinka. . . .'"

They stopped to rest and wait for Praskovya near a copse of young aspen-trees. Elizarov had long been a contractor in a small way, but he kept no horses, going on foot all over the district with nothing but a little bag in which there was bread and onions, and stalking along with big strides, swinging his arms. And it was difficult to walk with him.

At the entrance to the copse stood a milestone. Elizarov touched it; read it. Praskovya reached them out of breath. Her wrinkled and always scared-looking face was beaming with happiness; she had been at church to-day like anyone else, then she had been to the fair and there had drunk pear cider. For her this was unusual, and it even seemed to her now that she had lived for her own pleasure that day for the first time in her life. After resting they all three walked on side by side. The sun had already set, and its beams filtered through the copse, casting a light on the trunks of the trees. There was a faint sound of voices ahead. The Ukleevo girls had long before pushed on ahead but had lingered in the copse, prob-ably gathering mushrooms.

"Hey, wenches!" cried Elizarov. "Hey, my beauties!"

There was a sound of laughter in response.

"Crutch is coming! Crutch! The old horse-radish."

And the echo laughed, too. And then the copse was left behind. The tops of the factory chimneys came into view. The cross on the belfry glittered: this was the village: "the one at which the deacon ate all the caviare at the funeral." Now they were almost home; they only had to go down into the big ravine. Lipa and Praskovya, who had been walking barefooted, sat down on the grass to put on their boots; Elizarov sat down with them. If they looked down from above Ukleevo looked beautiful and peaceful with its willow-trees, its white church, and its little river, and the only blot on the picture was the roof of the factories, painted for the sake of cheapness a gloomy ashen grey. On the slope on the further side they could see the rye—some in stacks and sheaves here and there as though strewn about by the storm, and some freshly cut lying in swathes; the oats, too, were ripe and glistened now in the sun like mother-of-pearl. It was harvest-time. To-day was a holiday, to-morrow they would harvest the rye and carry the hay, and then Sunday a holiday again; every day there were mutterings of distant thunder. It was misty and looked like rain, and, gazing now at the fields, everyone thought, God grant we get the harvest in in time; and everyone felt gay and joyful and anxious at heart.

"Mowers ask a high price nowadays," said Praskovya. "One ruble and forty kopecks a day."

People kept coming and coming from the fair at Kazanskoe: peasant women, factory workers in new caps, beggars, children. . . . Here a cart would drive by stirring up the dust and behind it would run an unsold horse, and it seemed glad it had not been sold; then a cow was led along by the horns, resisting stubbornly; then a cart again, and in it drunken peasants swinging their legs. An old woman led a little boy in a big cap and big boots; the boy was tired out with the heat and the heavy boots which prevented his bending his legs at the knees, but yet blew unceasingly with all his might at a tin trumpet. They had gone down the slope and turned into the street, but the trumpet could still be heard.

"Our factory owners don't seem quite themselves . . ." said Elizarov. "There's trouble. Kostukov is angry with me. 'Too many boards have gone on the cornices.' 'Too many? As many have gone on it as were needed, Vassily Danilitch; I don't eat them with my porridge.' 'How can you speak to me like that?' said he, 'you good-for-nothing blockhead! Don't forget yourself! It was I made you a contractor.' 'That's nothing so wonderful,' said I. 'Even before I was a contractor I used to have tea every day.' 'You are a rascal . . .' he said. I said nothing. 'We are rascals in this world,' thought I, 'and you will be rascals in the next. . . .' Ha-ha-ha! The next day he was softer. 'Don't you bear malice against me for my words, Makaritch,' he said. 'If I said too much,' says he, 'what of it? I am a merchant of the first guild, your superior—you ought to hold your tongue.' 'You,' said I, 'are a merchant of the first guild and I am a carpenter, that's correct. And Saint Joseph was a carpenter, too. Ours is a righteous calling and pleasing to God, and if you are pleased to be my superior you are very welcome to it, Vassily Danilitch.' And later on, after that conversation I mean, I thought: 'Which was the superior? A merchant of the first guild or a carpenter?' The carpenter must be, my child!"

Crutch thought a minute and added:

"Yes, that's how it is, child. He who works, he who is patient is the superior."

By now the sun had set and a thick mist as white as milk was rising over the river, in the church enclosure, and in the open spaces round the factories. Now when the darkness was coming on rapidly, when lights were twinkling below, and when it seemed as though the mist were hiding a fathomless abyss, Lipa and her mother, who were born in poverty and prepared to live so till the end, giving up to others everything except their frightened, gentle souls, may have fancied for a minute perhaps that in the vast mysterious world, among the endless series of lives, they, too, counted for something, and they, too, were superior to someone; they liked sitting here at the top, they smiled happily and forgot that they must go down below again all the same.

At last they went home again. The mowers were sitting on the ground at the gates near the shop. As a rule the Ukleevo peasants did not go to Tsybukin's to work, and they had to hire strangers, and now in the darkness it seemed as though there were men sitting there with long black beards. The shop was open, and through the doorway they could see the deaf man playing draughts with a boy. The mowers were singing softly, scarcely audibly, or loudly demanding their wages for the previous day, but they were not paid for fear they should go away before to-morrow. Old Tsybukin, with his coat off, was sitting in his waistcoat with Aksinya under the birch-tree, drinking tea; a lamp was burning on the table.

"I say, grandfather," a mower called from outside the gates, as though taunting him, "pay us half anyway! Hey, grandfather."

And at once there was a sound of laughter, and then again they sang hardly audibly. . . . Crutch, too, sat down to have some tea.

"We have been at the fair, you know," he began telling them. "We have had a walk, a very nice walk, my children, praise the Lord. But an unfortunate thing happened: Sashka the blacksmith bought some tobacco and gave the shopman half a ruble, to be sure. And the half-ruble was a false one"—Crutch went on, and he meant to speak in a whisper, but he spoke in a smothered, husky voice which was audible to everyone. "The half-ruble turned out to be a bad one. He was asked where he got it. 'Anisim Tsybukin gave it me,' he said. 'When I went to his wedding,' he said. They called the police inspector, took the man away. . . . Look out, Grigory Petrovitch, that nothing comes of it, no talk. . . ."

"Gra-ndfather!" the same voice called tauntingly outside the gates. "Gra-andfather!"

A silence followed.

"Ah, little children, little children, little children . . ." Crutch muttered rapidly, and he got up. He was overcome with drowsiness. "Well, thank you for the tea, for the sugar, little children. It is time to sleep. I am like a bit of rotten timber nowadays, my beams are crumbling under me. Ho-ho-ho! I suppose it's time I was dead."

And he gave a gulp. Old Tsybukin did not finish his tea but sat on a little, pondering; and his face looked as though he were listening to the footsteps of Crutch, who was far away down the street.

"Sashka the blacksmith told a lie, I expect," said Aksinya, guessing his thoughts.

He went into the house and came back a little later with a parcel; he opened it, and there was the gleam of rubles—perfectly new coins. He took one, tried it with his teeth, flung it on the tray; then flung down another.

"The rubles really are false . . ." he said, looking at Aksinya and seeming perplexed. "These are those Anisim brought, his present. Take them, daughter," he whispered, and thrust the parcel into her hands. "Take them and throw them into the well . . . confound them! And mind there is no talk about it. Harm might come of it. . . . Take away the samovar, put out the light."

Lipa and her mother sitting in the barn saw the lights go out one after the other; only overhead in Varvara's room there were blue and red lamps gleaming, and a feeling of peace, content, and happy ignorance seemed to float down from there. Praskovya could never get used to her daughter's being married to a rich man, and when she came she huddled timidily in the outer room with a deprecating smile on her face, and tea and sugar were sent out to her. And Lipa, too, could not get used to it either, and after her husband had gone away she did not sleep in her bed, but lay down anywhere to sleep, in the kitchen or the barn, and every day she scrubbed the floor or washed the clothes, and felt as though she were hired by the day. And now, on coming back from the service, they drank tea in the kitchen with the cook, then they went into the barn and lay down on the ground between the sledge and the wall. It was dark here and smelt of harness. The lights went out about the house, then they could hear the deaf man shutting up the shop, the mowers settling themselves about the yard to sleep. In the distance at the Hrymin Juniors' they were playing on the expensive concertina. . . . Praskovya and Lipa began to go to sleep.

And when they were awakened by somebody's steps it was bright moonlight; at the entrance of the barn stood Aksinya with her bedding in her arms.

"Maybe it's a bit cooler here," she said; then she came in and lay down almost in the doorway so that the moonlight fell full upon her.

She did not sleep, but breathed heavily, tossing from side to side with the heat, throwing off almost all the bedclothes. And in the magic moonlight what a beautiful, what a proud animal she was! A little time passed, and then steps were heard again: the old father, white all over, appeared in the doorway.

"Aksinya," he called, "are you here?"

"Well?" she responded angrily.

"I told you just now to throw the money into the well, have you done so?"

"What next, throwing property into the water! I gave them to the mowers. . . ."

"Oh my God!" cried the old man, dumbfoundered and alarmed. "Oh my God! you wicked woman. . . ."

He flung up his hands and went out, and he kept saying something as he went away. And a little later Aksinya sat up and sighed heavily with annoyance, then got up and, gathering up her bedclothes in her arms, went out.

"Why did you marry me into this family, mother?" said Lipa.

"One has to be married, daughter. It was not us who ordained it."

And a feeling of inconsolable woe was ready to take possession of them. But it seemed to them that someone was looking down from the height of the heavens, out of the blue from where the stars were seeing everything that was going on in Ukleevo, watching over them. And however great was wickedness, still the night was calm and beautiful, and still in God's world there is and will be truth and justice as calm and beautiful, and everything on earth is only waiting to be made one with truth and justice, even as the moonlight is blended with the night.

And both, huddling close to one another, fell asleep comforted.

6

News had come long before that Anisim had been put in prison for coining and passing bad money. Months passed, more than half a year passed, the long winter was over, spring had begun, and everyone in the house and the village had grown used to the fact that Anisim was in prison. And when anyone passed by the house or the shop at night he would remember that Anisim was in prison; and when they rang at the churchyard for some reason, that, too, reminded them that he was in prison awaiting trial.

It seemed as though a shadow had fallen upon the house. The house looked darker, the roof was rustier, the heavy iron-bound door into the shop, which was painted green, was covered with cracks, or, as the deaf man expressed it, "blisters"; and old Tsybukin seemed to have grown dingy, too. He had given up cutting his hair and beard, and looked shaggy. He no longer sprang jauntily into his chaise, nor shouted to beggars: "God will provide!" His strength was on the wane, and that was evident in everything. People were less afraid of him now, and the police officer drew up a formal charge against him in the shop though he received his regular bribe as before; and three times the old man was called up to the town to be tried for illicit dealing in spirits, and the case was continually adjourned owing to the non-appearance of witnesses, and old Tsybukin was worn out with worry.

He often went to see his son, hired somebody, handed in a petition to somebody else, presented a holy banner to some church. He presented the governor of the prison in which Anisim was confined with a silver glass stand with a long spoon and the inscription: "The soul knows its right measure."

"There is no one to look after things for us," said Varvara. "Tut, tut. . . . You ought to ask someone of the gentlefolks, they would write to the head officials. . . . At least they might let him out on bail! Why wear the poor fellow out?"

She, too, was grieved, but had grown stouter and whiter; she lighted the lamps before the ikons as before, and saw that everything in the house was clean, and regaled the guests with jam and apple cheese. The deaf man and Aksinya looked after the shop. A new project was in progress—a brickyard in Butyokino—and Aksinya went there almost every day in the chaise. She drove herself, and when she met acquaintances she stretched out her neck like a snake out of the young rye, and smiled naïvely and enigmatically. Lipa spent her time playing with the baby which had been born to her before Lent. It was a tiny, thin, pitiful little baby, and it was strange that it should cry and gaze about and be considered a human being, and even be called Nikifor. He lay in his swinging cradle, and Lipa would walk away towards the door and say, bowing to him:

"Good day, Nikifor Anisimitch!"

And she would rush at him and kiss him. Then she would walk away to the door, bow again, and say:

"Good day, Nikifor Anisimitch!"

And he kicked up his little red legs, and his crying was mixed with laughter like the carpenter Elizarov's.

At last the day of the trial was fixed. Tsybukin went away five days before. Then they heard that the peasants called as witnesses had been fetched; their old workman who had received a notice to appear went too.

The trial was on a Thursday. But Sunday had passed, and Tsybukin was still not back, and there was no news. Towards the evening on Tuesday Varvara was sitting at the open window, listening for her husband to come. In the next room Lipa was playing with her baby. She was tossing him up in her arms and saying enthusiastically:

"You will grow up ever so big, ever so big. You will be a peasant, we shall go out to work together! We shall go out to work together!"

"Come, come," said Varvara, offended. "Go out to work, what an idea, you silly girl! He will be a merchant . . . !"

Lipa sang softly, but a minute later she forgot, and again:

"You will grow up ever so big, ever so big. You will be a peasant, we'll go out to work together."

"There she is at it again!"

Lipa, with Nikifor in her arms, stood still in the doorway and asked:

"Why do I love him so much, mamma? Why do I feel so sorry for him?" she went on in a quivering voice, and her eyes glistened with tears. "Who is he? What is he like? As light as a little feather, as a little crumb; but I love him; I love him like a real person. Here he can do nothing, he can't talk, and yet I know what he wants with his little eyes."

Varvara was listening; the sound of the evening train coming in to the station reached her. Had her husband come? She did not hear and she did not heed what Lipa was saying, she had no idea how the time passed, but only trembled all over—not from dread, but intense curiosity. She saw a cart full of peasants roll quickly by with a rattle. It was the witnesses coming back from the station. When the cart passed the shop the old workman jumped out and walked into the yard. She could hear him being greeted in the yard and being asked some questions. . . .

"Deprivation of rights and all his property," he said loudly, "and six years' penal servitude in Siberia."

She could see Aksinya come out of the shop by the back way; she had just been selling kerosene, and in one hand held a bottle and in the other a can, and in her mouth she had some silver coins.

"Where is father?" she asked, lisping.

"At the station," answered the labourer. " 'When it gets a little darker,' he said, 'then I shall come.' "

And when it became known all through the household that Anisim was sentenced to penal servitude, the cook in the kitchen suddenly broke into a wail as though at a funeral, imagining that this was demanded by the proprieties:

"There is no one to care for us now you have gone, Anisim Grigoritch, our bright falcon. . . ."

The dogs began barking in alarm. Varvara ran to the window, and rushing about in distress, shouted to the cook with all her might, straining her voice:

"Sto-op, Stepanida, sto-op! Don't harrow us, for Christ's sake!"

They forgot to set the samovar, they could think of nothing. Only Lipa could not make out what it was all about and went on playing with her baby.

When the old father arrived from the station they asked him no questions. He greeted them and walked through all the rooms in silence; he had no supper.

"There was no one to see about things . . ." Varvara began when they were alone. "I said you should have asked some of the gentry, you would not heed me at the time. . . . A petition would . . ."

"I saw to things," said her husband with a wave of his hand. "When Anisim was condemned I went to the gentleman who was defending him. 'It's no use now,' he said, 'it's too late'; and Anisim said the same; it's too late. But all the same as I came out of the court I made an agreement with a lawyer, I paid him something in advance. I'll wait a week and then I will go again. It is as God wills."

Again the old man walked through all the rooms, and when he went back to Varvara he said:

"I must be ill. My head's in a sort of . . . fog. My thoughts are in a maze."

He closed the door that Lipa might not hear, and went on softly:

"I am unhappy about my money. Do you remember on Low Sunday before his wedding Anisim's bringing me some new rubles and half-rubles? One parcel I put away at the time, but the others I mixed with my own money. When my uncle Dmitri Filatitch—the kingdom of heaven be his—was alive, he used constantly to go journeys to Moscow and to the Crimea to buy goods. He had a wife, and this same wife, when he was away buying goods, used to take up with other men. She had half a dozen children. And when uncle was in his cups he would laugh and say: 'I never can make out,' he used to say, 'which are my children and which are other people's.' An easy-going disposition, to be sure; and so I now can't distinguish which are genuine rubles and which are false ones. And it seems to me that they are all false."

"Nonsense, God bless you."

"I take a ticket at the station, I give the man three rubles, and I keep fancying they are false. And I am frightened. I must be ill."

"There's no denying it, we are all in God's hands. . . . Oh dear, dear . . ." said Varvara, and she shook her head. "You ought to think about this, Grigory Petrovitch: you never know, anything may happen, you are not a young man. See they don't wrong your grandchild when you are dead and gone. Oy, I am afraid they will be unfair to Nikifor! He has as good as no father, his mother's young and foolish . . . you ought to secure something for him, poor little boy, at least the land, Butyokino, Grigory Petrovitch, really! Think it over!" Varvara went on persuading him. "The pretty boy, one is sorry for him! You go to-morrow and make out a deed; why put it off?"

"I'd forgotten about my grandson," said Tsybukin. "I must go and have a look at him. So you say the boy is all right? Well, let him grow up, please God."

He opened the door and, crooking his finger, beckoned to Lipa. She went up to him with the baby in her arms.

"If there is anything you want, Lipinka, you ask for it," he said. "And eat anything you like, we don't grudge it, so long as it does you good. . . ." He made the sign of the cross over the baby. "And take care of my grandchild. My son is gone, but my grandson is left."

Tears rolled down his cheeks; he gave a sob and went away. Soon afterwards he went to bed and slept soundly after seven sleepless nights.

7

Old Tsybukin went to the town for a short time. Someone told Aksinya that he had gone to the notary to make his will and that he was leaving Butyokino, the very place where she had set up a brickyard, to Nikifor, his grandson. She was informed of this in the morning when old Tsybukin and Varvara were sitting near the steps under the birch-tree, drinking their tea. She closed the shop in the front and at the back, gathered together all the keys she had, and flung them at her father-in-law's feet.

"I am not going on working for you," she began in a loud voice, and suddenly broke into sobs. "It seems I am not your daughter-in-law, but a servant! Everybody's jeering and saying, 'See what a servant the Tsybukins have got hold of!' I did not come to you for wages! I am not a beggar, I am not a slave, I have a father and mother."

She did not wipe away her tears, she fixed upon her father-in-law eyes full of tears, vindictive, squinting with wrath; her face and neck were red and tense, and she was shouting at the top of her voice.

"I don't mean to go on being a slave!" she went on. "I am worn out. When it is work, when it is sitting in the shop day in and day out, scurrying out at night for vodka—then it is my share, but when it is giving away the land then it is for that convict's wife and her imp. She is mistress here, and I am her servant. Give her everything, the convict's wife, and may it choke her; I am going home! Find yourselves some other fool, you damned Herods!"

Tsybukin had never in his life scolded or punished his children, and had never dreamed that one of his family could speak to him rudely or behave disrespectfully; and now he was very much frightened; he ran into the house and there hid behind the cupboard. And Varvara was so much flustered that she could not get up from her seat, and only waved her hands before her as though she were warding off a bee.

"Oh Holy Saints! what's the meaning of it?" she muttered in horror. "What is she shouting? Oh dear, dear! . . . People will hear! Hush. Oh, hush!"

"He has given Butyokino to the convict's wife," Aksinya went on bawling. "Give her everything now, I don't want anything from you! Let me alone! You are all a gang of thieves here! I have seen my fill of it, I have had enough! You have robbed folks coming in and going out; you have robbed old and young alike, you brigands! And who has been selling vodka without a licence? And false money? You've filled boxes full of false coins, and now I am no more use!"

A crowd had by now collected at the open gate and was staring into the yard.

"Let the people look," bawled Aksinya. "I will shame you all! You shall burn with shame! You shall grovel at my feet. Hey! Stepan," she called to the deaf man, "let us go home this minute! Let us go to my father and mother; I don't want to live with convicts. Get ready!"

Clothes were hanging on lines stretched across the yard; she snatched off her petticoats and blouses still wet and flung them into the deaf man's arms. Then in her fury she dashed about the yard by the linen, tore down all of it, and what was not hers she threw on the ground and trampled upon.

"Holy Saints, take her away," moaned Varvara. "What a woman! Give her Butyokino! Give it her, for the Lord's sake!"

"Well! Wha-at a woman!" people were saying at the gate. "She's a wo-oman! She's going it—something like!"

Aksinya ran into the kitchen where washing was going on. Lipa was washing alone, the cook had gone to the river to rinse the clothes. Steam was rising from the trough and from the cauldron on the side of the stove, and the kitchen was thick and stifling from the steam. On the floor was a heap of unwashed clothes, and Nikifor, kicking up his little red legs, had been put down on a bench near them so that if he fell he should not hurt himself. Just as Aksinya went in Lipa took the former's chemise out of the heap and put it in the trough, and was just stretching out her hand to a big ladle of boiling water which was standing on the table.

"Give it here," said Aksinya, looking at her with hatred, and snatching the chemise out of the trough; "it is not your business to touch my linen! You are a convict's wife, and ought to know your place and who you are."

Lipa gazed at her, taken aback, and did not understand, but suddenly she caught the look Aksinya turned upon the child, and at once she understood and went numb all over.

"You've taken my land, so here you are!" Saying this Aksinya snatched up the ladle with the boiling water and flung it over Nikifor.

After this there was heard a scream such as had never been heard before in Ukleevo, and no one would have believed that a little weak creature like Lipa could scream like that. And it was suddenly silent in the yard.

Aksinya walked into the house with her old naïve smile. . . . The deaf man kept moving about the yard with his arms full of linen, then he began hanging it up again, in silence, without haste. And until the cook came back from the river no one ventured to go into the kitchen and see what was there.

8

Nikifor was taken to the district hospital, and towards evening he died there. Lipa did not wait for them to come for her, but wrapped the dead baby in its little quilt and carried it home.

The hospital, a new one recently built, with big windows, stood high up on a hill; it was glittering from the setting sun and looked as though it were on fire from inside. There was a little village below. Lipa went down along the road, and before reaching the village sat down by a pond. A woman brought a horse down to drink and the horse did not drink.

"What more do you want?" said the woman to it softly. "What do you want?"

A boy in a red shirt, sitting at the water's edge, was washing his father's boots. And not another soul was in sight either in the village or on the hill.

"It's not drinking," said Lipa, looking at the horse.

Then the woman with the horse and the boy with the boots walked away, and there was no one left at all. The sun went to bed wrapped in cloth of gold and purple, and long clouds, red and lilac, stretched across the sky, guarded its slumbers. Somewhere far away a bittern cried, a hollow, melancholy sound like a cow shut up in a barn. The cry of that mysterious bird was heard every spring, but no one knew what it was like or where it lived. At the top of the hill by the hospital, in the bushes close to the pond, and in the fields the nightingales were trilling. The cuckoo kept reckoning someone's years and losing count and beginning again. In the pond the frogs called angrily to one another, straining themselves to bursting, and one could even make out the words: "That's what you are! That's what you are!" What a noise there was! It seemed as though all these creatures were singing and shouting so that no one might sleep on that spring night, so that all, even the angry frogs, might appreciate and enjoy every minute: life is given only once.

A silver half-moon was shining in the sky; there were many stars. Lipa had no idea how long she sat by the pond, but when she got up and walked on everybody was asleep in the little village, and there was not a single light. It was probably about nine miles' walk home, but she had not the strength, she had not the power to think how to go: the moon gleamed now in front, now on the right, and the same cuckoo kept calling in a voice grown husky, with a chuckle as though gibing at her: "Oy, look out, you'll lose your way!" Lipa walked rapidly; she lost the kerchief from her head . . . she looked at the sky and wondered where her baby's soul was now: was it following her, or floating aloft yonder among the stars and thinking nothing now of his mother? Oh, how lonely it was in the open country at night, in the midst of that singing when one cannot sing oneself; in the midst of the incessant cries of joy when one cannot oneself be joyful, when the moon, which cares not whether it is spring or winter, whether men are alive or dead, looks down as lonely, too. . . . When there is grief in the heart it is hard to be without people. If only her mother, Praskovya, had been with her, or Crutch, or the cook, or some peasant!

"Boo-oo!" cried the bittern. "Boo-oo!"

And suddenly she heard clearly the sound of human speech:

"Put the horses in, Vavila!"

By the wayside a camp fire was burning ahead of her: the flames had died down, there were only red embers. She could hear the horses munching. In the darkness she could see the outlines of two carts, one with a barrel, the other, a lower one with sacks in it, and the figures of two men; one was leading a horse to put it into the shafts, the other was standing motionless by the fire with his hands behind his back. A dog growled by the carts. The one who was leading the horse stopped and said:

"It seems as though someone were coming along the road."

"Sharik, be quiet!" the other called to the dog.

And from the voice one could tell that the second was an old man. Lipa stopped and said:

"God help you."

The old man went up to her and answered not immediately:

"Good evening!"

"Your dog does not bite, grandfather?"

"No, come along, he won't touch you."

"I have been at the hospital," said Lipa after a pause. "My little son died there. Here I am carrying him home."

It must have been unpleasant for the old man to hear this, for he moved away and said hurriedly:

"Never mind, my dear. It's God's will. You are very slow, lad," he added, addressing his companion; "look alive!"

"Your yoke's nowhere," said the young man; "it is not to be seen."

"You are a regular Vavila."

The old man picked up an ember, blew on it—only his eyes and nose were lighted up—then, when they had found the yoke, he went with the light to Lipa and looked at her, and his look expressed compassion and tenderness.

"You are a mother," he said; "every mother grieves for her child."

And he sighed and shook his head as he said it. Vavila threw something on the fire, stamped on it—and at once it was very dark; the vision vanished, and as before there were only the fields, the sky with the stars, and the noise of the birds hindering each other from sleep. And the landrail called, it seemed, in the very place where the fire had been.

But a minute passed, and again she could see the two carts and the old man and lanky Vavila. The carts creaked as they went out on the road.

"Are you holy men?" Lipa asked the old man.

"No. We are from Firsanovo."

"You looked at me just now and my heart was softened. And the young man is so gentle. I thought you must be holy men."

"Are you going far?"

"To Ukleevo."

"Get in, we will give you a lift, as far as Kuzmenki, then you go straight on and we turn off to the left."

Vavila got into the cart with the barrel and the old man and Lipa got into the other. They moved at a walking pace, Vavila in front.

"My baby was in torment all day," said Lipa. "He looked at me with his little eyes and said nothing; he wanted to speak and could not. Holy Father, Queen of Heaven! In my grief I kept falling down on the floor. I stood up and fell down by the bedside. And tell me, grandfather, why a little thing should be tormented before his death? When a grown-up person, a man or woman, are in torment their sins are forgiven, but why a little thing, when he has no sins? Why?"

"Who can tell?" answered the old man.

They drove on for half an hour in silence.

"We can't know everything, how and wherefore," said the old man. "It is ordained for the bird to have not four wings but two because it is able to fly with two; and so it is ordained for man not to know everything but only a half or a quarter. As much as he needs to know so as to live, so much he knows."

"It is better for me to go on foot, grandfather. Now my heart is all of a tremble."

"Never mind, sit still."

The old man yawned and made the sign of the cross over his mouth.

"Never mind," he repeated. "Yours is not the worst of sorrows. Life is long, there will be good and bad to come, there will be everything. Great is mother Russia," he said, and looked round on each side of him. "I have been all over Russia, and I have seen everything in her, and you may believe my words, my dear. There will be good and there will be bad. I went as a delegate from my village to Siberia, and I have been to the Amur River and the Altai Mountains and I settled in Siberia; I worked the land there, then I was homesick for mother Russia and I came back to my native village. We came back to Russia on foot; and I remember we went on a steamer, and I was thin as thin, all in rags, barefoot, freezing with cold, and gnawing a crust, and a gentleman who was on the steamer —the kingdom of heaven be his if he is dead—looked at me pitifully, and the tears came into his eyes. 'Ah,' he said, 'your bread is black, your days are black. . . .' And when I got home, as the saying is, there was neither stick nor stall; I had a wife, but I left her behind in Siberia, she was buried there. So I am living as a day labourer. And yet I tell you: since then I have had good as well as bad. Here I do not want to die, my dear, I would be glad to live another twenty years; so there has been more of the good. And great is our mother Russia!" and again he gazed to each side and looked round.

"Grandfather," Lipa asked, "when anyone dies, how many days does his soul walk the earth?"

"Who can tell! Ask Vavila here, he has been to school. Now they teach them everything. Vavila!" the old man called to him.

"Yes!"

"Vavila, when anyone dies, how long does his soul walk the earth?"

Vavila stopped the horse and only then answered:

"Nine days. My uncle Kirilla died and his soul lived in our hut thirteen days after."

"How do you know?"

"Well, for thirteen days there was a knocking in the stove."

"Well, that's all right. Go on," said the old man, and it could be seen that he did not believe a word of all that.

Near Kuzmenki the cart turned into the high-road while Lipa went straight on. It was by now getting light. As she went down into the ravine the Ukleevo huts and the church were hidden in fog. It was cold, and it seemed to her that the same cuckoo was calling still.

When Lipa reached home the cattle had not yet been driven out; everyone was asleep. She sat down on the steps and waited. The old man was the first to come out; he understood all that had happened from the first glance at her, and for a long time he could not articulate a word, but only moved his lips without a sound.

"Ech, Lipa," he said, "you did not take care of my grandchild. . . ."

Varvara was awakened. She clasped her hands and broke into sobs, and immediately began laying out the baby.

"And he was a pretty child . . ." she said. "Oh dear, dear. . . . You only had the one child, and you did not take care enough of him, you silly girl. . . ."

There was a requiem service in the morning and the evening. The funeral took place the next day, and after it the guests and the priests ate a great deal, and with such greed that one might have thought that they had not tasted food for a long time. Lipa waited at table, and the priest, lifting his fork on which there was a salted mushroom, said to her:

"Don't grieve for the babe. For of such is the kingdom of heaven."

And only when they had all separated Lipa realized fully that there was no Nikifor and never would be, she realized it and broke into sobs. And she did not know what room to go into to sob, for she felt that now that her child was dead there was no place for her in the house, that she had no reason to be here, that she was in the way; and the others felt it, too.

"Now what are you bellowing for?" Aksinya shouted, suddenly appearing in the doorway; in honour of the funeral she was dressed all in new clothes and had powdered her face. "Shut up!"

Lipa tried to stop but could not, and sobbed louder than ever.

"Do you hear?" shouted Aksinya, and she stamped her foot in violent anger. "Who is it I am speaking to? Go out of the yard and don't set foot here again, you convict's wife. Get away."

"There, there, there," the old man put in fussily. "Aksinya, don't make such an outcry, my girl. . . . She is crying, it is only natural . . . her child is dead. . . ."

" 'It's only natural,' " Aksinya mimicked him. "Let her stay the night here, and don't let me see a trace of her here tomorrow! 'It's only natural!' she mimicked him again, and, laughing, she went into the shop.

Early next morning Lipa went off to her mother at Torguevo.

9

At the present time the steps and the front door of the shop have been repainted and are as bright as though they were new, there are gay geraniums in the windows as of old, and what happened in Tsybukin's house and yard three years ago is almost forgotten.

Grigory Petrovitch is looked upon as the master as he was in old days, but in reality everything has passed into Aksinya's hands; she buys and sells, and nothing can be done without her consent. The brickyard is working well; and as bricks are wanted for the railway the price has gone up to twenty-four rubles a thousand; peasant women and girls cart the bricks to the station and load them up in the trucks and earn a quarter-ruble a day for the work.

Aksinya has gone into partnership with the Hrymin Juniors, and their factory is now called Hrymin Juniors and Co. They have opened a tavern near the station, and now the expensive concertina is played not at the factory but at the tavern, and the head of the post office often goes there, and he, too, is engaged in some sort of traffic, and the station-master, too. Hrymin Juniors have presented the deaf man Stepan with a gold watch, and he is constantly taking it out of his pocket and putting it to his ear.

People say of Aksinya that she has become a person of power; and it is true that when she drives in the morning to her brickyard, handsome and happy, with the naïve smile on her face, and afterwards when she is giving orders there, one is aware of great power in her. Everyone is afraid of her in the house and in the village and in the brickyard. When she goes to the post the head of the postal department jumps up and says to her:

"I humbly beg you to be seated, Aksinya Abramovna!"

A certain landowner, middle-aged but foppish, in a tunic of fine cloth and patent leather high boots, sold her a horse, and was so carried away by talking to her that he knocked down the price to meet her wishes. He held her hand a long time and, looking into her merry, sly, naïve eyes, said:

"For a woman like you, Aksinya Abramovna, I should be ready to do anything you please. Only say when we can meet where no one will interfere with us?"

"Why, when you please."

And since then the elderly fop drives up to the shop almost every day to drink beer. And the beer is horrid, bitter as wormwood. The landowner shakes his head, but he drinks it.

Old Tsybukin does not have anything to do with the business now at all. He does not keep any money because he cannot distinguish between the good and the false, but he is silent, he says nothing of this weakness. He has become forgetful, and if they don't give him food he does not ask for it. They have grown used to having dinner without him, and Varvara often says:

"He went to bed again yesterday without any supper."

And she says it unconcernedly because she is used to it. For some reason, summer and winter alike, he wears a fur coat, and only in very hot weather he does not go out but sits at home. As a rule putting on his fur coat, wrapping it round him and turning up his collar, he walks about the village, along the road to the station, or sits from morning till night on the seat near the church gates. He sits there without stirring. Passers-by bow to him, but he does not respond, for as of old he dislikes the peasants. If he is asked a question he answers quite rationally and politely, but briefly.

There is a rumour going about in the village that his daughter-in-law turns him out of the house and gives him nothing to eat, and that he is fed by charity; some are glad, others are sorry for him.

Varvara has grown even fatter and whiter, and as before she is active in good works, and Aksinya does not interfere with her.

There is so much jam now that they have not time to eat it before the fresh fruit comes in; it goes sugary, and Varvara almost sheds tears, not knowing what to do with it.

They have begun to forget about Anisim. A letter has come from him written in verse on a big sheet of paper as though it were a petition, all in the same splendid handwriting. Evidently his friend Samorodov was sharing his punishment. Under the verses in an ugly, scarcely legible handwriting there was a single line: "I am ill here all the time; I am wretched, for Christ's sake help me!"

Towards evening—it was a fine autumn day—old Tsybukin was sitting near the church gates, with the collar of his fur coat turned up and nothing of him could be seen but his nose and the peak of his cap. At the other end of the long seat was sitting Elizarov the contractor, and beside him Yakov the school watchman, a toothless old man of seventy. Crutch and the watchman were talking.

"Children ought to give food and drink to the old. . . . Honour thy father and mother . . ." Yakov was saying with irritation, "while she, this daughter-in-law, has turned her father-in-law out of his own house; the old man has neither food nor drink, where is he to go? He has not had a morsel for these three days."

"Three days!" said Crutch, amazed.

"Here he sits and does not say a word. He has grown feeble. And why be silent? He ought to prosecute her, they wouldn't flatter her in the police court."

"Wouldn't flatter whom?" asked Crutch, not hearing.

"What?"

"The woman's all right, she does her best. In their line of business they can't get on without that . . . without sin, I mean. . . ."

"From his own house," Yakov went on with irritation. "Save up and buy your own house, then turn people out of it! She is a nice one, to be sure! A pla-ague!"

Tsybukin listened and did not stir.

"Whether it is your own house or others' it makes no difference so long as it is warm and the women don't scold . . ." said Crutch, and he laughed. "When I was young I was very fond of my Nastasya. She was a quiet woman. And she used to be always at it: 'Buy a house, Makaritch!

Buy a house, Makaritch! Buy a house, Makaritch!' She was dying and yet she kept on saying, 'Buy yourself a racing droshky, Makaritch, that you may not have to walk.' And I bought her nothing but gingerbread."

"Her husband's deaf and stupid," Yakov went on, not hearing Crutch; "a regular fool, just like a goose. He can't understand anything. Hit a goose on the head with a stick and even then it does not understand."

Crutch got up to go home to the factory. Yakov also got up, and both of them went off together, still talking. When they had gone fifty paces old Tsybukin got up too, and walked after them, stepping uncertainly as though on slippery ice.

The village was already plunged in the dusk of evening and the sun only gleamed on the upper part of the road which ran wriggling like a snake up the slope. Old women were coming back from the woods and children with them; they were bringing baskets of mushrooms. Peasant women and girls came in a crowd from the station where they had been loading the trucks with bricks, and their noses and their cheeks under their eyes were covered with red brick-dust. They were singing. Ahead of them all was Lipa singing in a high voice, with her eyes turned upwards to the sky, breaking into trills as though triumphant and ecstatic that at last the day was over and she could rest. In the crowd was her mother Praskovya, who was walking with a bundle in her arms and breathless as usual.

"Good evening, Makaritch!" cried Lipa, seeing Crutch. "Good evening, darling!"

"Good evening, Lipinka," cried Crutch, delighted. "Dear girls and women, love the rich carpenter! Ho-ho! My little children, my little children. (Crutch gave a gulp.) My dear little axes!"

Crutch and Yakov went on further and could still be heard talking. Then after them the crowd was met by old Tsybukin and there was a sudden hush. Lipa and Praskovya had dropped a little behind, and when the old man was on a level with them Lipa bowed down low and said:

"Good evening, Grigory Petrovitch."

Her mother, too, bowed down. The old man stopped and, saying nothing, looked at the two in silence; his lips were quivering and his eyes full of tears. Lipa took out of her mother's bundle a piece of savoury turnover and gave it him. He took it and began eating.

The sun had by now set; its glow died away on the road above. It grew dark and cool. Lipa and Praskovya walked on and for some time they kept crossing themselves.

QUESTIONS

1. How many distinct social classes are represented in the village of Ukleevo, as established in the first section of the story? As the story continues, which are the two classes which receive the major share of Chekhov's attention?

2. Is Chekhov's criticism of social injustice explicit or implicit or both? How would you summarize his view of the relationships between the classes in Ukleevo?

3. How many varieties of religious faith, or its absence, do you find in the story, distributed among the various characters?

4. Does it seem to you that Chekhov presents Varvara Nikolaevna, with her charity based on religion, as representing a solution to the social injustice that prevails in Ukleevo?

5. Does Chekhov have anything to say in the story about the role of bureaucracy in the society he is picturing, and if so, is his view of Russian bureaucracy at all comparable to Gogol's view in "The Overcoat"?

6. Are there any points in the story at which the fact that Ukleevo is situated in a ravine is used for the purposes of symbolism? Are the counterfeit rubles used as a symbol?

7. In what way are Aksinya and Lipa rivals? How does their rivalry represent the wider social conflict of the story? At what point does their rivalry reach a crisis? How is the crisis resolved, and what does its resolution suggest as to Chekhov's view of the stage reached in his time by the social conflict which the two women represent?

8. Why do you suppose Lipa thinks that the two wayfarers who give her a lift, in section 8, are holy men?

9. By the end of the story, what changes have been made in the lives of the principal characters? What changes have been made in the social conditions of life in Ukleevo?

STEPHEN CRANE

(1871–1900)

As we read *The Red Badge of Courage* or one of Crane's stories of the Civil War, such as the one reprinted here, it takes a certain small effort to realize that in these works Crane was describing episodes in a war that had ended before he was born. The first quality that strikes us in his work is the vivid exactitude with which in a few phrases, a sentence or two, he is able to convey a total impression of a scene, not only of its external air and look but also of the spiritual or emotional quality it holds for the characters he has placed within it. Sometimes he does this by focussing on one or two objective details—for example, in "The Little Regiment," the church spire, or the many signs of the former life of the captured town, or the soldiers' little pails of coffee. At other times, he puts us in immediate touch with the psychological elements of a situation by entering into it imaginatively himself and reporting it back to us from a carefully chosen and sometimes surprising angle. A good example of this latter habit is the description with which he begins "The Open Boat" (the story in which he describes the ordeal and the courageous effort of a little group of men at sea in an open boat after their ship has sunk), and especially its first sentence, "None of them knew the color of the sky."

Perhaps there is always a certain element of on-the-spot reporting in Crane's writing, and this is not surprising when we consider that for the larger part of his adult life he worked for newspapers as a reporter or correspondent. He was born in Newark, N. J., on Nov. 1, 1871, one of the many children of a Methodist minister. Although his father died in 1880, he was able through his own and his mother's efforts to go to college, first to Lafayette for a year, then to Syracuse University, but at his mother's death in 1890 he left college and went to New York. There he supported himself by reporting jobs, and there he saw at first hand the slum life which formed the background of his first work of fiction, *Maggie: A Girl of the Streets*. This book, which he published at his own expense in 1892, with borrowed money, was not a success, and he sold very few copies. His second novel, *The Red Badge of Courage*, first published as a book in 1895 after having been serialized in a newspaper, *was* a success, however, and not only established his reputation but to a large extent determined the outer form that his life was to take in the few years that were left to him.

At the time he wrote *The Red Badge of Courage* he had had no experience of war, working up the background for the novel from printed and pictorial accounts of the Civil War. In the next few years there were wars in various parts of the world—in Greece, in Cuba—, and newspaper editors, impressed with the expert touch displayed in *The Red Badge of Courage*, decided that Crane was the man to report them. His novel had also won him a distinct literary reputation in England as well as in America, and during the last two years of his life when he had settled in England (as far as it was possible for him to settle anywhere), he enjoyed the friendship of a circle of writers which included Ford Madox Hueffer, Henry James, and Joseph Conrad. But the years of success, perhaps even more than the years of struggle, had made serious inroads on his health, and he died of tuberculosis at Badenweiler, in Germany's Black Forest, on June 5, 1900, when he was not yet twenty-nine years old.

Occasionally Crane's work is disfigured by a patch of self-consciously vivid writing, by too great a trust in the picturesqueness of slang, by too great a fondness for the striking phrase. It may be that these faults betray his journalistic background, but whatever their origin, they are only momentary in their effect and do not endanger the total fabric of his work (except for *Maggie*, which has died the same death as the contemporary slang in which it was written). Crane is sometimes regarded as a writer whose work depends almost entirely for its success on *tour de force*, on his control of his own distinctive techniques of description. He is more justly to be seen as a writer who brought great imaginative insight to bear on a centrally important subject: how people stand up to the ordeals which life sends them.

These ordeals, Crane knew, could be encountered in many and widely different circumstances: on the battlefield, to be sure, or at sea, or in the streets and saloons of the Bowery, but also in such a pleasant American country town as his Whilomville. At times the occasion for heroism would present itself under conditions that were compounded of the serious and the comic, as in "The Bride Comes to Yellow Sky." And always Crane treats his reluctant heroes with a seriousness that has nothing of mere automatic solemnity in it but springs from his deep and tender respect for all that perfectly ordinary men and women are capable of when put to a crucial test.

Particularly, he displays a consistent respect and affection for the lives and deeds of soldiers. War was far from providing his only subject-matter, but it did provide him with the subject of his greatest single work as well as of some of his finest stories. In the years since the end of the first World War there have been many attempts to set down in works of fiction the reality of war, its horror, and the quality of the soldier's life. Yet *The Red Badge of Courage* has not been surpassed, nor, in their scope, have the stories that Crane published in 1896 under the title of *The Little Regiment and Other Episodes of the Civil War*.

Many recent writers of war fiction could have learned a valuable lesson from the restraint and the truly creative tact with which Crane handles the awkward matter of the language habitually used by soldiers. He had learned in writing *Maggie* that it is a mistake to reproduce contemporary slang, the language of a particular milieu, with complete accuracy, and the knowledge stood him in good stead when he came to write about the Civil War, a time already thirty years distant from him. We may be sure that Crane's soldiers used the language that is used by soldiers everywhere as a psychological armament against the special, deadly isolation which society has imposed upon them. Crane suggests this language, but does not reproduce it, and as a result his soldiers and their speech are as alive today as they were when he created them.

Crane's soldiers participate fully in the essential innocence of all Crane's humanity. There is evil in Crane's world, but it is not usually a human evil. More often than not, his men and women are pitted against natural forces—"falling trees, crashing boulders, the sea in a storm"—, and when the conflict is one of opposing human forces, blame is not attached to one side or the other with any finality. In his episodes of the Civil War, he is not interested in issues, or first causes, or taking sides, but only in the men who fought, the men in blue and the men in gray, and both sides have his respect, his pity, and his gently humorous affection as they make their stand against death and fear.

THE LITTLE REGIMENT

I

The fog made the clothes of the men of the column in the roadway seem of a luminous quality. It imparted to the heavy infantry overcoats a new colour, a kind of blue which was so pale that a regiment might have been merely a long, low shadow in the mist. However, a muttering, one part grumble, three parts joke, hovered in the air above the thick ranks, and blended in an undertoned roar, which was the voice of the column.

The town on the southern shore of the little river loomed spectrally, a faint etching upon the grey cloud-masses which were shifting with oily languor. A long row of guns upon the northern bank had been pitiless in their hatred, but a little battered belfry could be dimly seen still pointing with invincible resolution toward the heavens.

The enclouded air vibrated with noises made by hidden colossal things. The infantry tramplings, the heavy rumbling of the artillery, made the earth speak of gigantic preparation. Guns on distant heights thundered from time to time with sudden, nervous roar, as if unable to endure in silence a knowledge of hostile troops massing, other guns going to position. These sounds, near and remote, defined an immense battle-ground, described the tremendous width of the stage of the prospective drama. The voices of the guns, slightly casual, unexcited in their challenges and warnings, could not destroy the unutterable eloquence of the word in the air, a meaning of impending struggle which made the breath halt at the lips.

The column in the roadway was ankle-deep in mud. The men swore piously at the rain which drizzled upon them, compelling them to stand always very erect in fear of the drops that would sweep in under their coat collars. The fog was as cold as wet cloths. The men stuffed their hands deep into their pockets, and huddled their muskets in their arms. The machinery of orders had rooted these soldiers deeply into the mud, precisely as almighty nature roots mullein stalks.

They listened and speculated when a tumult of fighting came from the dim town across the river. When the noise lulled for a time they resumed their descriptions of the mud and graphically exaggerated the number of hours they had been kept waiting. The general commanding their division rode along the ranks, and they cheered admiringly, affectionately, crying out to him gleeful prophecies of the coming battle. Each man scanned him with a peculiarly keen personal interest, and afterward spoke of him with unquestioning devotion and confidence, narrating anecdotes which were mainly untrue.

When the jokers lifted the shrill voices which invariably belonged to them, flinging witticisms at their comrades, a loud laugh would sweep

REPRINTED from *Twenty Stories by Stephen Crane*, by permission of Alfred A. Knopf, Inc. Copyright 1940, by Alfred A. Knopf, Inc.

from rank to rank, and soldiers who had not heard would lean forward and demand repetition. When were borne past them some wounded men with gray and blood-smeared faces, and eyes that rolled in that helpless beseeching for assistance from the sky which comes with supreme pain, the soldiers in the mud watched intently, and from time to time asked of the bearers an account of the affair. Frequently they bragged of their corps, their division, their brigade, their regiment. Anon they referred to the mud and the cold drizzle. Upon this threshold of a wild scene of death they, in short, defied the proportion of events with that splendour of heedlessness which belongs only to veterans.

"Like a lot of wooden soldiers," swore Billie Dempster, moving his feet in the thick mass, and casting a vindictive glance indefinitely. "Standing in the mud for a hundred years."

"Oh, shut up!" murmured his brother Dan. The manner of his words implied that this fraternal voice near him was an indescribable bore.

"Why should I shut up?" demanded Billie.

"Because you're a fool," cried Dan, taking no time to debate it; "the biggest fool in the regiment."

There was but one man between them, and he was habituated. These insults from brother to brother had swept across his chest, flown past his face, many times during two long campaigns. Upon this occasion he simply grinned first at one, then at the other.

The way of these brothers was not an unknown topic in regimental gossip. They had enlisted simultaneously, with each sneering loudly at the other for doing it. They left their little town, and went forward with the flag exchanging protestations of undying suspicion. In the camp life they so openly despised each other that, when entertaining quarrels were lacking, their companions often contrived situations calculated to bring forth display of this fraternal dislike.

Both were large-limbed, strong young men, and often fought with friends in camp unless one was near to interfere with the other. This latter happened rather frequently, because Dan, preposterously willing for any manner of combat, had a very great horror of seeing Billie in a fight; and Billie, almost odiously ready himself, simply refused to see Dan stripped to his shirt and with his fists aloft. This sat queerly upon them, and made them the objects of plots.

When Dan jumped through a ring of eager soldiers and dragged forth his raving brother by the arm, a thing often predicted would almost come to pass. When Billie performed the same office for Dan, the prediction would again miss fulfilment by an inch. But indeed they never fought together, although they were perpetually upon the verge.

They expressed longing for such conflict. As a matter of truth, they had at one time made full arrangement for it, but even with the encouragement and interest of half of the regiment they somehow failed to achieve collision.

If Dan became a victim of police duty, no jeering was so destructive to the feelings as Billie's comment. If Billie got a call to appear at the head-quarters, none would so genially prophesy his complete undoing as Dan. Small misfortunes to one were, in truth, invariably greeted with hilarity by the other, who seemed to see in them great reinforcement of his opinion.

As soldiers, they expressed each for each a scorn intense and blasting. After a certain battle, Billie was promoted to corporal. When Dan was told of it, he seemed smitten dumb with astonishment and patriotic indig-nation. He stared in silence, while the dark blood rushed to Billie's fore-head, and he shifted his weight from foot to foot. Dan at last found his tongue, and said: "Well, I'm durned!" If he had heard that an army mule had been appointed to the post of corps commander, his tone could not have had more derision in it. Afterward, he adopted a fervid insubordina-tion, an almost religious reluctance to obey the new corporal's orders, which came near to developing the desired strife.

It is here finally to be recorded also that Dan, most ferociously profane in speech, very rarely swore in the presence of his brother; and that Billie, whose oaths came from his lips with the grace of falling pebbles, was sel-dom known to express himself in this manner when near his brother Dan.

At last the afternoon contained a suggestion of evening. Metallic cries rang suddenly from end to end of the column. They inspired at once a quick, business-like adjustment. The long thing stirred in the mud. The men had hushed, and were looking across the river. A moment later the shadowy mass of pale blue figures was moving steadily toward the stream. There could be heard from the town a clash of swift fighting and cheering. The noise of the shooting coming through the heavy air had its sharpness taken from it, and sounded in thuds.

There was a halt upon the bank above the pontoons. When the column went winding down the incline, and streamed out upon the bridge, the fog had faded to a great degree, and in the clearer dusk the guns on a distant ridge were enabled to perceive the crossing. The long whirling outcries of the shells came into the air above the men. An occasional solid shot struck the surface of the river, and dashed into view a sudden vertical jet. The distance was subtly illuminated by the lightning from the deep-booming guns. One by one the batteries on the northern shore aroused, the innumerable guns bellowing in angry oration at the distant ridge. The rolling thunder crashed and reverberated as a wild surf sounds on a still night, and to this music the column marched across the pontoons.

The waters of the grim river curled away in a smile from the ends of the great boats, and slid swiftly beneath the planking. The dark, riddled walls of the town upreared before the troops, and from a region hidden by these hammered and tumbled houses came incessantly the yells and firings of a prolonged and close skirmish.

When Dan had called his brother a fool, his voice had been so decisive, so brightly assured, that many men had laughed, considering it to be great humour under the circumstances. The incident happened to rankle deep in Billie. It was not any strange thing that his brother had called

him a fool. In fact, he often called him a fool with exactly the same amount
of cheerful and prompt conviction, and before large audiences, too. Billie
wondered in his own mind why he took such profound offence in this
case; but, at any rate, as he slid down the bank and on to the bridge with
his regiment, he was searching his knowledge for something that would
pierce Dan's blithesome spirit. But he could contrive nothing at this time,
and his impotency made the glance which he was once able to give his
brother still more malignant.

The guns far and near were roaring a fearful and grand introduction
for this column which was marching upon the stage of death. Billie felt
it, but only in a numb way. His heart was cased in that curious dissonant
metal which covers a man's emotions at such times. The terrible voices
from the hills told him that in this wide conflict his life was an insignificant fact, and that his death would be an insignificant fact. They por-
tended the whirlwind to which he would be as necessary as a butterfly's
waved wing. The solemnity, the sadness of it came near enough to make
him wonder why he was neither solemn nor sad. When his mind vaguely
adjusted events according to their importance to him, it appeared that the
uppermost thing was the fact that upon the eve of battle, and before many
comrades, his brother had called him a fool.

Dan was in a particularly happy mood. "Hurray! Look at 'em shoot,"
he said, when the long witches' croon of the shells came into the air. It
enraged Billie when he felt the little thorn in him, and saw at the same
time that his brother had completely forgotten it.

The column went from the bridge into more mud. At this southern
end there was a chaos of hoarse directions and commands. Darkness was
coming upon the earth, and regiments were being hurried up the slippery
bank. As Billie floundered in the black mud, amid the swearing, sliding
crowd, he suddenly resolved that, in the absence of other means of hurt-
ing Dan, he would avoid looking at him, refrain from speaking to him,
pay absolutely no heed to his existence; and this, done skilfully, would,
he imagined, soon reduce his brother to a poignant sensitiveness.

At the top of the bank the column again halted and rearranged itself,
as a man after a climb rearranges his clothing. Presently the great steel-
backed brigade, an infinitely graceful thing in the rhythm and ease of its
veteran movement, swung up a little narrow, slanting street.

Evening had come so swiftly that the fighting on the remote borders
of the town was indicated by thin flashes of flame. Some building was
on fire, and its reflection upon the clouds was an oval of delicate pink.

II

All demeanour of rural serenity had been wrenched violently from the
little town by the guns and by the waves of men which had surged
through it. The hand of war laid upon this village had in an instant
changed it to a thing of remnants. It resembled the place of a monstrous
shaking of the earth itself. The windows, now mere unsightly holes, made

the tumbled and blackened dwellings seem skeletons. Doors lay splintered to fragments. Chimneys had flung their bricks everywhere. The artillery fire had not neglected the rows of gentle shade-trees which had lined the streets. Branches and heavy trunks cluttered the mud in driftwood tangles, while a few shattered forms had contrived to remain dejectedly, mournfully upright. They expressed an innocence, a helplessness, which perforce created a pity for their happening into this cauldron of battle. Furthermore, there was under foot a vast collection of odd things reminiscent of the charge, the fight, the retreat. There were boxes and barrels filled with earth, behind which riflemen had lain snugly, and in these little trenches were the dead in blue with the dead in gray, the poses eloquent of the struggles for possession of the town, until the history of the whole conflict was written plainly in the streets.

And yet the spirit of this little city, its quaint individuality, poised in the air above the ruins, defying the guns, the sweeping volleys; holding in contempt those avaricious blazes which had attacked many dwellings. The hard earthen sidewalks proclaimed the games that had been played there during long lazy days, in the careful shadows of the trees. "General Merchandise," in faint letters upon a long board, had to be read with a slanted glance, for the sign dangled by one end; but the porch of the old store was a palpable legend of wide-hatted men, smoking.

This subtle essence, this soul of the life that had been, brushed like invisible wings the thoughts of the men in the swift columns that came up from the river.

In the darkness a loud and endless humming arose from the great blue crowds bivouacked in the streets. From time to time a sharp spatter of firing from far picket lines entered this bass chorus. The smell from the smouldering ruins floated on the cold night breeze.

Dan, seated ruefully upon the doorstep of a shot-pierced house, was proclaiming the campaign badly managed. Orders had been issued forbidding campfires.

Suddenly he ceased his oration and, scanning the group of his comrades, said: "Where's Billie? Do you know?"

"Gone on picket."

"Get out! Has he?" said Dan. "No business to go on picket. Why don't some of them other corporals take their turn?"

A bearded private was smoking his pipe of confiscated tobacco, seated comfortably upon a horse-hair trunk which he had dragged from the house. He observed: "*Was* his turn."

"No such thing," cried Dan. He and the man on the horse-hair trunk held discussion in which Dan stoutly maintained that if his brother had been sent on picket it was an injustice. He ceased his argument when another soldier, upon whose arms could faintly be seen the two stripes of a corporal, entered the circle. "Humph," said Dan, "where you been?"

The corporal made no answer. Presently Dan said: "Billie, where you been?"

His brother did not seem to hear these inquiries. He glanced at the house which towered above them, and remarked casually to the man on the horse-hair trunk: "Funny, ain't it? After the pelting this town got, you'd think there wouldn't be one brick left on another."

"Oh," said Dan, glowering at his brother's back. "Getting mighty smart, ain't you?"

The absence of camp-fires allowed the evening to make apparent its quality of faint silver light in which the blue clothes of the throng became black, and the faces became white expanses, void of expression. There was considerable excitement a short distance from the group around the doorstep. A soldier had chanced upon a hoop-skirt, and arrayed in it he was performing a dance amid the applause of his companions. Billie and a greater part of the men immediately poured over there to witness the exhibition.

"What's the matter with Billie?" demanded Dan of the man upon the horse-hair trunk.

"How do I know?" rejoined the other in mild resentment. He arose and walked away. When he returned he said briefly, in a weather-wise tone, that it would rain during the night.

Dan took a seat upon one end of the horse-hair trunk. He was facing the crowd around the dancer, which in its hilarity swung this way and that way. At times he imagined that he could recognize his brother's face.

He and the man on the other end of the trunk thoughtfully talked of the army's position. To their minds, infantry and artillery were in a most precarious jumble in the streets of the town; but they did not grow nervous over it, for they were used to having the army appear in a precarious jumble to their minds. They had learned to accept such puzzling situations as a consequence of their position in the ranks, and were now usually in possession of a simple but perfectly immovable faith that somebody understood the jumble. Even if they had been convinced that the army was a headless monster, they would merely have nodded with the veteran's singular cynicism. It was none of their business as soldiers. Their duty was to grab sleep and food when occasion permitted, and cheerfully fight wherever their feet were planted until more orders came. This was a task sufficiently absorbing.

They spoke of other corps, and, this talk being confidential, their voices dropped to tones of awe. "The Ninth"—"The First"—"The Fifth"—"The Sixth"—"The Third"—the simple numerals rang with eloquence, each having a meaning which was to float through many years as no intangible arithmetical mist, but as pregnant with individuality as the names of cities.

Of their own corps they spoke with a deep veneration, an idolatry, a supreme confidence which apparently would not blanch to see it match against everything.

It was as if their respect for other corps was due partly to a wonder that organizations not blessed with their own famous numeral could take such an interest in war. They could prove that their division was the best in the corps, and that their brigade was the best in the division. And their regiment—it was plain that no fortune of life was equal to the chance which caused a man to be born, so to speak, into this command, the keystone of the defending arch.

At times Dan covered with insults the character of a vague, unnamed general to whose petulance and busy-body spirit he ascribed the order which made hot coffee impossible.

Dan said that victory was certain in the coming battle. The other man seemed rather dubious. He remarked upon the fortified line of hills, which had impressed him even from the other side of the river. "Shucks," said Dan. "Why, we—" He pictured a splendid overflowing of these hills by the sea of men in blue. During the period of this conversation Dan's glance searched the merry throng about the dancer. Above the babble of voices in the street a far-away thunder could sometimes be heard, evidently from the very edge of the horizon—the boom-boom of restless guns.

III

Ultimately the night deepened to the tone of black velvet. The outlines of the fireless camp were like the faint drawings upon ancient tapestry. The glint of a rifle, the shine of a button, might have been of threads of silver and gold sewn upon the fabric of the night. There was little presented to the vision, but to a sense more subtle there was discernible in the atmosphere something like a pulse; a mystic beating which would have told a stranger of the presence of a giant thing—the slumbering mass of regiments and batteries.

With fire forbidden, the floor of a dry old kitchen was thought to be a good exchange for the cold earth of December, even if a shell had exploded in it and knocked it so out of shape that when a man lay curled in his blanket his last waking thought was likely to be of the wall that bellied out above him, as if strongly anxious to topple upon the score of soldiers.

Billie looked at the bricks ever about to descend in a shower upon his face, listened to the industrious pickets plying their rifles on the border of the town, imagined some measure of the din of the coming battle, thought of Dan and Dan's chagrin, and, rolling over in his blanket, went to sleep with satisfaction.

At an unknown hour he was aroused by the creaking of boards. Lifting himself upon his elbow, he saw a sergeant prowling among the sleeping forms. The sergeant carried a candle in an old brass candlestick. He would have resembled some old farmer on an unusual midnight tour if it were not for the significance of his gleaming buttons and striped sleeves.

Billie blinked stupidly at the light until his mind returned from the journeys of slumber. The sergeant stooped among the unconscious soldiers, holding the candle close, and peering into each face.

"Hello, Haines," said Billie. "Relief?"

"Hello, Billie," said the sergeant. "Special duty."

"Dan got to go?"

"Jameson, Hunter, McCormack, D. Dempster. Yes.—Where is he?"

"Over there by the winder," said Billie, gesturing. "What is it for, Haines?"

"You don't think I know, do you?" demanded the sergeant. He began to pipe sharply but cheerily at men upon the floor. "Come, Mac, get up there. Here's a special for you. Wake up, Jameson. Come along, Dannie, me boy."

Each man at once took this call to duty as a personal affront. They pulled themselves out of their blankets, rubbed their eyes, and swore at whoever was responsible. "Them's orders," cried the sergeant. "Come! Get out of here." An undetailed head with dishevelled hair thrust out from a blanket, and a sleepy voice said: "Shut up, Haines, and go home."

When the detail clanked out of the kitchen, all but one of the remaining men seemed to be again asleep. Billie, leaning on his elbow, was gazing into darkness. When the footsteps died to silence, he curled himself into his blanket.

At the first cool lavender lights of daybreak he aroused again, and scanned his recumbent companions. Seeing a wakeful one he asked: "Is Dan back yet?"

The man said: "Hain't seen 'im."

Billie put both hands behind his head, and scowled into the air. "Can't see the use of these cussed details in the night-time," he muttered in his most unreasonable tones. "Darn nuisances. Why can't they—?" He grumbled at length and graphically.

When Dan entered with the squad, however, Billie was convincingly asleep.

IV

The regiment trotted in double time along the street, and the colonel seemed to quarrel over the right of way with many artillery officers. Batteries were waiting in the mud, and the men of them, exasperated by the bustle of this ambitious infantry, shook their fists from saddle and caisson, exchanging all manner of taunts and jests. The slanted guns continued to look reflectively at the ground.

On the outskirts of the crumbled town a fringe of blue figures was firing into the fog. The regiment swung out into skirmish lines, and the fringe of blue figures departed, turning their backs and going joyfully around the flank.

The bullets began a low moan off toward a ridge which loomed faintly in the heavy mist. When the swift crescendo had reached its climax, the missiles zipped just overhead, as if piercing an invisible curtain. A battery on the hill was crashing with such tumult that it was as if the guns had quarrelled and had fallen pell-mell and snarling upon each other. The shells howled on their journey toward the town. From short-range distance there came a spatter of musketry, sweeping along an invisible line and making faint sheets of orange light.

Some in the new skirmish lines were beginning to fire at various shadows discerned in the vapour—forms of men suddenly revealed by some humour of the laggard masses of clouds. The crackle of musketry began to dominate the purring of the hostile bullets. Dan, in the front rank, held his rifle poised, and looked into the fog keenly, coldly, with the air of a sportsman. His nerves were so steady that it was as if they had been drawn from his body, leaving him merely a muscular machine; but his numb heart was somehow beating to the pealing march of the fight.

The waving skirmish line went backward and forward, ran this way and that way. Men got lost in the fog, and men were found again. Once they got too close to the formidable ridge, and the thing burst out as if repulsing a general attack. Once another blue regiment was apprehended on the very edge of firing into them. Once a friendly battery began an elaborate and scientific process of extermination. Always as busy as brokers, the men slid here and there over the plain, fighting their foes, escaping from their friends, leaving a history of many movements in the wet yellow turf, cursing the atmosphere, blazing away every time they could identify the enemy.

In one mystic changing of the fog, as if the fingers of spirits were drawing aside these draperies, a small group of the gray skirmishers, silent, statuesque, was suddenly disclosed to Dan and those about him. So vivid and near were they that there was something uncanny in the revelation.

There might have been a second of mutual staring. Then each rifle in each group was at the shoulder. As Dan's glance flashed along the barrel of his weapon, the figure of a man suddenly loomed as if the musket had been a telescope. The short black beard, the slouch hat, the pose of the man as he sighted to shoot, made a quick picture in Dan's mind. The same moment, it would seem, he pulled his own trigger, and the man, smitten, lurched forward, while his exploding rifle made a slanting crimson streak in the air, and the slouch hat fell before the body. The billows of the fog, governed by singular impulses, rolled between.

"You got that feller sure enough," said a comrade to Dan. Dan looked at him absent-mindedly.

V

When the next morning calmly displayed another fog, the men of the regiment exchanged eloquent comments; but they did not abuse it at length, because the streets of the town now contained enough galloping aides to make three troops of cavalry, and they knew that they had come to the verge of the great fight.

Dan conversed with the man who had once possessed a horse-hair trunk; but they did not mention the line of hills which had furnished them in more careless moments with an agreeable topic. They avoided it now

as condemned men do the subject of death, and yet the thought of it
stayed in their eyes as they looked at each other and talked gravely of
other things.

The expectant regiment heaved a long sigh of relief when the sharp
call "Fall in," repeated indefinitely, arose in the streets. It was inevitable
that a bloody battle was to be fought, and they wanted to get it off their
minds. They were, however, doomed again to spend a long period planted
firmly in the mud. They craned their necks, and wondered where some
of the other regiments were going.

At last the mists rolled carelessly away. Nature made at this time all
provisions to enable foes to see each other, and immediately the roar of
guns resounded from every hill. The endless cracking of the skirmishers
swelled to rolling crashes of musketry. Shells screamed with panther-like
noises at the houses. Dan looked at the man of the horse-hair trunk, and
the man said: "Well, here she comes!"

The tenor voices of younger officers and the deep and hoarse voices
of the older ones rang in the streets. These cries pricked like spurs.
The masses of men vibrated from the suddenness with which they were
plunged into the situation of troops about to fight. That the orders were
long expected did not concern the emotion.

Simultaneous movement was imparted to all these thick bodies of men
and horses that lay in the town. Regiment after regiment swung rapidly
into the streets that faced the sinister ridge.

This exodus was theatrical. The little sober-hued village had been like
the cloak which disguises the king of drama. It was now put aside, and
an army, splendid thing of steel and blue, stood forth in the sunlight.

Even the soldiers in the heavy columns drew deep breaths at the sight,
more majestic than they had dreamed. The heights of the enemy's position were crowded with men who resembled people come to witness
some mighty pageant. But as the column moved steadily to their positions, the guns, matter-of-fact warriors, doubled their number, and shells
burst with red thrilling tumult on the crowded plain. One came into the
ranks of the regiment, and after the smoke and the wrath of it had faded,
leaving motionless figures, every one stormed according to the limits of
his vocabulary, for veterans detest being killed when they are not busy.

The regiment sometimes looked sidewise at its brigade companions,
composed of men who had never been in battle; but no frozen blood
could withstand the heat of the splendour of this army before the eyes
on the plain, these lines so long that the flanks were little streaks, this
mass of men of one intention. The recruits carried themselves heedlessly.
At the rear was an idle battery, and three artillerymen in a foolish row
on a caisson nudged each other and grinned at the recruits. "You'll catch
it pretty soon," they called out. They were impersonally gleeful, as if
they themselves were not also likely to catch it pretty soon. But with this
picture of an army in their hearts, the new men perhaps felt the devotion
which the drops may feel for the wave; they were of its power and glory;

they smiled jauntily at the foolish row of gunners, and told them to go to blazes.

The column trotted across some little bridges, and spread quickly into lines of battle. Before them was a bit of plain, and in back of the plain was the ridge. There was no time left for consideration. The men were staring at the plain, mightily wondering how it would feel to be out there, when a brigade in advance yelled and charged. The hill was all gray smoke and fire-points.

That fierce elation in the terrors of war, catching a man's heart and making it burn with such ardour that he becomes capable of dying, flashed in the faces of the men like coloured lights, and made them resemble leashed animals, eager, ferocious, daunting at nothing. The line was really in its first leap before the wild, hoarse crying of the orders.

The greed for close quarters which is the emotion of a bayonet charge came then into the minds of the men and developed until it was a madness. The field, with its faded grass of a Southern winter, seemed to this fury miles in width.

High, slow-moving masses of smoke, with an odour of burning cotton, engulfed the line until the men might have been swimmers. Before them the ridge, the shore of this gray sea, was outlined, crossed, and re-crossed by sheets of flame. The howl of the battle arose to the noise of innumerable wind demons.

The line, galloping, scrambling, plunging like a herd of wounded horses, went over a field that was sown with corpses, the records of other charges.

Directly in front of the black-faced, whooping Dan, carousing in this onward sweep like a new kind of fiend, a wounded man appeared, raising his shattered body, and staring at this rush of men down upon him. It seemed to occur to him that he was to be trampled; he made a desperate, piteous effort to escape; then finally huddled in a waiting heap. Dan and the soldier near him widened the interval between them without looking down, without appearing to heed the wounded man. This little clump of blue seemed to reel past them as boulders reel past a train.

Bursting through a smoke-wave, the scampering, unformed bunches came upon the wreck of the brigade that had preceded them, a floundering mass stopped afar from the hill by the swirling volleys.

It was as if a necromancer had suddenly shown them a picture of the fate which awaited them; but the line with muscular spasm hurled itself over this wreckage and onward, until men were stumbling amid the relics of other assaults, the point where the fire from the ridge consumed.

The men, panting, perspiring, with crazed faces, tried to push against it; but it was as if they had come to a wall. The wave halted, shuddered in an agony from the quick struggle of its two desires, then toppled, and broke into a fragmentary thing which has no name.

Veterans could now at last be distinguished from recruits. The new regiments were instantly gone, lost, scattered, as if they never had been.

But the sweeping failure of the charge, the battle, could not make the veterans forget their business. With a last throe, the band of maniacs drew itself up and blazed a volley at the hill, insignificant to those iron entrenchments, but nevertheless expressing that singular final despair which enables men coolly to defy the walls of a city of death.

After this episode the men· renamed their command. They called it the Little Regiment.

VI

"I seen Dan shoot a feller yesterday. Yes sir. I'm sure it was him that done it. And maybe he thinks about that feller now, and wonders if *he* tumbled down just about the same way. Them things come up in a man's mind."

Bivouac fires upon the sidewalks, in the streets, in the yards, threw high their wavering reflections, which examined, like slim red fingers, the dingy scarred walls and the piles of tumbled brick. The droning of voices again arose from great blue crowds.

The odour of frying bacon, the fragrance from countless little coffee-pails floated among the ruins. The rifles, stacked in the shadows, emitted flashes of steely light. Wherever a flag lay horizontally from one stack to another was the bed of an eagle which had led men into the mystic smoke.

The men about a particular fire were engaged in holding in check their jovial spirits. They moved whispering around the blaze, although they looked at it with a certain fine contentment, like labourers after a day's hard work.

There was one who sat apart. They did not address him save in tones suddenly changed. They did not regard him directly, but always in little sidelong glances.

At last a soldier from a distant fire came into this circle of light. He studied for a time the man who sat apart. Then he hesitatingly stepped closer, and said: "Got any news, Dan?"

"No," said Dan.

The new-comer shifted his feet. He looked at the fire, at the sky, at the other men, at Dan. His face expressed a curious despair; his tongue was plainly in rebellion. Finally, however, he contrived to say: "Well, there's some chance yet, Dan. Lots of the wounded are still lying out there, you know. There's some chance yet."

"Yes," said Dan.

The soldier shifted his feet again, and looked miserably into the air. After another struggle he said; "Well, there's some chance yet, Dan." He moved hastily away.

One of the men of the squad, perhaps encouraged by this example, now approached the still figure. "No news yet, hey?" he said, after coughing behind his hand.

"No," said Dan.

"Well," said the man, "I've been thinking of how he was fretting about you the night you went on special duty. You recollect? Well, sir, I was surprised. He couldn't say enough about it. I swan, I don't believe he slep' a wink after you left, but just lay awake cussing special duty and worrying. I was surprised. But there he lay cussing. He—"

Dan made a curious sound, as if a stone had wedged in his throat. He said: "Shut up, will you?"

Afterward the men would not allow his moody contemplation of the fire to be interrupted.

"Oh, let him alone, can't you?"

"Come away from there, Casey!"

"Say, can't you leave him be?"

They moved with reverence about the immovable figure, with its countenance of mask-like invulnerability.

VII

After the red round eye of the sun had stared long at the little plain and its burden, darkness, a sable mercy, came heavily upon it, and the wan hands of the dead were no longer seen in strange frozen gestures.

The heights in front of the plain shone with tiny camp-fires, and from the town in the rear, small shimmerings ascended from the blazes of the bivouac. The plain was a black expanse upon which, from time to time, dots of light, lanterns, floated slowly here and there. These fields were long steeped in grim mystery.

Suddenly, upon one dark spot, there was a resurrection. A strange thing had been groaning there, prostrate. Then it suddenly dragged itself to a sitting posture, and became a man.

The man stared stupidly for a moment at the lights on the hill, then turned and contemplated the faint colouring over the town. For some moments he remained thus, staring with dull eyes, his face unemotional, wooden.

Finally he looked around him at the corpses dimly to be seen. No change flashed into his face upon viewing these men. They seemed to suggest merely that his information concerning himself was not too complete. He ran his fingers over his arms and chest, bearing always the air of an idiot upon a bench at an almshouse door.

Finding no wound in his arms nor in his chest, he raised his hand to his head, and the fingers came away with some dark liquid upon them. Holding these fingers close to his eyes, he scanned them in the same stupid fashion, while his body gently swayed.

The soldier rolled his eyes again toward the town. When he arose, his clothing peeled from the frozen ground like wet paper. Hearing the sound of it, he seemed to see reason for deliberation. He paused and looked at the ground, then at his trousers, then at the ground.

Finally he went slowly off toward the faint reflection, holding his hands palm outward before him, and walking in the manner of a blind man.

VIII

The immovable Dan again sat unaddressed in the midst of comrades who did not joke aloud. The dampness of the usual morning fog seemed to make the little camp-fires furious.

Suddenly a cry arose in the streets, a shout of amazement and delight. The men making breakfast at the fire looked up quickly. They broke forth in clamorous exclamation: "Well! Of all things! Dan! Dan! Look who's coming! Oh, Dan!"

Dan the silent raised his eyes and saw a man, with a bandage of the size of a helmet about his head, receiving a furious demonstration from the company. He was shaking hands, and explaining, and haranguing to a high degree.

Dan started. His face of bronze flushed to his temples. He seemed about to leap from the ground, but then suddenly he sank back, and resumed his impassive gazing.

The men were in a flurry. They looked from one to the other. "Dan! Look! See who's coming!" some cried again. "Dan! Look!"

He scowled at last, and moved his shoulders sullenly. "Well, don't I know it?"

But they could not be convinced that his eyes were in service. "Dan, why can't you look? See who's coming!"

He made a gesture then of irritation and rage. "Curse it! Don't I know it?"

The man with a bandage of the size of a helmet moved forward, always shaking hands and explaining. At times his glance wandered to Dan, who saw with his eyes riveted.

After a series of shiftings, it occurred naturally that the man with the bandage was very near to the man who saw the flames. He paused, and there was a little silence. Finally he said: "Hello, Dan."

"Hello, Billie."

QUESTIONS

1. What seem to you to be the keynotes of Crane's opening description of the column of soldiers, the battle-ground, etc.? What are some of the principal sensory images which help to build up the total impression a reader receives?

2. At what point does a reader begin to suspect that the story will not take a primarily tragic approach to the subject of men at war? How would you describe Crane's attitude towards this subject, as represented in this particular story?

3. What is the somewhat unusual human situation which forms the anecdotal basis of Crane's story? If it were a story told orally, rather than a written story with its full, careful treatment, what would it consist in?

4. What are the stages by which Crane prepares for the incident which constitutes the story's climax? Why is such preparation necessary, why wouldn't it have been possible to describe the incident which extends over sections VI, VII, and VIII by itself, with possibly a brief preliminary explanation?

JAMES JOYCE

(1882–1941)

Ever since the publication of his second novel, *Ulysses,* in Paris in 1922, James Joyce has been one of the most commanding figures in the literary history of the present century. This great and engaging work, with its full exploitation of a wide variety of novel literary techniques and the frank inclusiveness with which it recreates the daily warp and woof of human life, brought Joyce a mixture of fame and notoriety. Not only was the book regarded in many quarters as incomprehensible, but until the early 1930's it was banned both in the United States and in England. Since that time, happily, its intelligibility and its innocence have been recognized by a wide public, as have its penetration, its imposing structure, and its full, mordant Irish humor. This recognition might have been arrived at earlier, and even more widely, if so many of the novel's early readers had not insisted on seeing the book as an isolated production rather than as what it is, Joyce's third work of fiction, closely related in subject-matter, in style, and in many aspects of technique to the two works which had preceded it. These are *Dubliners,* a volume of short stories (from which the story printed below is taken) completed by 1905 but not published until 1914, and *A Portrait of the Artist as a Young Man,* published in 1916.

Joyce had been born in the Dublin suburb of Rathgar on February 2, 1882. While recent biographies provide a detailed picture of his life, it may be said, with the usual caution against taking fiction as factual truth, that we also find a very detailed picture of his own life in the autobiographical first novel and in the parts of *Ulysses* which continue it. Like Stephen Dedalus, the hero of the first novel and a central figure in the second, Joyce had gone as a small boy to Clongowes Wood College, then to Belvedere College, and in 1898 to University College, Dublin. *A Portrait of the Artist as a Young Man* takes the story of Stephen—and of Joyce—up to the time of his first leaving for Paris in 1902, to live by and for his art, "in secrecy, exile, and cunning," as Stephen puts it: "to forge the conscience of my race in the smithy of my soul." Joyce was recalled to Dublin by a telegram received on Good Friday, 1903, saying that his mother was dying. He remained in Dublin—it was his last visit of any length—until October 8, 1904, when he left once more for the Continent with his newly married wife. The entire action of *Ulysses* takes place on a single day during this period—to be exact, from the morning of June 16, 1904, until the early hours of June 17.

Joyce was in Ireland for the last time in September, 1912, but although he thus lived abroad—in Paris, in Trieste, in Zurich, and again in Paris—for the last two-thirds of his life, his subject was always his native Dublin, and the mode in which Dublin impinged on his own mind and soul. This is true even of his last book, *Finnegans Wake* (1939), written in all but hermetic language to transcribe the life of dream, as it is true of *A Por-*

189

trait of the Artist, of *Ulysses,* and of the uncompromisingly lucid, daylight-clear stories that make up *Dubliners.*

Among the documents relating to the difficulties which hindered the publication of *Dubliners* for nine years, there is a letter from Joyce to Grant Richards, a London publisher, in which he states incisively his fundamental purpose in writing the book. "My intention was to write a chapter of the moral history of my country and I chose Dublin because that city seemed to me the centre of paralysis. . . . I have written it for the most part in a style of scrupulous meanness and with the conviction that he is a very bold man who dares to alter in the presentment, still more to deform, whatever he has seen and heard." Two elements may be singled out from this statement as accounting at least in part for the characteristic strength of the volume: the presence of a guiding moral judgment, and the insistence on complete objectivity of presentation.

Dubliners consists of fifteen stories, in each of which is presented a revealing incident, or brief sequence of incidents, in the life of one of the citizens of Dublin. Although each of the stories can perfectly well be read by itself, the entire collection holds together as a single, unified work in a way for which it is hard to find parallels in even the most closely integrated volumes by other short-story writers. This is largely because of the central moral purpose to which reference has already been made, the *total* subject being the moral life of Joyce's people and each story presenting a single facet of that life. Among the central characters of the several stories, all age groups are represented, from childhood through youth and maturity up to old age, and these characters come from many walks of middle-class life.

It was one of Joyce's fundamental concepts as a writer of fiction that the meaning and quality of the life of a given time and place could be apprehended by focussing sharply on single lives and single days in that time and place. In *Ulysses,* which was at first to have been one of the stories in *Dubliners,* and to have been called "Mr. Bloom's Day," Stephen thinks: "Every life is many days, day after day. We walk through ourselves, meeting robbers, ghosts, giants, old men, young men, wives, widows, brothers-in-love. But always meeting ourselves." And it may be that in each of the stories in *Dubliners,* however foreign the objective circumstances of some of them may seem to Joyce's own life, he was exploring a quality, a failing which he had detected not only in his country but in himself.

It is with *Dubliners* that one should begin to read Joyce, because it comes first chronologically in his development as a writer of fiction and because it provides a backdrop of objectivity against which the later, more directly subjective books will have their existence. But quite aside from its place in Joyce's total work, the volume occupies a place of high distinction in the history of the modern short story, standing as one of the greatest single achievements in the form. This distinction is partly the result of the unusually serious and coherent purpose within which the whole collection was conceived. But it also results from the presence of qualities which are observable in each of the individual stories: the finesse of the prose, for example, which at first sight appears to be so resolutely flat but on closer inspection reveals the most subtle and appropriate modulations from point to point in the story. Closely connected with the style of the stories is another quality common to all of them: the balance that is maintained between an often relentless exposure of weakness and failure, and a poignant sympathy which Joyce has ready for the innocent, the victims, even if he does not always extend it to the guilty.

But if one were to single out the greatest strength of these stories—it is one of the greatest strengths of all of Joyce's work—it might well be the firmness with which Joyce holds his subject fixed before his vision, and ours. In these stories, as in *Ulysses,* he holds his subject as if in a vise, doing with it what he will, at his leisure. If the simile suggests too great a rigidity in the relationship between writer and subject, the suggestion can not altogether be denied. Nevertheless, another comparison might better express the satisfaction with which we apprehend this quality in Joyce's best work. As we read *Dubliners,* or many pages of *A Portrait of the Artist as a Young Man,* or *Ulysses,* it is as if the final skillful adjustment had been given to a microscope so that what had before been indistinct or invisible is revealed to us, firmly centered, patent in all its detail, and bathed in light.

A PAINFUL CASE

Mr. James Duffy lived in Chapelizod because he wished to live as far as possible from the city of which he was a citizen and because he found all the other suburbs of Dublin mean, modern and pretentious. He lived in an old sombre house and from his windows he could look into the disused distillery or upwards along the shallow river on which Dublin is built. The lofty walls of his uncarpeted room were free from pictures. He had himself bought every article of furniture in the room: a black iron bedstead, an iron washstand, four cane chairs, a clothes-rack, a coal-scuttle, a fender and irons and a square table on which lay a double desk. A bookcase had been made in an alcove by means of shelves of white wood. The bed was clothed with white bedclothes and a black and scarlet rug covered the foot. A little hand-mirror hung above the washstand and during the day a white-shaded lamp stood as the sole ornament of the mantelpiece. The books on the white wooden shelves were arranged from below upwards according to bulk. A complete Wordsworth stood at one end of the lowest shelf and a copy of the *Maynooth Catechism,* sewn into the cloth cover of a notebook, stood at one end of the top shelf. Writing materials were always on the desk. In the desk lay a manuscript translation of Hauptmann's *Michael Kramer,* the stage directions of which were writ-

FROM *The Portable James Joyce.* Copyright 1946, 1947 by The Viking Press, Inc., New York.

ten in purple ink, and a little sheaf of papers held together by a brass pin. In these sheets a sentence was inscribed from time to time and, in an ironical moment, the headline of an advertisement for *Bile Beans* had been pasted on to the first sheet. On lifting the lid of the desk a faint fragrance escaped—the fragrance of new cedarwood pencils or of a bottle of gum or of an over-ripe apple which might have been left there and forgotten.

Mr. Duffy abhorred anything which betokened physical or mental disorder. A mediæval doctor would have called him saturnine. His face, which carried the entire tale of his years, was of the brown tint of Dublin streets. On his long and rather large head grew dry black hair and a tawny moustache did not quite cover an unamiable mouth. His cheekbones also gave his face a harsh character; but there was no harshness in the eyes which, looking at the world from under their tawny eyebrows, gave the impression of a man ever alert to greet a redeeming instinct in others but often disappointed. He lived at a little distance from his body, regarding his own acts with doubtful side-glances. He had an odd autobiographical habit which led him to compose in his mind from time to time a short sentence about himself containing a subject in the third person and a predicate in the past tense. He never gave alms to beggars and walked firmly, carrying a stout hazel.

He had been for many years cashier of a private bank in Baggot Street. Every morning he came in from Chapelizod by tram. At midday he went to Dan Burke's and took his lunch—a bottle of lager beer and a small trayful of arrowroot biscuits. At four o'clock he was set free. He dined in an eating-house in George's Street where he felt himself safe from the society of Dublin's gilded youth and where there was a certain plain honesty in the bill of fare. His evenings were spent either before his landlady's piano or roaming about the outskirts of the city. His liking for Mozart's music brought him sometimes to an opera or a concert: these were the only dissipations of his life.

He had neither companions nor friends, church nor creed. He lived his spiritual life without any communion with others, visiting his relatives at Christmas and escorting them to the cemetery when they died. He performed these two social duties for old dignity's sake but conceded nothing further to the conventions which regulate the civic life. He allowed himself to think that in certain circumstances he would rob his bank but, as these circumstances never arose, his life rolled out evenly—an adventureless tale.

One evening he found himself sitting beside two ladies in the Rotunda. The house, thinly peopled and silent, gave distressing prophecy of failure. The lady who sat next him looked round at the deserted house once or twice and then said:

"What a pity there is such a poor house tonight! It's so hard on people to have to sing to empty benches."

He took the remark as an invitation to talk. He was surprised that she seemed so little awkward. While they talked he tried to fix her permanently in his memory. When he learned that the young girl beside her was her daughter he judged her to be a year or so younger than himself. Her face, which must have been handsome, had remained intelligent. It was an oval face with strongly marked features. The eyes were very dark blue and steady. Their gaze began with a defiant note but was confused by what seemed a deliberate swoon of the pupil into the iris, revealing for an instant a temperament of great sensibility. The pupil reasserted itself quickly, this half-disclosed nature fell again under the reign of prudence, and her astrakhan jacket, moulding a bosom of a certain fulness, struck the note of defiance more definitely.

He met her again a few weeks afterwards at a concert in Earlsfort Terrace and seized the moments when her daughter's attention was diverted to become intimate. She alluded once or twice to her husband but her tone was not such as to make the allusion a warning. Her name was Mrs. Sinico. Her husband's great-great-grandfather had come from Leghorn. Her husband was captain of a mercantile boat plying between Dublin and Holland; and they had one child.

Meeting her a third time by accident he found courage to make an appointment. She came. This was the first of many meetings; they met always in the evening and chose the most quiet quarters for their walks together. Mr. Duffy, however, had a distaste for underhand ways and, finding that they were compelled to meet stealthily, he forced her to ask him to her house. Captain Sinico encouraged his visits, thinking that his daughter's hand was in question. He had dismissed his wife so sincerely from his gallery of pleasures that he did not suspect that anyone else would take an interest in her. As the husband was often away and the daughter out giving music lessons Mr. Duffy had many opportunities of enjoying the lady's society. Neither he nor she had had any such adventure before and neither was conscious of any incongruity. Little by little he entangled his thoughts with hers. He lent her books, provided her with ideas, shared his intellectual life with her. She listened to all.

Sometimes in return for his theories she gave out some fact of her own life. With almost maternal solicitude she urged him to let his nature open to the full: she became his confessor. He told her that for some time he had assisted at the meetings of an Irish Socialist Party where he had felt himself a unique figure amidst a score of sober workmen in a garret lit by an inefficient oil-lamp. When the party had divided into three sections, each under its own leader and in its own garret, he had discontinued his attendances. The workmen's discussions, he said, were too timorous; the interest they took in the question of wages was inordinate. He felt that they were hard-featured realists and that they resented an exactitude which was the produce of a leisure not within their reach. No social revolution, he told her, would be likely to strike Dublin for some centuries.

She asked him why did he not write out his thoughts. For what, he asked her, with careful scorn. To compete with phrasemongers, incapable of thinking consecutively for sixty seconds? To submit himself to the criticisms of an obtuse middle class which entrusted its morality to police-men and its fine arts to impresarios?

He went often to her little cottage outside Dublin; often they spent their evenings alone. Little by little, as their thoughts entangled, they spoke of subjects less remote. Her companionship was like a warm soil about an exotic. Many times she allowed the dark to fall upon them, re-fraining from lighting the lamp. The dark discreet room, their isolation, the music that still vibrated in their ears united them. This union exalted him, wore away the rough edges of his character, emotionalised his men-tal life. Sometimes he caught himself listening to the sound of his own voice. He thought that in her eyes he would ascend to an angelical stature; and, as he attached the fervent nature of his companion more and more closely to him, he heard the strange impersonal voice which he recognised as his own, insisting on the soul's incurable loneliness. We cannot give ourselves, it said: we are our own. The end of these discourses was that one night during which she had shown every sign of unusual excitement, Mrs. Sinico caught up his hand passionately and pressed it to her cheek.

Mr. Duffy was very much surprised. Her interpretation of his words disillusioned him. He did not visit her for a week; then he wrote to her asking her to meet him. As he did not wish their last interview to be troubled by the influence of their ruined confessional they met in a little cakeshop near the Parkgate. It was cold autumn weather but in spite of the cold they wandered up and down the roads of the Park for nearly three hours. They agreed to break off their intercourse: every bond, he said, is a bond to sorrow. When they came out of the Park they walked in silence towards the tram; but here she began to tremble so violently that, fearing another collapse on her part, he bade her good-bye quickly and left her. A few days later he received a parcel containing his books and music.

Four years passed. Mr. Duffy returned to his even way of life. His room still bore witness of the orderliness of his mind. Some new pieces of music encumbered the music-stand in the lower room and on his shelves stood two volumes by Nietzsche: *Thus Spake Zarathustra* and *The Gay Science*. He wrote seldom in the sheaf of papers which lay in his desk. One of his sentences, written two months after his last interview with Mrs. Sinico, read: Love between man and man is impossible because there must not be sexual intercourse and friendship between man and woman is impossible because there must be sexual intercourse. He kept away from concerts lest he should meet her. His father died; the junior partner of the bank retired. And still every morning he went into the city by tram and every evening walked home from the city after having dined moder-ately in George's Street and read the evening paper for dessert.

One evening as he was about to put a morsel of corned beef and cab-bage into his mouth his hand stopped. His eyes fixed themselves on a para-graph in the evening paper which he had propped against the water-carafe. He replaced the morsel of food on his plate and read the paragraph attentively. Then he drank a glass of water, pushed his plate to one side, doubled the paper down before him between his elbows and read the paragraph over and over again. The cabbage began to deposit a cold white grease on his plate. The girl came over to him to ask was his dinner not properly cooked. He said it was very good and ate a few mouthfuls of it with difficulty. Then he paid his bill and went out.

He walked along quickly through the November twilight, his stout hazel stick striking the ground regularly, the fringe of the buff *Mail* peeping out of a side-pocket of his tight reefer over-coat. On the lonely road which leads from the Parkgate to Chapelizod he slackened his pace. His stick struck the ground less emphatically and his breath, issuing irregularly, almost with a sighing sound, condensed in the wintry air. When he reached his house he went up at once to his bedroom and, taking the paper from his pocket, read the paragraph again by the failing light of the window. He read it not aloud, but moving his lips as a priest does when he reads the prayers *Secreto*. This was the paragraph:

DEATH OF A LADY AT SYDNEY PARADE

A Painful Case

To-day at the City of Dublin Hospital the Deputy Coroner (in the absence of Mr. Leverett) held an inquest on the body of Mrs. Emily Sinico, aged forty-three years, who was killed at Sydney Parade Station yesterday evening. The evidence showed that the deceased lady, while attempting to cross the line, was knocked down by the engine of the ten o'clock slow train from Kingstown, thereby sustaining injuries of the head and right side which led to her death.

James Lennon, driver of the engine, stated that he had been in the employment of the railway company for fifteen years. On hearing the guard's whistle he set the train in motion and a second or two afterwards brought it to rest in response to loud cries. The train was going slowly.

P. Dunne, railway porter, stated that as the train was about to start he observed a woman attempting to cross the lines. He ran towards her and shouted, but, before he could reach her, she was caught by the buffer of the engine and fell to the ground.

A juror. "You saw the lady fall?"

Witness. "Yes."

Police Sergeant Croly deposed that when he arrived he found the deceased lying on the platform apparently dead. He had the body taken to the waiting-room pending the arrival of the ambulance.

Constable 57E corroborated.

Dr. Halpin, assistant house surgeon of the City of Dublin Hospital, stated that the deceased had two lower ribs fractured and had sustained severe contusions of the right shoulder. The right side of the head had been injured in the fall. The injuries were not sufficient to have caused death in a normal person. Death, in his opinion, had been probably due to shock and sudden failure of the heart's action.

Mr. H. B. Patterson Finlay, on behalf of the railway company, expressed his deep regret at the accident. The company had always taken every precaution to prevent people crossing the lines except by the bridges, both by placing notices in every station and by the use of patent spring gates at level crossings. The deceased had been in the habit of crossing the lines late at night from platform to platform and, in view of certain other circumstances of the case, he did not think the railway officials were to blame.

Captain Sinico, of Leoville, Sydney Parade, husband of the deceased, also gave evidence. He stated that the deceased was his wife. He was not in Dublin at the time of the accident as he had arrived only that morning from Rotterdam. They had been married for twenty-two years and had lived happily until about two years ago when his wife began to be rather intemperate in her habits.

Miss Mary Sinico said that of late her mother had been in the habit of going out at night to buy spirits. She, witness, had often tried to reason with her mother and had induced her to join a League. She was not at home until an hour after the accident.

The jury returned a verdict in accordance with the medical evidence and exonerated Lennon from all blame.

The Deputy Coroner said it was a most painful case, and expressed great sympathy with Captain Sinico and his daughter. He urged on the railway company to take strong measures to prevent the possibility of similar accidents in the future. No blame attached to anyone.

Mr. Duffy raised his eyes from the paper and gazed out of his window on the cheerless evening landscape. The river lay quiet beside the empty distillery and from time to time a light appeared in some house on the Lucan road. What an end! The whole narrative of her death revolted him and it revolted him to think that he had ever spoken to her of what he held sacred. The threadbare phrases, the inane expressions of sympathy, the cautious words of a reporter won over to conceal the details of a commonplace vulgar death attacked his stomach. Not merely had she degraded herself; she had degraded him. He saw the squalid tract of her vice, miserable and malodorous. His soul's companion! He thought of the hobbling wretches whom he had seen carrying cans and bottles to be filled by the barman. Just God, what an end! Evidently she had been unfit to live, without any strength of purpose, an easy prey to habits, one of the wrecks on which civilisation has been reared. But that she could have sunk so low! Was it possible he had deceived himself so utterly about her? He remembered her outburst of that night and interpreted it in a harsher sense than he had ever done. He had no difficulty now in approving of the course he had taken.

As the light failed and his memory began to wander he thought her hand touched his. The shock which had first attacked his stomach was now attacking his nerves. He put on his over-coat and hat quickly and went out. The cold air met him on the threshold; it crept into the sleeves of his coat. When he came to the public-house at Chapelizod Bridge he went in and ordered a hot punch.

The proprietor served him obsequiously but did not venture to talk. There were five or six workingmen in the shop discussing the value of a gentleman's estate in County Kildare. They drank at intervals from their huge pint tumblers and smoked, spitting often on the floor and sometimes dragging the sawdust over their spits with their heavy boots. Mr. Duffy sat on his stool and gazed at them, without seeing or hearing them. After a while they went out and he called for another punch. He sat a long time over it. The shop was very quiet. The proprietor sprawled on the counter reading the *Herald* and yawning. Now and again a tram was heard swishing along the lonely road outside.

As he sat there, living over his life with her and evoking alternately the two images in which he now conceived her, he realised that she was dead, that she had ceased to exist, that she had become a memory. He began to feel ill at ease. He asked himself what else could he have done. He could not have carried on a comedy of deception with her; he could not have lived with her openly. He had done what seemed to him best. How was he to blame? Now that she was gone he understood how lonely her life must have been, sitting night after night alone in that room. His life would be lonely too until he, too, died, ceased to exist, became a memory —if anyone remembered him.

It was after nine o'clock when he left the shop. The night was cold and gloomy. He entered the Park by the first gate and walked along under the gaunt trees. He walked through the bleak alleys where they had walked four years before. She seemed to be near him in the darkness. At moments he seemed to feel her voice touch his ear, her hand touch his. He stood still to listen. Why had he withheld life from her? Why had he sentenced her to death? He felt his moral nature falling to pieces.

When he gained the crest of the Magazine Hill he halted and looked along the river towards Dublin, the lights of which burned redly and hospitably in the cold night. He looked down the slope and, at the base, in the shadow of the wall of the Park, he saw some human figures lying. Those venal and furtive loves filled him with despair. He gnawed the rectitude of his life; he felt that he had been outcast from life's feast. One human being had seemed to love him and he had denied her life and happiness: he had sentenced her to ignominy, a death of shame. He knew that the prostrate creatures down by the wall were watching him and wished him gone. No one wanted him; he was outcast from life's feast. He turned his eyes to the grey gleaming river, winding along towards Dublin. Beyond the river he saw a goods train winding out of Kingsbridge Station, like a worm with a fiery head winding through the darkness, obstinately and laboriously. It passed slowly out of sight; but still he heard in his ears the laborious drone of the engine reiterating the syllables of her name.

He turned back the way he had come, the rhythm of the engine pounding in his ears. He began to doubt the reality of what memory told him. He halted under a tree and allowed the rhythm to die away. He could not feel her near him in the darkness nor her voice touch his ear. He waited for some minutes listening. He could hear nothing: the night was perfectly silent. He listened again: perfectly silent. He felt that he was alone.

QUESTIONS

1. In the first four paragraphs, Mr. Duffy is presented by means of a detailed, objective description of his mode of living, his surroundings, his tastes, and his habits. How would you summarize, in abstract terms, the character that is thus revealed?

2. What do you think of Mr. Duffy's convictions, such as that "Every bond is a bond to sorrow," or that "We cannot give ourselves—we are our own"? What connection do you see between such convictions and "the evenness of his life," "the orderliness of his mind"?

3. At what point does the action of the story reach a crisis?

4. What does Joyce gain for his story by citing the newspaper report in its entirety, without comment? What seem to you to be the flavor and tone of the phrase "a painful case," which Joyce uses three times? Is it true, as the concluding sentence of the report states, that "no blame attached to anyone"?

5. Is Mr. Duffy any different at the end of the story than he was at the beginning? Has any element been added to his character, or has any unsuspected element been discovered? How would you summarize what happens to him over the course of the events described in the story?

D. H. LAWRENCE

The years between the end of World War I and the beginning of World War II were, for the English novel, a time of striking experiment and of very great achievement. There were many novelists, of course, who continued to make use of techniques and forms that had been developed some time before, but it seemed during those years that in the works of fiction being written by Virginia Woolf, by Aldous Huxley, by James Joyce, by E. M. Forster, and by D. H. Lawrence, new and fruitful de-

mands were being made of the novel, new conceptions were being developed of the seriousness and completeness with which the novel could
undertake its task of representing life, new forms were constantly being
invented for it. A characteristic feature of the literary history of the time
is the very great difficulty which two of the writers mentioned above experienced with the censorship and prohibition of their books, both in England and America: both Joyce and Lawrence, in their belief that fiction, if
it was to give a serious and valid account of human life, must be allowed
to give a *complete* account of it, included in some of their books elements
which the government censorship deemed unprintable. Times change and
serious writers sometimes win their battle for the right to address adult
readers in an adult way—the ban on Joyce's *Ulysses* was lifted in this
country in 1933, and although the ban on Lawrence's *Lady Chatterley's
Lover* is still in force both here and in England, his other books circulate
freely in both countries. As Lawrence pointed out to Rhys Davies in 1928,
"All you young writers have me to thank for what freedom you enjoy, for
being able to say much that you couldn't even hint at before I appeared.
It was I who set about smashing down the barriers." ["D. H. Lawrence in
Bandol," *Horizon*, October, 1940.]

Now, approximately thirty years after his death, Lawrence's reputation
seems to be both higher than it has ever been and more accurately centered on what his work really is, what it really says. While he was alive
and in the years immediately following his death, many readers and many
critics misjudged his work because they seized on certain isolated aspects
of a given novel or story and failed to see the work, and its meaning, as
a whole. Lawrence was a prophetic writer, one who wrote in the grip of
a vision of truth which he believed would regenerate the failing sources
of modern life. He believed that the individual self should be completely
realized, that it should be allowed to come to consciousness not only in
the intellect but also in the blood, which had for too long been unheeded
and repressed in the people of the England he knew. He did not, however,
believe merely in a blind mindlessness, as he is sometimes misunderstood
to have done, but in the fullest, most delicately poised balance of all the
forces and faculties of the individual being. Above all, he believed in
the love between man and woman as the fulfillment and culmination of
the identity of each: not, be it noted, in terms of a merging of one in the
other, but as a balance of distinct polarities—the "star balance" of *Women
in Love*. The achievement of this balance without the sacrifice of one or
the other of the identities necessarily involved a good deal of preliminary
conflict, conflict which rages up and down the pages of his novels and
which he knew, and recognized humorously, in his own life. (Writing
from Bavaria in 1912, about him and his wife, "You needn't think we
spend all our time billing and cooing, and nibbling grapes and white
sugar. Oh no—the great war is waged in this little flat on the Isarthal, just
as much as anywhere else." [*The Letters of D. H. Lawrence*, ed. Aldous
Huxley, p. 44.])

The great war is waged in the story "Wintry Peacock," too. There is
certainly room for differing individual judgments as to how it will come

out, as to what the marriage of the Goytes will come to in the future, but it could perhaps be agreed that Lawrence has chosen to focus on the couple at a moment of armed truce—or maybe it's not a truce at all, but a silent pitched battle—between the two principals. He focusses on this relationship through the eyes of his narrator, and with the figure of the peacock in the foreground, as it were, of his picture. The peacock is certainly one of the main forces in the situation—the wife has set it up as her husband's rival, the equivalent and opposite of the girl in Belgium. Moreover, it is rendered with the most beautiful completeness as a real bird, with the extra dimension that is always present in Lawrence's rendering of birds, beasts, and flowers. At first there is a temptation to look for a symbolic meaning in the peacock—indeed in all the peacocks, particularly in the first paragraph where they seem to represent something out of balance, something removed from its element—but it is more important, if we are to see the story as a powerful and grotesque grouping of tensions to be resolved one way or another, to realize that this wintry peacock is present as a force in its own right.

WINTRY PEACOCK

There was thin, crisp snow on the ground, the sky was blue, the wind very cold, the air clear. Farmers were just turning out the cows for an hour or so in the midday, and the smell of cowsheds was unendurable as I entered Tible. I noticed the ash-twigs up in the sky were pale and luminous, passing into the blue. And then I saw the peacocks. There they were in the road before me, three of them, and tailless, brown, speckled birds, with dark-blue necks and ragged crests. They stepped archly over the filigree snow, and their bodies moved with slow motion, like small, light, flat-bottomed boats. I admired them, they were curious. Then a gust of wind caught them, heeled them over as if they were three frail boats, opening their feathers like ragged sails. They hopped and skipped with discomfort, to get out of the draught of the wind. And then, in the lee of the walls, they resumed their arch, wintry motion, light and unballasted now their tails were gone, indifferent. They were indifferent to my presence. I might have touched them. They turned off to the shelter of an open shed.

As I passed the end of the upper house, I saw a young woman just coming out of the back door. I had spoken to her in the summer. She recognized me at once, and waved to me. She was carrying a pail, wearing a white apron that was longer than her preposterously short skirt, and

From *England, My England* by D. H. Lawrence. Copyright 1922 by Thomas Seltzer, Inc., 1959 by Frieda Lawrence. Reprinted by permission of The Viking Press, Inc., New York.

she had on the cotton bonnet. I took off my hat to her and was going on. But she put down her pail and darted with a swift, furtive movement after me.

"Do you mind waiting a minute?" she said. "I'll be out in a minute."

She gave me a slight, odd smile, and ran back. Her face was long and sallow and her nose rather red. But her gloomy black eyes softened caressively to me for a moment, with that momentary humility which makes a man lord of the earth.

I stood in the road, looking at the fluffy, dark-red young cattle that mooed and seemed to bark at me. They seemed happy, frisky cattle, a little impudent, and either determined to go back into the warm shed, or determined not to go back. I could not decide which.

Presently the woman came forward again, her head rather ducked. But she looked up at me and smiled, with that odd, immediate intimacy, something witchlike and impossible.

"Sorry to keep you waiting," she said. "Shall we stand in this cart-shed —it will be more out of the wind."

So we stood among the shafts of the open cart-shed that faced the road. Then she looked down at the ground, a little sideways, and I noticed a small black frown on her brows. She seemed to brood for a moment. Then she looked straight into my eyes, so that I blinked and wanted to turn my face aside. She was searching me for something and her look was too near. The frown was still on her keen, sallow brow.

"Can you speak French?" she asked me abruptly.

"More or less," I replied.

"I was supposed to learn it at school," she said. "But I don't know a word." She ducked her head and laughed, with a slightly ugly grimace and a rolling of her black eyes.

"No good keeping your mind full of scraps," I answered.

But she had turned aside her sallow, long face, and did not hear what I said. Suddenly again she looked at me. She was searching. And at the same time she smiled at me, and her eyes looked softly, darkly, with infinite trustful humility into mine. I was being cajoled.

"Would you mind reading a letter for me, in French," she said, her face immediately black and bitter-looking. She glanced at me, frowning.

"Not at all," I said.

"It's a letter to my husband," she said, still scrutinizing.

I looked at her, and didn't quite realize. She looked too far into me, my wits were gone. She glanced round. Then she looked at me shrewdly. She drew a letter from her pocket, and handed it to me. It was addressed from France to Lance-Corporal Goyte, at Tible. I took out the letter and began to read it, as mere words. "Mon cher Alfred"—it might have been a bit of a torn newspaper. So I followed the script: the trite phrases of a letter from a French-speaking girl to an English soldier. "I think of you always, always. Do you think sometimes of me?" And then I vaguely realized that I was reading a man's private correspondence. And yet, how could one consider these trivial, facile French phrases private! Nothing more trite and **vulgar** in the world, than such a love-letter—no newspaper more obvious.

Therefore I read with a callous heart the effusions of the Belgian damsel. But then I gathered my attention. For the letter went on, "Notre cher petit bébé—our dear little baby was born a week ago. Almost I died, knowing you were far away, and perhaps forgetting the fruit of our perfect love. But the child comforted me. He has the smiling eyes and virile air of his English father. I pray to the Mother of Jesus to send me the dear father of my child, that I may see him with my child in his arms, and that we may be united in holy family love. Ah, my Alfred, can I tell you how I miss you, how I weep for you. My thoughts are with you always, I think of nothing but you, I live for nothing but you and our dear baby. If you do not come back to me soon, I shall die, and our child will die. But no, you cannot come back to me. But I can come to you, come to England with our child. If you do not wish to present me to your good mother and father, you can meet me in some town, some city, for I shall be so frightened to be alone in England with my child, and no one to take care of us. Yet I must come to you, I must bring my child, my little Alfred to his father, the big, beautiful Alfred that I love so much. Oh, write and tell me where I shall come. I have some money, I am not a penniless creature. I have money for myself and my dear baby—"

I read to the end. It was signed: "Your very happy and still more unhappy Elise." I suppose I must have been smiling.

"I can see it makes you laugh," said Mrs. Goyte, sardonically. I looked up at her.

"It's a love-letter, I know that," she said. "There's too many 'Alfreds' in it."

"One too many," I said.

"Oh, yes— And what does she say—Eliza? We know her name's Eliza, that's another thing." She grimaced a little, looking up at me with a mocking laugh.

"Where did you get this letter?" I said.

"Postman gave it me last week."

"And is your husband at home?"

"I expect him home to-night. He's been wounded, you know, and we've been applying for him home. He was home about six weeks ago—he's been in Scotland since then. Oh, he was wounded in the leg. Yes, he's all right, a great strapping fellow. But he's lame, he limps a bit. He expects he'll get his discharge—but I don't think he will. We married? We've been married six years—and he joined up the first day of the war. Oh, he thought he'd like the life. He'd been through the South African War. No, he was sick of it, fed up. I'm living with his father and mother—I've no home of my own now. My people had a big farm—over a thousand acres —in Oxfordshire. Not like here—no. Oh, they're very good to me, his father and mother. Oh, yes, they couldn't be better. They think more of me than of their own daughters. But it's not like being in a place of your own, is it? You can't *really* do as you like. No, there's only me and his father and mother at home. Before the war? Oh, he was anything. He's had a good education—but he liked the farming better. Then he was a chauffeur. That's how he knew French. He was driving a gentleman in France for a long time—"

At this point the peacocks came round the corner on a puff of wind.

"Hello, Joey!" she called, and one of the birds came forward, on delicate legs. Its grey speckled back was very elegant, it rolled its full, dark blue neck as it moved to her. She crouched down. "Joey, dear," she said, in an odd, saturnine caressive voice, "you're bound to find me, aren't you?" She put her face forward, and the bird rolled his neck, almost touching her face with his beak, as if kissing her.

"He loves you," I said.

She twisted her face up at me with a laugh.

"Yes," she said, "he loves me, Joey does,"—then, to the bird—"and I love Joey, don't I. I *do* love Joey." And she smoothed his feathers for a moment. Then she rose, saying: "He's an affectionate bird."

I smiled at the roll of her "bir-rrd."

"Oh, yes, he is," she protested. "He came with me from my home seven years ago. Those others are his descendants—but they're not like Joey—*are they, dee-urr?*" Her voice rose at the end with a witch-like cry.

Then she forgot the birds in the cart-shed and turned to business again.

"Won't you read that letter?" she said. "Read it, so that I know what it says."

"It's rather behind his back," I said.

"Oh, never mind him," she cried. "He's been behind my back long enough—all these four years. If he never did no worse things behind my back than I do behind his, he wouldn't have cause to grumble. You read me what it says."

Now I felt a distinct reluctance to do as she bid, and yet I began—"'My dear Alfred'."

"I guessed that much," she said. "Eliza's dear Alfred." She laughed. "How do you say it in French? *Eliza?*"

I told her, and she repeated the name with great contempt—*Elise*.

"Go on," she said. "You're not reading."

So I began—"'I have been thinking of you sometimes—have you been thinking of me?—'"

"Of several others as well, beside her, I'll wager," said Mrs. Goyte.

"Probably not," said I, and continued. "'A dear little baby was born here a week ago. Ah, can I tell you my feelings when I take my darling little brother into my arms—'"

"I'll bet it's *his*," cried Mrs. Goyte.

"No," I said. "It's her mother's."

"Don't you believe it," she cried. "It's a blind. You mark, it's her own right enough—and his."

"No," I said, "it's her mother's. 'He has sweet smiling eyes, but not like your beautiful English eyes—'"

She suddenly struck her hand on her skirt with a wild motion, and bent down, doubled with laughter. Then she rose and covered her face with her hand.

"I'm forced to laugh at the beautiful English eyes," she said.

"Aren't his eyes beautiful?" I asked.

"Oh, yes—*very!* Go on!—*Joey, dear, dee-urr, Joey!*"—this to the peacock.

—"Er—'We miss you very much. We all miss you. We wish you were here to see the darling baby. Ah, Alfred, how happy we were when you stayed with us. We all loved you so much. My mother will call the baby Alfred so that we shall never forget you—' "

"Of course it's his right enough," cried Mrs. Goyte.

"No," I said. "It's the mother's. Er—'My mother is very well. My father came home yesterday—on leave. He is delighted with his son, my little brother, and wishes to have him named after you, because you were so good to us all in that terrible time, which I shall never forget. I must weep now when I think of it. Well, you are far away in England, and perhaps I shall never see you again. How did you find your dear mother and father? I am so happy that your wound is better, and that you can nearly walk—' "

"How did he find his dear *wife?*" cried Mrs. Goyte. "He never told her he had one. Think of taking the poor girl in like that!"

" 'We are so pleased when you write to us. Yet now you are in England you will forget the family you served so well—' "

"A bit too well—eh, *Joey?*" cried the wife.

" 'If it had not been for you we should not be alive now, to grieve and to rejoice in this life, that is so hard for us. But we have recovered some of our losses, and no longer feel the burden of poverty. The little Alfred is a great comfort to me. I hold him to my breast and think of the big, good Alfred, and I weep to think that those times of suffering were perhaps the times of a great happiness that is gone for ever'."

"Oh, but isn't it a shame, to take a poor girl in like that!" cried Mrs. Goyte. "Never to let on that he was married, and raise her hopes—I call it beastly, I do."

"You don't know," I said. "You know how anxious women are to fall in love, wife or no wife. How could he help it, if she was determined to fall in love with him?"

"He could have helped it if he'd wanted."

"Well," I said, "we aren't all heroes."

"Oh, but that's different! The big, good Alfred!—did ever you hear such tommy-rot in your life! Go on—what does she say at the end?"

"Er—'We shall be pleased to hear of your life in England. We all send many kind regards to your good parents. I wish you all happiness for your future days. Your very affectionate and ever-grateful, Elise'."

There was silence for a moment, during which Mrs. Goyte remained with her head dropped, sinister and abstracted. Suddenly she lifted her face, and her eyes flashed.

"Oh, but I call it beastly, I call it mean, to take a girl in like that."

"Nay," I said. "Probably he hasn't taken her in at all. Do you think those French girls are such poor innocent things? I guess she's a great deal more downy than he."

"Oh, he's one of the biggest fools that ever walked," she cried.

"There you are!" said I.

"But it's his child right enough," she said.

"I don't think so," said I.

"I'm sure of it."

"Oh, well," I said, "if you prefer to think that way."

"What other reason has she for writing like that—"

I went out into the road and looked at the cattle.

"Who is this driving the cows?" I said. She too came out.

"It's the boy from the next farm," she said.

"Oh, well," said I, "those Belgian girls! You never know where their letters will end. And, after all, it's his affair—you needn't bother."

"Oh—!" she cried, with rough scorn—"it's not *me* that bothers. But it's the nasty meanness of it—me writing him such loving letters"—she put her hand before her face and laughed malevolently—"and sending him parcels all the time. You bet he fed that gurrl on my parcels—I know he did. It's just like him. I'll bet they laughed together over my letters. I'll bet anything they did—"

"Nay," said I. "He'd burn your letters for fear they'd give him away."

There was a black look on her yellow face. Suddenly a voice was heard calling. She poked her head out of the shed, and answered coolly:

"All right!" Then turning to me: "That's his mother looking after me."

She laughed into my face, witch-like, and we turned down the road.

When I awoke, the morning after this episode, I found the house darkened with deep, soft snow, which had blown against the large west windows, covering them with a screen. I went outside, and saw the valley all white and ghastly below me, the trees beneath black and thin-looking like wire, the rock-faces dark between the glistening shroud, and the sky above sombre, heavy, yellowish-dark, much too heavy for this world below of hollow bluey whiteness figured with black. I felt I was in a valley of the dead. And I sensed I was a prisoner, for the snow was everywhere deep, and drifted in places. So all the morning I remained indoors, looking up the drive at the shrubs so heavily plumed with snow, at the gate-posts raised high with a foot or more of extra whiteness. Or I looked down into the white-and-black valley that was utterly motionless and beyond life, a hollow sarcophagus.

Nothing stirred the whole day—no plume fell off the shrubs, the valley was as abstracted as a grove of death. I looked over at the tiny, half-buried farms away on the bare uplands beyond the valley hollow, and I thought of Tible in the snow, of the black witch-like little Mrs. Goyte. And the snow seemed to lay me bare to influences I wanted to escape.

In the faint glow of the half-clear light that came about four o'clock in the afternoon, I was roused to see a motion in the snow away below, near where the thorn-trees stood very black and dwarfed, like a little savage group, in the dismal white. I watched closely. Yes, there was a flapping and a struggle—a big bird, it must be, labouring in the snow. I wondered. Our biggest birds, in the valley, were the large hawks that often hung flickering opposite my windows, level with me, but high above some prey on the steep valley-side. This was much too big for a hawk—too big for any known bird. I searched in my mind for the largest English wild birds, geese, buzzards.

Still it laboured and strove, then was still, a dark spot, then struggled again. I went out of the house and down the steep slope, at risk of breaking my leg between the rocks. I knew the ground so well—and yet I got well shaken before I drew near the thorn-trees.

Yes, it was a bird. It was Joey. It was the grey-brown peacock with a blue neck. He was snow-wet and spent.

"Joey—Joey, de-urr!" I said, staggering unevenly towards him. He looked so pathetic, rowing and struggling in the snow, too spent to rise, his blue neck stretching out and lying sometimes on the snow, his eye closing and opening quickly, his crest all battered.

"Joey dee-urr!" I said caressingly to him. And at last he lay still, blinking, in the surged and furrowed snow, whilst I came near and touched him, stroked him, gathered him under my arm. He stretched his long, wetted neck away from me as I held him, none the less he was quiet in my arm, too tired, perhaps, to struggle. Still he held his poor, crested head away from me, and seemed sometimes to droop, to wilt, as if he might suddenly die.

He was not so heavy as I expected, yet it was a struggle to get up to the house with him again. We set him down, not too near the fire, and gently wiped him with cloths. He submitted, only now and then stretched his soft neck away from us, avoiding us helplessly. Then we set warm food by him. I *put* it to his beak, tried to make him eat. But he ignored it. He seemed to be ignorant of what we were doing, recoiled inside himself inexplicably. So we put him in a basket with cloths, and left him crouching oblivious. His food we put near him. The blinds were drawn, the house was warm, it was night. Sometimes he stirred, but mostly he huddled still, leaning his queer crested head on one side. He touched no food, and took no heed of sounds or movements. We talked of brandy or stimulants. But I realized we had best leave him alone.

In the night, however, we heard him thumping about. I got up anxiously with a candle. He had eaten some food, and scattered more, making a mess. And he was perched on the back of a heavy arm-chair. So I concluded he was recovered, or recovering.

The next day was clear, and the snow had frozen, so I decided to carry him back to Tible. He consented, after various flappings, to sit in a big fish-bag with his battered head peeping out with wild uneasiness. And so

I set off with him, slithering down into the valley, making good progress down in the pale shadow beside the rushing waters, then climbing painfully up the arrested white valley-side, plumed with clusters of young pine trees, into the paler white radiance of the snowy, upper regions, where the wind cut fine. Joey seemed to watch all the time with wide, anxious, unseeing eye, brilliant and inscrutable. As I drew near to Tible township he stirred violently in the bag, though I do not know if he had recognized the place. Then, as I came to the sheds, he looked sharply from side to side, and stretched his neck out long. I was a little afraid of him. He gave a loud, vehement yell, opening his sinister beak, and I stood still, looking at him as he struggled in the bag, shaken myself by his struggles, yet not thinking to release him.

Mrs. Goyte came darting past the end of the house, her head sticking forward in sharp scrutiny. She saw me, and came forward.

"Have you got Joey!" she cried sharply, as if I were a thief.

I opened the bag, and he flopped out, flapping as if he hated the touch of the snow now. She gathered him up, and put her lips to his beak. She was flushed and handsome, her eyes bright, her hair slack, thick, but more witch-like than ever. She did not speak.

She had been followed by a grey-haired woman with a round, rather sallow face and a slightly hostile bearing.

"Did you bring him with you, then?" she asked sharply. I answered that I had rescued him the previous evening.

From the background slowly approached a slender man with a grey moustache and large patches on his trousers.

"You've got 'im back 'gain, ah see," he said to his daughter-in-law. His wife explained how I had found Joey.

"Ah," went on the grey man. "It wor our Alfred scarred him off, back your life. He must'a flyed ower t'valley. Tha ma' thank thy stars as 'e wor fun, Maggie. 'E'd a bin froze. They a bit nesh, you know," he concluded to me.

"They are," I answered. "This isn't their country."

"No, it isna," replied Mr. Goyte. He spoke very slowly and deliberately, quietly, as if the soft pedal were always down in his voice. He looked at his daughter-in-law as she crouched, flushed and dark, before the peacock, which would lay its long blue neck for a moment along her lap. In spite of his grey moustache and thin grey hair, the elderly man had a face young and almost delicate, like a young man's. His blue eyes twinkled with some inscrutable source of pleasure, his skin was fine and tender, his nose delicately arched. His grey hair being slightly ruffled, he had a debonair look, as of a youth who is in love.

"We mun tell 'im it's come," he said slowly, and turning he called: "Alfred—Alfred! Wheer's ter gotten to?"

Then he turned again to the group.

"Get up then, Maggie, lass, get up wi' thee. Tha ma'es too much o' th' bod."

A young man approached, wearing rough khaki and knee-breeches. He was Danish-looking, broad at the loins.

"I's come back then," said the father to the son; "leastwise, he's bin browt back, flyed ower the Griff Low."

The son looked at me. He had a devil-may-care bearing, his cap on one side, his hands stuck in the front pockets of his breeches. But he said nothing.

"Shall you come in a minute, Master," said the elderly woman, to me.

"Ay, come in an' ha'e a cup o' tea or summat. You'll do wi' summat, carrin' that bod. Come on, Maggie wench, let's go in."

So we went indoors, into the rather stuffy, overcrowded living room, that was too cosy, and too warm. The son followed last, standing in the doorway. The father talked to me. Maggie put out the tea-cups. The mother went into the dairy again.

"Tha'lt rouse thysen up a bit again, now, Maggie," the father-in-law said —and then to me: " 'ers not bin very bright sin' Alfred come whoam, an' the bod flyed awee. 'E come whoam a Wednesday night, Alfred did. But ay, you knowed, didna yer. Ay, 'e comed 'a Wednesday—an' I reckon there wor a bit of a to-do between 'em, worn't there, Maggie?"

He twinkled maliciously to his daughter-in-law, who was flushed, brilliant and handsome.

"Oh, be quiet, Father. You're wound up, by the sound of you," she said to him, as if crossly. But she could never be cross with him.

" 'Ers got 'er colour back this mornin'," continued the father-in-law slowly. "It's bin heavy weather wi' 'er this last two days. Ay—'er's bin north-east sin 'er seed you a Wednesday."

"Father, do stop talking. You'd wear the leg off an iron pot. I can't think where you've found your tongue, all of a sudden," said Maggie, with caressive sharpness.

"Ah've found it wheer I lost it. Aren't goin' ter come in an' sit thee down, Alfred?"

But Alfred turned and disappeared.

" 'E's got th' monkey on 'is back ower this letter job," said the father secretly to me. "Mother, 'er knows nowt about it. Lot o' tom-foolery, isn't it? Ay! What's good o'makkin' a peck o' trouble over what's far enough off, an' ned niver come no nigher. No—not a smite o' use. That's what I tell 'er. 'Er should ta'e no notice on't. Ty, what can y' expect."

The mother came in again, and the talk became general. Maggie flashed her eyes at me from time to time, complacent and satisfied, moving among the men. I paid her little compliments, which she did not seem to hear. She attended to me with a kind of sinister, witch-like graciousness, her dark head ducked between her shoulders, at once humble and powerful. She was happy as a child attending to her father-in-law and to me. But there was something ominous between her eyebrows, as if a dark moth were settled there—and something ominous in her bent, hulking bearing.

She sat on a low stool by the fire, near her father-in-law. Her head was dropped, she seemed in a state of abstraction. From time to time she would suddenly recover, and look up at us, laughing and chatting. Then she would forget again. Yet in her hulked black forgetting she seemed very near to us.

The door having been opened, the peacock came slowly in, prancing calmly. He went near to her and crouched down, coiling his blue neck. She glanced at him, but almost as if she did not observe him. The bird sat silent, seeming to sleep, and the woman also sat hulked and silent, seemingly oblivious. Then once more there was a heavy step, and Alfred entered. He looked at his wife, and he looked at the peacock crouching by her. He stood large in the doorway, his hands stuck in front of him, in his breeches pockets. Nobody spoke. He turned on his heel and went out again.

I rose also to go. Maggie started as if coming to herself.

"Must you go?" she asked, rising and coming near to me, standing in front of me, twisting her head sideways and looking up at me. "Can't you stop a bit longer? We can all be cosy to-day, there's nothing to do outdoors." And she laughed, showing her teeth oddly. She had a long chin.

I said I must go. The peacock uncoiled and coiled again his long blue neck, as he lay on the hearth. Maggie still stood close in front of me, so that I was acutely aware of my waistcoat buttons.

"Oh, well," she said, "you'll come again, won't you? Do come again."

I promised.

"Come to tea one day—yes, do!"

I promised—one day.

The moment I went out of her presence I ceased utterly to exist for her —as utterly as I ceased to exist for Joey. With her curious abstractedness she forgot me again immediately. I knew it as I left her. Yet she seemed almost in physical contact with me while I was with her.

The sky was all pallid again, yellowish. When I went out there was no sun; the snow was blue and cold. I hurried away down the hill, musing on Maggie. The road made a loop down the sharp face of the slope. As I went crunching over the laborious snow I became aware of a figure striding down the steep scarp to intercept me. It was a man with his hands in front of him, half stuck in his breeches pockets, and his shoulders square—a real farmer of the hills; Alfred, of course. He waited for me by the stone fence.

"Excuse me," he said as I came up.

I came to a halt in front of him and looked into his sullen blue eyes. He had a certain odd haughtiness on his brows. But his blue eyes stared insolently at me.

"Do you know anything about a letter—in French—that my wife opened—a letter of mine—?"

"Yes," said I. "She asked me to read it to her."

He looked square at me. He did not know exactly how to feel.

"What was there in it?" he asked.

"Why?" I said. "Don't you know?"

"She makes out she's burnt it," he said.

"Without showing it you?" I asked.

He nodded slightly. He seemed to be meditating as to what line of action he should take. He wanted to know the contents of the letter: he must know: and therefore he must ask me, for evidently his wife had taunted him. At the same time, no doubt, he would like to wreak untold vengeance on my unfortunate person. So he eyed me, and I eyed him, and neither of us spoke. He did not want to repeat his request to me. And yet I only looked at him, and considered.

Suddenly he threw back his head and glanced down the valley. Then he changed his position—he was a horse-soldier. Then he looked at me more confidentially.

"She burnt the blasted thing before I saw it," he said.

"Well," I answered slowly, "she doesn't know herself what was in it."

He continued to watch me narrowly. I grinned to myself.

"I didn't like to read her out what there was in it," I continued.

He suddenly flushed so that the veins in his neck stood out, and he stirred again uncomfortably.

"The Belgian girl said her baby had been born a week ago, and that they were going to call it Alfred," I told him.

He met my eyes. I was grinning. He began to grin, too.

"Good luck to her," he said.

"Best of luck," said I.

"And what did you tell *her?*" he asked.

"That the baby belonged to the old mother—that it was brother to your girl, who was writing to you as a friend of the family.

He stood smiling, with the long, subtle malice of a farmer.

"And did she take it in?" he asked.

"As much as she took anything else."

He stood grinning fixedly. Then he broke into a short laugh.

"Good for *her!*" he exclaimed cryptically.

And then he laughed aloud once more, evidently feeling he had won a big move in his contest with his wife.

"What about the other woman?" I asked.

"Who?"

"Elise."

"Oh"—he shifted uneasily—"she was all right—"

"You'll be getting back to her," I said.

He looked at me. Then he made a grimace with his mouth.

"Not me," he said. "Back your life it's a plant."

"You don't think the *cher petit bébé* is a little Alfred?"

"It might be," he said.

"Only might?"

"Yes—an' there's lots of mites in a pound of cheese." He laughed boisterously but uneasily.

"What did she say, exactly?" he asked.

I began to repeat, as well as I could, the phrases of the letter:

"*Mon cher Alfred— Figure-toi comme je suis désolée—*"

He listened with some confusion. When I had finished all I could remember, he said:

"They know how to pitch you out a letter, those Belgian lasses."

"Practice," said I.

"They get plenty," he said.

There was a pause.

"Oh, well," he said. "I've never got that letter, anyhow."

The wind blew fine and keen, in the sunshine, across the snow. I blew my nose and prepared to depart.

"And *she* doesn't know anything?" he continued, jerking his head up the hill in the direction of Tible.

"She knows nothing but what I've said—that is, if she really burnt the letter."

"I believe she burnt it," he said, "for spite. She's a little devil, she is. But I shall have it out with her." His jaw was stubborn and sullen. Then suddenly he turned to me with a new note.

"Why?" he said. "Why didn't you wring that b— peacock's neck—that b— Joey?"

"Why?" I said. "What for?"

"I hate the brute," he said. "I had a shot at him—"

I laughed. He stood and mused.

"Poor little Elise," he murmured.

"Was she small—petite?" I asked. He jerked up his head.

"No," he said. "Rather tall."

"Taller than your wife, I suppose."

Again he looked into my eyes. And then once more he went into a loud burst of laughter that made the still, snow-deserted valley clap again.

"God, it's a knock-out!" he said, thoroughly amused. Then he stood at ease, one foot out, his hands in his breeches pockets, in front of him, his head thrown back, a handsome figure of a man.

"But I'll do that blasted Joey in—" he mused.

I ran down the hill, shouting with laughter.

QUESTIONS

1. What impression of Mrs. Goyte do we receive, especially in the long opening scene with the narrator, from Lawrence's notations of her tone of voice, the emotional tone of her remarks, her facial expression?

2. Do you find any points of resemblance between the qualities brought out in the temperament and physical appearance of Mrs. Goyte and the qualities Lawrence stresses in describing the peacock? If so, what are the points of similarity and what significance do they have for the story?

3. What color-words are used most consistently? How—and in your opinion, for what expressive purpose—does Lawrence make Mrs. Goyte,

the peacock, and the wintry valley fit into the same restricted color pattern?

4. What part does the peacock play in furthering the action of the story? What is its place in the plot?

5. What do you think is likely to happen to the Goytes after the point at which the story leaves them? In what way would things have turned out differently if (a) the narrator had told Mrs. Goyte the truth about the contents of the letter or (b) she had confronted her husband with it instead of destroying it?

RING LARDNER

(1885–1933)

Ring Lardner was born in Niles, Michigan, where he grew up and where he went to high school. By profession he was for most of his life a newspaper reporter and journalist. He began newspaper work in his very early twenties, as a reporter on the South Bend *Times*, covering ballgames, among other beats. Baseball was always to be one of his major interests, and baseball players were to be among the leading subjects of his stories and sketches. His knowledge of the baseball world had been gained at first hand as a reporter assigned to cover the teams both when they were training and when they were playing, and it is both professional and human. He had his first success as a writer—it amounted to popularity on a national scale—with his stories of a baseball player, Jack Keefe, which were first published in *The Saturday Evening Post* beginning in 1914 and then collected under the title *You Know Me, Al* in 1916. The stories took the form of the baseball player's letters to a friend, and one of the chief reasons for their charm and freshness was that they reproduced his baseball-player's language and letter-writing style with complete accuracy. Unlike many other attempts to get down on paper the slang and colloquialisms of a particular period and milieu (Stephen Crane's *Maggie*, for example), the language of Ring Lardner's ball-players or caddies or stenographers from the 1920's is still alive and expressive.

The Jack Keefe stories were very funny indeed, as all Lardner's stories were funny, at least in part. Moreover, what he wrote still seems funny, even with the passage of time. But Lardner was far from being a humorist pure and simple, and it may be that the bitter irony and the pathos of many of his stories have acted as a preservative for the humor (or perhaps it is the other way around). At any rate, what he gives us, underneath the light-hearted slang and the insouciance, is a deeply-felt picture of American middle-class life in the 1920's. It is the era of Coolidge and prohibition (the trusted bootlegger appears as a family friend), of Paul Whiteman and Ed Wynn, of Channel swimmers and a dreadfully complicated game called

Mahjong, of the Twentieth Century Limited and the Follies. Other times have other bywords for glamor and zest, but we still recognize ourselves and our problems, we still encounter many home truths in Lardner's stories. Golf was somewhat newer to America when Lardner wrote "A Caddy's Diary," and the patterns of life which emerged from country-club activities had an arresting novelty which they have since lost. Nevertheless, his caddy's-eye view of the country-club, banking-and-business set (and their wives) is still sharply applicable today. It may be that in the 1920's elderly couples retired to Florida with a feckless optimism which has been somewhat moderated since, but the picture of innocent, garrulous, uprooted old age which Lardner presents in "The Golden Honeymoon" has a power that is as overwhelming today as it ever was—and again, it is a story that has its funny side. Sometimes his simultaneous exposure of the fatuity and the pathos of little lives is almost more than we can bear to contemplate, but it was almost more than he could bear to contemplate, too, and there is nothing of the pert, irresponsible jester about him.

His stories appeared in a number of separate volumes, among which may be mentioned *How to Write Short Stories* (1924) with its brilliantly satiric title essay, *What of It* (1925), and *The Love Nest* (1929). In 1929 the stories, but not the sketches (including the marvellous modern-slang versions of "Cinderella" and "Red Riding Hood"), were gathered into one volume called *Round Up*, later published in The Modern Library under the title of *The Collected Short Stories of Ring Lardner*.

ANNIVERSARY

Mrs. Taylor shuffled a worn pack of cards and began her evening session at solitaire. She would play probably forty games before she went to bed, and she would win thirty of them. What harm if she cheated a little? Russian Bank was more fun, but it cannot be played alone, and her husband was bored by it. He had been unable to learn bridge in spite of the patient and more or less expert teaching of the Hammonds, who lived three blocks away.

The thirty-four-dollar synthetic radio had done nothing but croak since the day following its installation. The cheap piano's D and G above middle C were mute. The town's Carnegie Library acquired very few "hot" books and the few were nearly always out. Picture plays hurt Louis' eyes and he would not let her go out nights by herself, though he had no scruples against leaving her at home from eight to eleven Wednesdays, when he attended lodge and bowled.

So Mrs. Taylor shuffled her cards and tried to listen when Louis read aloud from the Milton Daily Star or the Milton Weekly Democrat, or recounted stories she had heard six times before and would hear six times again.

She had awakened this morning to the realization that it was the twelfth day of November, the ninth anniversary of her marriage. Louis had remembered that date for the first six years of their life together; for the last three years it had been to him just November the twelfth.

Nine years ago the Star and the Democrat had called her one of Milton's most charming and beautiful young women, and they had been right. They had referred to Louis as a model young man, sober, industrious and "solid"; a young man whom any girl should be proud and glad to have as a husband. They were right again.

Now Mrs. Taylor, at thirty-three, was good-looking, but in a cold, indifferent sort of way. She no longer bothered to embellish her natural attractiveness and she lacked the warmth and vivacity which had won the adoration of most of Milton's male youth, notably Walter Frayne, Jim Satterly and Louis Taylor himself.

Louis was still a model young man, sober, industrious and "solid." When you thought of the precarious existence of the women who had married his chief rivals, you couldn't help feeling that wisdom and good luck had been on Mrs. Taylor's side when she made her choice.

Walter had attended college for one semester, at the end of which he came home with a perfect record of studies, 4; Flunks, 4. He had run amuck in Milton and ultimately, turned down by the girl he really cared for, had married an orphan whose parents had left her $150,000—but not for long. After this tidy sum had been poured away Walter was almost continuously unemployed and people wondered how he and his wife lived. And why.

There was nothing of the gay dog about Jim Satterly. He had graduated from high school and gone into the Milton Gas Company's office as bookkeeper at eight dollars per week. He was now thirty-five years old and still with the gas company, but his salary had been steadily increased until it was twenty-two dollars. His wife gave weekly piano lessons to a class of four pupils at fifty cents a half-hour each. She had borne Jim three children, or kiddies. The Satterlys seemed to enjoy their kiddies and an occasional picture show, but no magazine editor had ever sent a staff man to get a success story out of Jim.

Louis Taylor was secretary to the town's only wealthy man, old Thomas Parvis, who owned a controlling interest in the Interurban Railway. Louis worked long hours and was paid four thousand a year, big money in Milton. It was enough to keep the childless Taylors in comfort; in comparative luxury, even. Couples with smaller incomes owned cars, took trips to near-by lake resorts and to Harper City, where a stock company presented worth-while plays. But Louis was saving for a rainy day and his wife had long ago given up praying for rain.

Mrs. Taylor was winning her fourth successive victory over solitaire by the simple expedient of pretending that a black queen was red.

"It says here," stated her husband, "that there are 27,650,267 automobiles in the world, according to a census just completed."

It was Mrs. Taylor's own fault that Louis had contracted the habit of reciting interesting tidbits from the paper. Back in May, 1924, he had asked her whether she would like to hear the news of the Loeb-Leopold case. She had already read it, but she said yes, thinking it would be more thrilling even in repetition, than one of Louis' own experiences, also in repetition. Since then, she had listened every evening—except Wednesday, when Louis went out, and Sundays, when there was no paper—to excerpts from the Star, consisting principally of what is known in newspaper offices as filler—incontrovertible statistics about men and things in all parts of the world, facts that seemed to smite her husband like a bolt from the blue.

"Think of it!" he said. "Nearly twenty-eight million automobiles!"

"Heavens!" said Mrs. Taylor.

"And speaking of automobiles: 'Storms have made roads so bad in parts of Chile that drivers have not dared to go into the rural districts.' That's the trouble with owning a car. If you don't stay right on the paved streets or paved roads, you're liable to get stuck and maybe walk home. Besides that, you've got to be a mechanic yourself or else, when there's something wrong, you have to take it to a garage and lay it up a week till they consent to look at it and find out what's the matter, and then they don't know themselves nine times out of ten. But they charge you just the same and they charge you plenty. Did I tell you about Walter Trumbull's trip to Harper City?"

"Yes," said Mrs. Taylor.

"I don't believe I did. It was only last Friday night; no, Thursday night, the night after the Spartans beat us by one pin, when I had a chance to get a 202 and hit the head pin just a little too full and they split on me. That was the night Berger showed up so drunk he couldn't bowl and we had to use Tommy and he shot 123.

"So it was the night after that when Walter and Marjorie started over to the City to see the 'Seventh Heaven,' and about five miles the other side of Two Oaks the engine died and Walter couldn't get it going again. His flash-light wouldn't work and Marjorie wouldn't let him strike matches with the hood up to see what the trouble was. As it turned out, it wouldn't have done him any good anyway.

"Finally he left poor Marjorie in the car and walked way back to Two Oaks, but the garage was closed up for the night and the whole town was asleep, so he went back to the car and by that time of course it was too late to see the show. He hailed three or four cars coming from the other way, trying to get a ride home, but it wasn't till after ten o'clock that he could get a car to stop and pick them up. The next morning he sent Charlie Thomas out to fix up the car so it would run or else tow it in, and Charlie found out there was nothing the matter with it except it was out of gas. When Walter told me about it, I said that was what he deserved for not patronizing the Interurban."

"We don't patronize it ourselves."

"I hear enough about it in the daytime without riding on it at night."

Mrs. Taylor shuffled the cards and Louis resumed perusal of the Star.

"The old U. S. is a pretty good country after all," he said presently. "Listen to this: 'The Netherlands' unemployed now include 26,000 skilled and 24,000 unskilled workers.' And listen: 'A large proportion of Belgium's population still wear wooden shoes.' You wouldn't think that was possible in this day and age!"

"I imagine," said Mrs. Taylor, "that there are some places in the United States where people don't wear any shoes at all."

"Oh, sure, but not a large proportion; probably a few of those backwoods Tennessee mountaineers. And of course the colored people in the small towns in Georgia and South Carolina. You see lots of them, passing through on the train, that never had a shoe on in their life. I remember a place named Jesup, Georgia, a kind of junction. There was—— No, that wasn't Jesup; it was some other place, some place the boss and I went through on the way to Daytona that time. I guess I told you about it."

"Yes," said Mrs. Taylor.

"You wouldn't believe the way some of those people live. Not all colored people, either; white people, too. Poor white trash, they call them. Or rather, 'po' white trash.' Families of four and five in one room. Mr. Parvis said it was a crime and kept wishing he could do something for them."

"Why didn't he?"

"Well, he's hardly got money enough to house and clothe the whole South and it wouldn't do any good to just pick out some one town and try and better conditions there."

"Why not?"

"It would be a drop in the bucket, and besides, other towns would hear about it and pester the life out of him. I reminded him he was taking the trip to get away from care and worry for a while and he ought not to fret himself about other people's business. Then, too, if he was going to practise some of his philanthrophy down there, I'd probably be put in charge of it. We might have even had to live there a year or two. I guess you wouldn't like that, would you?"

"It wouldn't make any difference to me," said Mrs. Taylor.

"What! Live in one of those God-forsaken holes, without any friends or anybody you'd want to make friends with! Nothing to do all day and all night but eat and sleep and——"

"Play solitaire," suggested Mrs. Taylor.

"You may think you wouldn't mind it, but that's because you've never seen it. Those Georgia villages are an interesting study, but as for making your home in one of them, you'd die of loneliness. Of course there's some spots in Florida that are pretty close to heaven. Take Daytona, for instance. But I've told you what it's like."

"Yes."

"They've got a beach that's so hard and smooth that they have automobile races on it. It's beautiful. And it's right close to Ormond, where Rockefeller spends his winters. Mr. Parvis and I saw him playing golf on the Ormond course. I can't see anything in golf myself, but maybe I would if I had a chance to get interested in it. When I'm as old as he is, I'll try it out, providing I've got as much time and one-millionth as much money."

"There's no reason why you shouldn't have fully as much money."

"I know what you mean by that. You're digging at my thriftiness, though I suppose you call it stinginess. You'll look at it differently when we're old."

"I hope I won't be here to look at it at all."

"No, you don't. But what was I saying? Oh, yes. Daytona is where I'd like to live in winter, if I had the means. I must have told you about running into Harry Riker down there."

"You did."

"It certainly was a funny thing, running into him! We hadn't seen each other for twenty-two years and he recognized me the minute he set eyes on me. I wouldn't have known him from Adam's off ox.

"It sure did take me back, running into Harry. He recalled one time, just before I left Shelbyville, when his father and mother were away on a visit somewhere. Harry's aunt, Mr. Riker's sister, was supposed to be taking care of Harry while his father and mother was away, but she was kind of old and she used to go to sleep right after supper.

"Well, there were a couple of girls, sisters, named Lindsay. They lived out in the country, but came in town to school. Harry and I thought we were stuck on them, so one night after supper, when Harry's aunt had gone to sleep, we hitched up Mr. Riker's horse and buggy and drove seven miles out in the country to call on the Lindsay girls. When we got out there it was raining, so we unhitched the horse and put him in the barn and——"

"He got loose, didn't he? And ran all the way home?"

"Yes, but that comes later. We put him in Lindsay's barn and we thought we had him tied all right, and Harry and I went in the house and sat around with the girls. Mrs. Lindsay stayed right in the room with us and did most of the talking——"

"You're sure of that?"

"I certainly am! She was one of these women that talk all the time. She never stopped. So about half past nine she said the girls would have to go to bed, and that was telling us to get out. Well, to make a long story short, the horse wasn't in the barn and Harry and I walked home seven miles in the pouring rain. We found the horse in his own stall and Harry had to ride him out to Lindsay's next day and get the buggy. That was the last time we ever called on the Lindsay girls."

"Kind of hard on them," said Mrs. Taylor.

"Oh, we were all just kids and there wasn't anything serious between us. Harry's in the insurance business now in Indianapolis, doing fine, he told me."

Louis was almost, but not quite, through with his paper.

"Here's a funny thing," he said. "Although Edinburgh, Scotland, had only 237 ice-cream parlors last season, the number was fifty more than were in the city a year ago."

"I should think that was enough ice-cream parlors."

"Not for the size of the town. Let's see. How big is Edinburgh? I'll have to look it up."

He was on his way to the bookcase when the door-bell rang. He went to the door and admitted Florence Hammond.

"Hello, Louis. Hello, Bess. This isn't a social call. We're out here with a flat tire and Perce wants to borrow your flash."

"There's automobiles for you!" said Louis. "More trouble than they're worth."

"I tried to persuade Perce to take it to the garage and have them fix it, but he's afraid driving it even that far would ruin the rim or the shoe or whatever you call it."

"I'll get the flash and see if I can help him," said Louis.

"And you sit down, Florence, and keep me company," said Mrs. Taylor. "I haven't been out of the house for three days and I'm dying to hear what's going on in Milton."

"You take the Star, don't you?"

"I'm afraid we do, but it hasn't been very thrilling lately."

"You can't blame the paper for that," said Mrs. Hammond. "Nothing exciting has happened; that is, in Milton."

"Has anything happened anywhere?"

"Yes. In Clyde."

"Clyde. That's where your sister lives, isn't it?"

"If you call it living. I'd rather be dead! Honestly, Bess, you and I ought to thank the Lord that we married men who are at least sane and normal. Louis and Perce may not be as good-looking or 'brilliant' as Ed, but anyway we always know where they are and what to expect of them."

"That's true," said Mrs. Taylor.

"I wrote Grace a letter today and told her she was simply crazy not to leave him, especially after this last mess. But she won't give him up. I believe he's got her hypnotized. And she still loves him. She admits his faults and excuses him and expects everybody to do the same. If she didn't, she'd keep her troubles to herself and not write me all the details. I realize everybody has their weakness, but it seems to me there are some things I couldn't forgive. And one of them is a punch in the eye."

"You don't mean——"

"Yes, I do. And Grace took it and accepted his apology when he made one. When I think of it, I simply boil!"

"What was the occasion?"

"No special occasion. Just Saturday night. Everybody in Clyde goes to the Yacht Club Saturday nights. There's no river or lake and no yachts, but they have a sunset gun, so I suppose they're entitled to call it a yacht club. Grace hated it at first and let Ed go alone, but that only made him drink more and get home later Sunday mornings. Besides, she's always been a little jealous, and probably with reason. So she decided to go with him and try to enjoy herself. Grace loves to dance and there are some awfully good dancers in Clyde; that is, early in the evening, before they begin to flounder and reel.

"Of course nobody can say Ed married her under false pretenses. She went into it with her eyes wide open. She saw him for the first time at one of those parties and she fell in love with him when he got mad at a man and knocked him down for cutting in on a dance. The man was about half Ed's size and Ed hit him when he wasn't looking. That didn't make any difference to Grace. And it didn't seem to make any difference to the Yacht Club. Anybody else would have been expelled, but Ed begged everyone's pardon and wasn't even scolded.

"That first night he asked Grace to let him drive her home. She was visiting Helen Morse, and Helen advised her not to take the chance. Ed didn't seem to be in very good driving condition. But Grace was so crazy about him that she told him yes. And then he forgot all about it, went home with another girl and left Grace at the club with some people she hardly knew. She had to call up the Morses and get them to come back after her.

"Well, they met again the next week and Grace thought she would put him in his place by ignoring him entirely, but that didn't work because he didn't remember having seen her before. He was comparatively sober this time and awfully nice and attentive. I'll admit Ed can be nice when he wants to. After that they played tennis together two or three times and then Ed proposed and Grace accepted him and he said he couldn't wait for a big wedding and she agreed to marry him secretly at Colby, a town about thirty miles from Clyde. She was to be in front of the Clyde post-office at twelve o'clock on a certain day and he was to pick her up in his car and drive to Colby and be married.

"The day came and she waited for him an hour and then went back to the Morses'. That evening he telephoned that he had made a mistake in the day and had just discovered it, and would she please forgive him and meet him the next day at the same place. I blush to say she succumbed, though she suspected what she found out later to be true—Ed had been on a bat and was sleeping it off at the time he was supposed to do his eloping.

"They were married and Ed behaved beautifully on the honeymoon. They spent two weeks in New York and went to the theatre every night and sightseeing in the mornings and afternoons. He had men friends of his to dinner once or twice and gave them all they wanted to drink, but wouldn't touch anything himself.

"When they got back to Clyde, Ed bought a lovely house already furnished, and the furniture was just what Grace would have picked out. Grace was so happy it seemed as if it couldn't last, and it didn't.

"They had been in Clyde a week when Ed announced that he had to go away on a trip. He didn't trouble to say where or why or how long. He just went, stayed away five days and came home looking as if he had had five or six operations. Grace tried to get him to tell her where he had been, but he just laughed and said it was a secret.

"And that's the way things have gone on ever since. Ed's got plenty of money and he gives Grace all she can possibly spend, besides buying her presents that are always lovely and terribly expensive. He'll be as good as pie for weeks and weeks—except for the Saturday night carousal—and then he'll disappear for a few days and she won't know where he is or when to expect him home. Her life is one surprise after another. But when he suddenly hits her in the eye, it's more than a surprise. It's a kind of a shock. At least it would be to me."

"When did it happen?" asked Mrs. Taylor.

"A week ago Saturday," said Mrs. Hammond. "There was the usual party at the Yacht Club and Ed took more than his usual amount to drink. Along about midnight he disappeared, and so did a girl named Eva Grayson.

"Finally Grace went home, but she sat up and waited for Ed. He came in about four o'clock, pie-eyed. He walked right to where Grace was sitting and without saying anything at all, he hit her, not hard enough to knock her out of her chair but with enough force to really hurt. Then, still not saying anything, he went to bed without taking the time to undress.

"In the morning, or whenever he woke up, he noticed that Grace's eye was discolored and asked her what had happened. She told him and he made no attempt to deny it. All he said was, 'Dearest, I can't tell you how sorry I am. You must believe me when I say I had no idea it was you. I thought it was Eva Grayson. And she deserved to be hit.'

"Can you imagine forgiving a man for a thing like that? Can you imagine continuing to live with him and love him? I'd kill myself before I'd stand it! And Grace excuses him and writes me the full details, just as if it were something she was proud of. I tell you, Bess, you and I can consider ourselves lucky——"

The front door opened and Louis came in with his flash-light.

"You're all set, Florence," said he. "I asked Perce in, but he thinks it's time to drive on."

"I know it is," said Mrs. Hammond. "We're going to play bridge out at the Cobbs' and we're terribly late. I ought to have phoned them, but I guess they'll sit up for us. Good night, Bess. I hope I didn't bore you with my long monolog."

"You didn't," said Mrs. Taylor.

Louis sat down to finish the Star. Mrs. Taylor shuffled her cards and started a new game, but in the middle of it she rose from the table and went close to her husband's chair.

"Do you know what day this is?" she said.

"Why, yes," Louis replied. "It's Tuesday."

"It's Tuesday, November twelfth. Our anniversary."

"Gosh! That's right! I wish I'd remembered it. I'd have bought you some flowers. Will it do tomorrow?"

"I don't want any flowers. But there is something I would like you to give me. And you don't have to wait till tomorrow."

"What is it?"

"A punch in the eye," said Mrs. Taylor.

"You're feeling kind of funny, aren't you? Did Florence have a shot of their home-made gin in her bag?"

"No. And I'm not feeling funny. I'm just sleepy. I think I'll go to bed." Louis was reading again.

"It says: 'Experiments in the raising of sisal are being made in Haiti.' I don't suppose you happen to know what sisal is."

But Mrs. Taylor was on her way up-stairs.

QUESTIONS

1. In what *specific* respects might the Taylors and their friends lead a rather different kind of life today from the life Ring Lardner pictures them as leading in the 1920's? Has his picture of small-town life retained its general validity or not, in your estimation?

2. Is this primarily a comic story or a story of pathos? How would you describe the exact balance which Lardner has tried to establish between the two elements?

3. Is the Taylors' marriage more, or less, successful than the marriage of the Goytes in "Wintry Peacock"?

ERNEST HEMINGWAY

(1898–   )

It is possible that of all the American writers of fiction who achieved prominence in the years between the two world wars—Sherwood Anderson, Thomas Wolfe, William Faulkner, F. Scott Fitzgerald, to name only a few of the others—Ernest Hemingway has been the most widely popular and also the most widely influential. His influence has been felt not only in the realm of fictional form and style, where indeed it has been very great both in America and in Europe, but also in the development of quite specific new attitudes towards experience.

His first important novel, *The Sun Also Rises* (1926), presented a classic picture of the post-war "lost" generation living in exile in Paris, its deeper subject being the hidden, long-term ways in which war disturbs and stultifies life. *A Farewell to Arms* (1928) was the no less classic story —in a major key this time, despite the understatement and the playing down of heroics—of love against the background of war, life trying to hold out against death. In *For Whom the Bell Tolls* (1940), the Spanish Civil War provides situations which test courage and which throw into sharp relief the need for human solidarity.

No doubt these novels have been the largest single factor in shaping Hemingway's fame and in giving currency to the modes of feeling and response which he has come to stand for so widely. His own personal legend has also contributed to this effect, so that his activities as a reporter, his experience of three wars, his travels, his interest in bull-fighting, in big-game hunting, in deep-sea fishing have become elements of a frequently encountered twentieth-century conception of the writer as seeker and recorder of vigorous and colorful experience wherever it is to be found. Sometimes those who have set out to follow Hemingway's example, to model their literary careers after what has seemed to be the pattern he has set, have overlooked the most important single element in that pattern: Hemingway's great and original artistry.

This artistry is nowhere more brilliantly apparent than in his short stories, which are by no means to be regarded as a minor aspect of Hemingway's achievement. Some of the shorter ones—stories like "In Another Country" or "Cat in the Rain" or even "The Killers"—might at first sight seem hardly to be stories at all, but as we become more familiar with them we realize that in the purity and intensity with which they seize and communicate a single mood, a single, unified effect, they are clear vindications of Poe's high claims for the short story as an art form. Hemingway achieves an almost poetic intensity of effect by a considerable range of characteristic technical and stylistic devices. These devices include understatement, absence of commentary or explanation on the part of the author, the barest possible transcription of the relevant events, the most skillful evocation of all kinds of sensuous experience, and a style from which all non-essentials and circumlocution have been pared away. Their total result is to give us the data as directly as possible, and from the data we are left to draw our own conclusions. Often two or more sets of data are juxtaposed, and a reader's success in responding to the whole story will depend on the alertness and fullness of his response to the separate strands and his ability to allow them to combine and react on one another in his own mind. Perhaps something of the sort happens when we read "The Killers," where we have a chance to witness, though very briefly, the varying responses of a small set of characters to a single ugly and terrible event, so that we weigh and contrast the responses against one another and, in doing so, both take in the event itself and come to some conclusion about what is the most valid and complete way to view it.

In "The Capital of the World" there is another sort of juxtaposition set up among a number of "unexplained" entities. What, we want to know, is the significant link between what happens to Paco, the lives of the three matadors who live at the pension where he is a waiter, and all the people in Madrid who were being disappointed in the movie version of *Anna Christie* at the time Paco's story takes place? There is nothing particularly recondite about the way we find the answer to this question. It is the way we use in life, where we learn about people and the meaning of their lives by observing what they do and say, for ourselves. But while Hemingway's story reproduces the conditions of life insofar as it offers no direct explanation, by an omniscient observer, of the events that take place before our eyes, it is *not* life but a work of art whose elements have been assembled with a certain pattern of significance in mind, a pattern in which every facet of the story, including the title, has a place. (What is the Capital of the World if not Hollywood, sometimes known as the Dream Factory?)

Hemingway's stories appeared in three principal separate volumes: *In Our Time* (1925), *Men without Women* (1927), and *Winner Take Nothing* (1933). A collected volume, *The Fifth Column and the First Forty-Nine Stories*, was published in 1938, and in it "The Capital of the World," originally published in *Esquire* in June, 1936, under the title "The Horns of the Bull," first appeared in book form. A long story, or novella, *The Old Man and the Sea*, was first published in 1952, and won the Pulitzer Prize in 1953; in the next year, Hemingway won the Nobel Prize for Literature. His stories are at present most conveniently obtainable in *The Short Stories of Ernest Hemingway* (Scribner's).

THE CAPITAL
OF THE WORLD

Madrid is full of boys named Paco, which is the diminutive of the name Francisco, and there is a Madrid joke about a father who came to Madrid and inserted an advertisement in the personal columns of *El Liberal* which said: PACO MEET ME AT HOTEL MONTANA NOON TUESDAY ALL IS FORGIVEN PAPA and how a squadron of Guardia Civil had to be called out to disperse the eight hundred young men who answered the advertisement. But this Paco, who waited on table at the Pension Luarca, had no father to forgive him nor anything for the father to forgive. He had two older sisters who were chambermaids at the Luarca, who had gotten their place through coming from the same small village as a former Luarca chambermaid who had proven hardworking and honest and hence given her village and its products a good name; and these sisters had paid his way on the auto-bus to Madrid and gotten him his job as an apprentice waiter. He came from a village in a part of Extramadura where conditions were incredibly primitive, food scarce, and comforts unknown and he had worked hard ever since he could remember.

He was a well built boy with very black, rather curly hair, good teeth and a skin that his sisters envied, and he had a ready and unpuzzled smile. He was fast on his feet and did his work well and he loved his sisters, who seemed beautiful and sophisticated; he loved Madrid, which was still an unbelievable place, and he loved his work, which, done under bright lights, with clean linen, the wearing of evening clothes, and abundant food in the kitchen, seemed romantically beautiful.

There were from eight to a dozen other people who lived at the Luarca and ate in the dining room but for Paco, the youngest of the three waiters who served at table, the only ones who really existed were the bull fighters.

Second-rate matadors lived at the pension because the address in the Calle San Jeronimo was good, the food was excellent and the room and board was cheap. It is necessary for a bull fighter to give the appearance, if not of prosperity, at least of respectability, since decorum and dignity rank above courage as the virtues most highly prized in Spain, and bull fighters stayed at the Luarca until their last pesetas were gone. There is no record of any bull fighter having left the Luarca for a better or more expensive hotel; second-rate bull fighters never became first rate; but the descent from the Luarca was swift since any one could stay there who was making anything at all and a bill was never presented to a guest unasked until the woman who ran the place knew that the case was hopeless.

At this time there were three full matadors living at the Luarca as well as two very good picadors, and one excellent banderillero. The Luarca was luxury for the picadors and the banderilleros who, with their families in Seville, required lodging in Madrid during the Spring season; but they were well paid and in the fixed employ of fighters who were heavily contracted during the coming season and the three of these subalterns would probably make much more apiece than any of the three matadors. Of the three matadors one was ill and trying to conceal it; one had passed his short vogue as a novelty; and the third was a coward.

The coward had at one time, until he had received a peculiarly atrocious horn wound in the lower abdomen at the start of his first season as a full matador, been exceptionally brave and remarkably skilful and he still had many of the hearty mannerisms of his days of success. He was jovial to excess and laughed constantly with and without provocation. He had, when successful, been very addicted to practical jokes but he had given them up now. They took an assurance that he did not feel. This matador had an intelligent, very open face and he carried himself with much style.

The matador who was ill was careful never to show it and was meticulous about eating a little of all the dishes that were presented at the table. He had a great many handkerchiefs which he laundered himself in his room and, lately, he had been selling his fighting suits. He had sold one, cheaply, before Christmas and another in the first week of April. They had been very expensive suits, had always been well kept and he had one more. Before he had become ill he had been a very promising, even a sensational, fighter and, while he himself could not read, he had clippings which said that in his debut in Madrid he had been better than Belmonte. He ate alone at a small table and looked up very little.

The matador who had once been a novelty was very short and brown and very dignified. He also ate alone at a separate table and he smiled very rarely and never laughed. He came from Valladolid, where the people are extremely serious, and he was a capable matador; but his style had become old-fashioned before he had ever succeeded in endearing himself to the public through his virtues, which were courage and a calm capability, and his name on a poster would draw no one to a bull ring. His novelty had been that he was so short that he could barely see over the bull's withers, but there were other short fighters, and he had never succeeded in imposing himself on the public's fancy.

Of the picadors one was a thin, hawk-faced, gray-haired man, lightly built but with legs and arms like iron, who always wore cattle-men's boots under his trousers, drank too much every evening and gazed amorously at any woman in the pension. The other was huge, dark, brown-faced, good-looking, with black hair like an Indian and enormous hands. Both were great picadors although the first was reputed to have lost much of his ability through drink and dissipation, and the second was said to be too head-strong and quarrelsome to stay with any matador more than a single season.

The banderillero was middle-aged, gray, cat-quick in spite of his years and, sitting at the table he looked a moderately prosperous business man. His legs were still good for this season, and when they should go he was intelligent and experienced enough to keep regularly employed for a long time. The difference would be that when his speed of foot would be gone he would always be frightened where now he was assured and calm in the ring and out of it.

On this evening every one had left the dining room except the hawk-faced picador who drank too much, the birthmarked-faced auctioneer of watches at the fairs and festivals of Spain, who also drank too much, and two priests from Galicia who were sitting at a corner table and drinking if not too much certainly enough. At that time wine was included in the price of the room and board at the Luarca and the waiters had just brought fresh bottles of Valdepeñas to the tables of the auctioneer, then to the picador and, finally, to the two priests.

The three waiters stood at the end of the room. It was the rule of the house that they should all remain on duty until the diners whose tables they were responsible for should all have left, but the one who served the table of the two priests had an appointment to go to an Anarcho-Syndicalist meeting and Paco had agreed to take over his table for him.

Upstairs the matador who was ill was lying face down on his bed alone. The matador who was no longer a novelty was sitting looking out of his window preparatory to walking out to the café. The matador who was a coward had the older sister of Paco in his room with him and was trying to get her to do something which she was laughingly refusing to do. This matador was saying, "Come on, little savage."

"No," said the sister. "Why should I?"

"For a favor."

"You've eaten and now you want me for dessert."

"Just once. What harm can it do?"

"Leave me alone. Leave me alone, I tell you."

"It is a very little thing to do."

"Leave me alone, I tell you."

Down in the dining room the tallest of the waiters, who was overdue at the meeting, said, "Look at those black pigs drink."

"That's no way to speak," said the second waiter. "They are decent clients. They do not drink too much."

"For me it is a good way to speak," said the tall one. "There are the two curses of Spain, the bulls and the priests."

"Certainly not the individual bull and the individual priest," said the second waiter.

"Yes," said the tall waiter. "Only through the individual can you attack the class. It is necessary to kill the individual bull and the individual priest. All of them. Then there are no more."

"Save it for the meeting," said the other waiter.

"Look at the barbarity of Madrid," said the tall waiter. "It is now half-past eleven o'clock and these are still guzzling."

"They only started to eat at ten," said the other waiter. "As you know there are many dishes. That wine is cheap and these have paid for it. It is not a strong wine."

"How can there be solidarity of workers with fools like you?" asked the tall waiter.

"Look," said the second waiter who was a man of fifty. "I have worked all my life. In all that remains of my life I must work. I have no complaints against work. To work is normal."

"Yes, but the lack of work kills."

"I have always worked," said the older waiter. "Go on to the meeting. There is no necessity to stay."

"You are a good comrade," said the tall waiter. "But you lack all ideology."

"*Mejor si me falta eso que el otro,*" said the older waiter (meaning it is better to lack that than work). "Go on to the *mitin.*"

Paco had said nothing. He did not yet understand politics but it always gave him a thrill to hear the tall waiter speak of the necessity for killing the priests and the Guardia Civil. The tall waiter represented to him revolution and revolution also was romantic. He himself would like to be a good catholic, a revolutionary, and have a steady job like this, while, at the same time, being a bull fighter.

"Go on to the meeting, Ignacio," he said. "I will respond for your work."

"The two of us," said the older waiter.

"There isn't enough for one," said Paco. "Go on to the meeting."

"*Pues, me voy,*" said the tall waiter. "And thanks."

In the meantime, upstairs, the sister of Paco had gotten out of the embrace of the matador as skilfully as a wrestler breaking a hold and said, now angry, "These are the hungry people. A failed bullfighter. With your ton-load of fear. If you have so much of that, use it in the ring."

"That is the way a whore talks."

"A whore is also a woman, but I am not a whore."

"You'll be one."

"Not through you."

"Leave me," said the matador who, now, repulsed and refused, felt the nakedness of his cowardice returning.

"Leave you? What hasn't left you?" said the sister. "Don't you want me to make up the bed? I'm paid to do that."

"Leave me," said the matador, his broad good-looking face wrinkled into a contortion that was like crying. "You whore. You dirty little whore."

"Matador," she said, shutting the door. "My matador."

Inside the room the matador sat on the bed. His face still had the contortion which, in the ring, he made into a constant smile which frightened those people in the first rows of seats who knew what they were watching. "And this," he was saying aloud. "And this. And this."

He could remember when he had been good and it had only been three years before. He could remember the weight of the heavy gold-brocaded fighting jacket on his shoulders on that hot afternoon in May when his voice had still been the same in the ring as in the café, and how he sighted along the point-dipping blade at the place in the top of the shoulders where it was dusty in the short-haired black hump of muscle above the wide, wood-knocking, splintered-tipped horns that lowered as he went in to kill, and how the sword pushed in as easy as into a mound of stiff butter with the palm of his hand pushing the pommel, his left arm crossed low, his left shoulder forward, his weight on his left leg, and then his weight wasn't on his leg. His weight was on his lower belly and as the bull raised his head the horn was out of sight in him and he swung over on it twice before they pulled him off it. So now when he went in to kill, and it was seldom, he could not look at the horns and what did any whore know about what he went through before he fought? And what had they been through that laughed at him? They were all whores and they knew what they could do with it.

Down in the dining room the picador sat looking at the priests. If there were women in the room he stared at them. If there were no women he would stare with enjoyment at a foreigner, *un inglés,* but lacking women or strangers, he now stared with enjoyment and insolence at the two priests. While he stared the birthmarked auctioneer rose and folding his napkin went out, leaving over half the wine in the last bottle he had ordered. If his accounts had been paid up at the Luarca he would have finished the bottle.

The two priests did not stare back at the picador. One of them was saying, "It is ten days since I have been here waiting to see him and all day I sit in the ante-chamber and he will not receive me."

"What is there to do?"

"Nothing. What can one do? One cannot go against authority."

"I have been here for two weeks and nothing. I wait and they will not see me."

"We are from the abandoned country. When the money runs out we can return."

"To the abandoned country. What does Madrid care about Galicia? We are a poor province."

"One understands the action of our brother Basilio."

"Still I have no real confidence in the integrity of Basilio Alvarez."

"Madrid is where one learns to understand. Madrid kills Spain."

"If they would simply see one and refuse."

"No. You must be broken and worn out by waiting."

"Well, we shall see. I can wait as well as another."

At this moment the picador got to his feet, walked over to the priests' table and stood, gray-headed and hawk-faced, staring at them and smiling.

"A torero," said one priest to the other.

"And a good one," said the picador and walked out of the dining room, gray-jacketed, trim-waisted, bow-legged, in tight breeches over his high-heeled cattleman's boots that clicked on the floor as he swaggered quite steadily, smiling to himself. He lived in a small, tight, professional world of personal efficiency, nightly alcoholic triumph, and insolence. Now he lit a cigar and tilting his hat at an angle in the hallway went out to the café.

The priests left immediately after the picador, hurriedly conscious of being the last people in the dining room, and there was no one in the room now but Paco and the middle-aged waiter. They cleared the tables and carried the bottles into the kitchen.

In the kitchen was the boy who washed the dishes. He was three years older than Paco and was very cynical and bitter.

"Take this," the middle-aged waiter said, and poured out a glass of the Valdepeñas and handed it to him.

"Why not?" the boy took the glass.

"Tu, Paco?" the older waiter asked.

"Thank you," said Paco. The three of them drank.

"I will be going," said the middle-aged waiter.

"Good night," they told him.

He went out and they were alone. Paco took a napkin one of the priests had used and standing straight, his heels planted, lowered the napkin and with head following the movement, swung his arms in the motion of a slow sweeping veronica. He turned and advancing his right foot slightly, made the second pass, gained a little terrain on the imaginary bull and made a third pass, slow, perfectly timed and suave, then gathered the napkin to his waist and swung his hips away from the bull in a media-veronica.

The dishwasher, whose name was Enrique, watched him critically and sneeringly.

"How is the bull?" he said.

"Very brave," said Paco. "Look."

Standing slim and straight he made four more perfect passes, smooth, elegant and graceful.

"And the bull?" asked Enrique standing against the sink, holding his wine glass and wearing his apron.

"Still has lots of gas," said Paco.

"You make me sick," said Enrique.

"Why?"

"Look."

Enrique removed his apron and citing the imaginary bull he sculptured four perfect, languid gypsy veronicas and ended up with a rebolera that made the apron swing in a stiff arc past the bull's nose as he walked away from him.

"Look at that," he said. "And I wash dishes."

"Why?"

"Fear," said Enrique. "*Miedo*. The same fear you would have in a ring with a bull."

"No," said Paco. "I wouldn't be afraid."

"*Leche!*" said Enrique. "Every one is afraid. But a torero can control his fear so that he can work the bull. I went in an amateur fight and I was so afraid I couldn't keep from running. Every one thought it was very funny. So would you be afraid. If it wasn't for fear every bootblack in Spain would be a bull fighter. You, a country boy, would be frightened worse than I was."

"No," said Paco.

He had done it too many times in his imagination. Too many times he had seen the horns, seen the bull's wet muzzle, the ear twitching, then the head go down and the charge, the hoofs thudding and the hot bull pass him as he swung the cape, to re-charge as he swung the cape again, then again, and again, and again, to end winding the bull around him in his great media-veronica, and walk swingingly away, with bull hairs caught in the gold ornaments of his jacket from the close passes; the bull standing hypnotized and the crowd applauding. No, he would not be afraid. Others, yes. Not he. He knew he would not be afraid. Even if he ever was afraid he knew that he could do it anyway. He had confidence. "I wouldn't be afraid," he said.

Enrique said, "*Leche*," again.

Then he said, "If we should try it?"

"How?"

"Look," said Enrique. "You think of the bull but you do not think of the horns. The bull has such force that the horns rip like a knife, they stab like a bayonet, and they kill like a club. Look," he opened a table drawer and took out two meat knives. "I will bind these to the legs of a chair. Then I will play bull for you with the chair held before my head. The knives are the horns. If you make those passes then they mean something."

"Lend me your apron," said Paco. "We'll do it in the dining room."

"No," said Enrique, suddenly not bitter. "Don't do it, Paco."

"Yes," said Paco. "I'm not afraid."

"You will be when you see the knives come."

"We'll see," said Paco. "Give me the apron."

At this time, while Enrique was binding the two heavy-bladed razor-sharp meat knives fast to the legs of the chair with two soiled napkins holding the haft of each knife, wrapping them tight and then knotting them, the two chambermaids, Paco's sisters, were on their way to the cinema to see Greta Garbo in "Anna Christie." Of the two priests, one was sitting in his underwear reading his breviary and the other was wearing a nightshirt and saying the rosary. All the bullfighters except the one who was ill had made their evening appearance at the Café Fornos, where the big, dark-haired picador was playing billiards, the short, serious matador was sitting at a crowded table before a coffee and milk, along with the middle-aged banderillero and other serious workmen.

The drinking, gray-headed picador was sitting with a glass of cazalas brandy before him staring with pleasure at a table where the matador whose courage was gone sat with another matador who had renounced the sword to become a banderillero again, and two very houseworn-looking prostitutes.

The auctioneer stood on the street corner talking with friends. The tall waiter was at the Anarcho-Syndicalist meeting waiting for an opportunity to speak. The middle-aged waiter was seated on the terrace of the Café Alvarez drinking a small beer. The woman who owned the Luarca was already asleep in her bed, where she lay on her back with the bolster between her legs; big, fat, clean, easy-going, very religious and never having ceased to miss or pray daily for her husband, dead, now, twenty years. In his room, alone, the matador who was ill lay face down on his bed with his mouth against a handkerchief.

Now, in the deserted dining room, Enrique tied the last knot in the napkins that bound the knives to the chair legs and lifted the chair. He pointed the legs with the knives on them forward and held the chair over his head with the two knives pointing straight ahead, one on each side of his head.

"It's heavy," he said. "Look, Paco. It is very dangerous. Don't do it." He was sweating.

Paco stood facing him, holding the apron spread, holding a fold of it bunched in each hand, thumbs up, first finger down, spread to catch the eye of the bull.

"Charge straight," he said. "Turn like a bull. Charge as many times as you want."

"How will you know when to cut the pass?" asked Enrique. "It's better to do three and then a media."

"All right," said Paco. "But come straight. Huh, torito! Come on, little bull!"

Running with head down Enrique came toward him and Paco swung the apron just ahead of the knife blade as it passed close in front of his belly and as it went by it was, to him, the real horn, white-tipped, black, smooth, and as Enrique passed him and turned to rush again it was the hot, blood-flanked mass of the bull that thudded by, then turned like a cat and came again as he swung the cape slowly. Then the bull turned and came again and, as he watched the onrushing point, he stepped his left foot two inches too far forward and the knife did not pass, but had slipped in as easily as into a wineskin and there was a hot scalding rush above and around the sudden inner rigidity of steel and Enrique shouting, "Ay! Ay! Let me get it out! Let me get it out!" and Paco slipped forward on the chair, the apron cape still held, Enrique pulling on the chair as the knife turned in him, in him, Paco.

The knife was out now and he sat on the floor in the widening warm pool.

"Put the napkin over it. Hold it!" said Enrique. "Hold it tight. I will run for the doctor. You must hold in the hemorrhage."

"There should be a rubber cup," said Paco. He had seen that used in the ring.

"I came straight," said Enrique, crying. "All I wanted was to show the danger."

"Don't worry," said Paco, his voice sounding far away. "But bring the doctor."

In the ring they lifted you and carried you, running with you, to the operating room. If the femoral artery emptied itself before you reached there they called the priest.

"Advise one of the priests," said Paco, holding the napkin tight against his lower abdomen. He could not believe that this had happened to him.

But Enrique was running down the Carrera San Jeronimo to the all-night first-aid station and Paco was alone, first sitting up, then huddled over, then slumped on the floor, until it was over, feeling his life go out of him as dirty water empties from a bathtub when the plug is drawn. He was frightened and he felt faint and he tried to say an act of contrition and he remembered how it started but before he had said, as fast as he could, "Oh, my God, I am heartily sorry for having offended Thee who art worthy of all my love and I firmly resolve . . . ," he felt too faint and he was lying face down on the floor and it was over very quickly. A severed femoral artery empties itself faster than you can believe.

As the doctor from the first-aid station came up the stairs accompanied by a policeman who held on to Enrique by the arm, the two sisters of

Paco were still in the moving-picture palace of the Gran Via, where they were intensely disappointed in the Garbo film, which showed the great star in miserable low surroundings when they had been accustomed to see her surrounded by great luxury and brilliance. The audience disliked the film thoroughly and were protesting by whistling and stamping their feet. All the other people from the hotel were doing almost what they had been doing when the accident happened, except that the two priests had finished their devotions and were preparing for sleep, and the gray-haired picador had moved his drink over to the table with the two house-worn prostitutes. A little later he went out of the café with one of them. It was the one for whom the matador who had lost his nerve had been buying drinks.

The boy Paco had never known about any of this nor about what all these people would be doing on the next day and on other days to come. He had no idea how they really lived nor how they ended. He did not even realize they ended. He died, as the Spanish phrase has it, full of illusions. He had not had time in his life to lose any of them, nor even, at the end, to complete an act of contrition.

He had not even had time to be disappointed in the Garbo picture which disappointed all Madrid for a week.

QUESTIONS

1. How many degrees of character development and presentation do you find in the story, from Paco, who is in a sense the most fully presented, down to characters who are mentioned in only a sentence or two?

2. Does it seem to you that the story gives you one *fully* developed character against a background of a great many minor characters? Do you know more in the end about Paco than you know about the bullfighters, or the waiters, or Paco's sisters, or the priests?

3. What is the relationship between Paco's life and the lives of the other personages in the story, with some of whom he has no real contact at all? Is it merely that all are living in the same place at the same time, or does some particular significance emerge from the close juxtaposition of their lives?

4. How would you analyze Hemingway's method of pacing his story, the varying rates of speed at which he switches from one character to another?

5. What does the presence of the movie *Anna Christie*, and Madrid's reaction to it, add to the story? What does it have to do with Paco?

F SCOTT FITZGERALD

(1896–1940)

With the publication of his first novel, *This Side of Paradise*, in 1920, F. Scott Fitzgerald suddenly found himself a success when he was still in his early twenties. He had been born in St. Paul, Minnesota, he had gone to private schools in preparation for Princeton, where he spent four years, leaving without taking a degree in 1917. What Princeton meant to him and did for him we know from many places in his writing, and from the whole of *This Side of Paradise*. (Returning to Princeton on a visit in 1927, he saw again "the college windows open to the spring—open, open to everything in life. . . .") He served in the Army as an infantry lieutenant until 1919 but did not go overseas. The first money he earned by his writing was thirty dollars for a story accepted by *Smart Set*, edited by H. L. Mencken and George Jean Nathan. His first novel not only brought him financial success but also established him squarely in the middle of the literary scene as the chronicler and interpreter of "The Jazz Age."

In an essay he wrote in 1931, "Echoes of the Jazz Age," Fitzgerald described the course of this brief and frenetic episode in American life, from its beginnings about 1919 in the cynicism and disillusion—as well as the unspent energy—which the war had left behind it, to its end in 1929 when the Stock Market crash made visible a failure of nerve which had for some time been lurking beneath the gay, extravagant, illogical surface. In another autobiographical essay, "My Lost City" (1932), he described the strange and bewildering position in which he found himself, as a result of the publicity which was suddenly accorded him as the author of *This Side of Paradise*, in his first months in New York. "For just a moment, before it was demonstrated that I was unable to play the role, I, who knew less of New York than any reporter of six months standing and less of its society than any hallroom boy in a Ritz stag line, was pushed into the position not only of spokesman for the time but of the typical product of that same moment." Sometimes, so completely and vividly has he presented the life of the Jazz Age in his earlier novels and stories, we find ourselves thinking of him not only as its chronicler and representative but also as its impresario.

From the time of his first success until his tragic early death in 1940, Fitzgerald wrote three more novels and many short stories. The novels are: *The Beautiful and Damned* (1922), *The Great Gatsby* (1925), and *Tender is the Night* (1934). They have been frequently reprinted in the last few years, both here and in England, and *The Last Tycoon*, a novel about Hollywood which was unfinished at the time of Fitzgerald's death, was published in its incomplete form in 1941. The short stories appeared in four successive volumes during Fitzgerald's lifetime: *Flappers and Philosophers* (1921), *Tales of the Jazz Age* (1922), *All the Sad Young Men* (1926), and *Taps at Reveille* (1935). *The Stories of F. Scott Fitzgerald; a Selection of 28 Stories*, with an Introduction by Malcolm Cowley, was published in 1951.

If Fitzgerald had been only a chronicler of the manners and morals of a particular era, now past, it is unlikely that interest in his books would have continued to grow as it has. But it seems to be true that readers who had not yet been born in the 1920's can read Fitzgerald's evocations of the era without feeling that they are looking at something that belongs in a museum. The people of his novels and stories live within a fully detailed and documented representation of their times, but they *do live*, and as a result of their vitality their times live too. Fitzgerald is never deserted by his own imaginative vitality or by his intelligence, and it is perhaps surprising that, as a writer who treats experience in a way that in other hands leads inevitably to clichés of thought and feeling, he never falls into them. He can write a frankly nostalgic autobiographical sketch, in which he tries to fix in a sentence or two the impression of each of the hotels he and his wife had stayed at in a decade of wandering, without ever becoming boring or sentimental. For example, he describes a moment at a Swiss resort in 1931, looking back through it to an earlier time, and the little description has more poetry and more salt in it than many a more pretentious production by a less gifted writer: "We walked at night towards a café blooming with Japanese lanterns, white shoes gleaming like radium in the damp darkness. It was like the good gone times when we still believed in summer hotels and the philosophies of popular songs."

Then too, Fitzgerald has a subject that is larger than any particular time. Much of his writing is at least obliquely autobiographical, and all of it makes use of the places, the kinds of people he had known in his own life: boys and masters at private schools, undergraduates at Princeton, the rich and the not-so-rich in New York and on Long Island, the exiled writers and artists, the footloose Americans in Paris and on the Riviera (as well as those who were not footloose but merely lost). What he understands, not only about himself but about all the people whose lives had interested him, is their aspirations, their motives, the specific form taken in each instance by an intense eagerness for life. His general subject is the pursuit of happiness and, often, the bitter end of disillusion and emptiness to which that pursuit can lead. But what he presents is a specific individual who is convinced that if he can only master the rules laid down for *his* life by the society which governs it, he will achieve happiness, success, a place in which to stand, a valid and admired identity. This is as true of Gatsby as it is of Basil Lee, in the story reprinted here. In a sense, Basil is too young to take his full part in the world, he is still waiting in the wings until it is time to go on. In another sense, he is fully representative of Fitzgerald's adult heroes. His eagerness to do all the things that are waiting to be done, his anxiety lest he not do them right, his fear and his courage in the face of the enemies who surround him are exactly parallel with the corresponding forces in the lives of Anthony Patch, of Gatsby, or of Dick Diver.

THE FRESHEST BOY

It was a hidden Broadway restaurant in the dead of the night, and a brilliant and mysterious group of society people, diplomats and members of the underworld were there. A few minutes ago the sparkling wine had been flowing and a girl had been dancing gaily upon a table, but now the whole crowd were hushed and breathless. All eyes were fixed upon the masked but well-groomed man in the dress suit and opera hat who stood nonchalantly in the door.

"Don't move, please," he said, in a well-bred, cultivated voice that had, nevertheless, a ring of steel in it. "This thing in my hand might—go off."

His glance roved from table to table—fell upon the malignant man higher up with his pale saturnine face, upon Heatherly, the suave secret agent from a foreign power, then rested a little longer, a little more softly perhaps, upon the table where the girl with dark hair and dark tragic eyes sat alone.

"Now that my purpose is accomplished, it might interest you to know who I am." There was a gleam of expectation in every eye. The breast of the dark-eyed girl heaved faintly and a tiny burst of subtle French perfume rose into the air. "I am none other than that elusive gentleman, Basil Lee, better known as the Shadow."

Taking off his well-fitting opera hat, he bowed ironically from the waist. Then, like a flash, he turned and was gone into the night.

"You get up to New York only once a month," Lewis Crum was saying, "and then you have to take a master along."

Slowly, Basil Lee's glazed eyes returned from the barns and billboards of the Indiana countryside to the interior of the Broadway Limited. The hypnosis of the swift telegraph poles faded and Lewis Crum's stolid face took shape against the white slip-cover of the opposite bench.

"I'd just duck the master when I got to New York," said Basil.

"Yes, you would!"

"I bet I would."

"You try it and you'll see."

"What do you mean saying I'll see, all the time, Lewis? What'll I see?"

His very bright dark-blue eyes were at this moment fixed upon his companion with boredom and impatience. The two had nothing in common except their age, which was fifteen, and the lifelong friendship of their fathers—which is less than nothing. Also they were bound from the same Middle-Western city for Basil's first and Lewis' second year at the same Eastern school.

But, contrary to all the best traditions, Lewis the veteran was miserable and Basil the neophyte was happy. Lewis hated school. He had grown entirely dependent on the stimulus of a hearty vital mother, and as he felt her slipping farther and farther away from him, he plunged deeper into misery and homesickness. Basil, on the other hand, had lived with such intensity on so many stories of boarding-school life that, far from being homesick, he had a glad feeling of recognition and familiarity. Indeed, it was with some sense of doing the appropriate thing, having the traditional rough-house, that he had thrown Lewis' comb off the train at Milwaukee last night for no reason at all.

To Lewis, Basil's ignorant enthusiasm was distasteful—his instinctive attempt to dampen it had contributed to the mutual irritation.

"I'll tell you what you'll see," he said ominously. "They'll catch you smoking and put you on bounds."

"No, they won't, because I won't be smoking. I'll be in training for football."

"Football! Yeah! Football!"

"Honestly, Lewis, you don't like anything, do you?"

"I don't like football. I don't like to go out and get a crack in the eye." Lewis spoke aggressively, for his mother had canonized all his timidities as common sense. Basil's answer, made with what he considered kindly intent, was the sort of remark that creates lifelong enmities.

"You'd probably be a lot more popular in school if you played football," he suggested patronizingly.

Lewis did not consider himself unpopular. He did not think of it in that way at all. He was astounded.

"You wait!" he cried furiously. "They'll take all that freshness out of you."

"Clam yourself," said Basil, coolly plucking at the creases of his first long trousers. "Just clam yourself."

"I guess everybody knows you were the freshest boy at the Country Day!"

"Clam yourself," repeated Basil, but with less assurance. "Kindly clam yourself."

"I guess I know what they had in the school paper about you—"

Basil's own coolness was no longer perceptible.

"If you don't clam yourself," he said darkly, "I'm going to throw your brushes off the train too."

The enormity of this threat was effective. Lewis sank back in his seat, snorting and muttering, but undoubtedly calmer. His reference had been to one of the most shameful passages in his companion's life. In a periodical issued by the boys of Basil's late school there had appeared, under the heading Personals:

If someone will please poison young Basil, or find some other means to stop his mouth, the school at large and myself will be much obliged.

The two boys sat there fuming wordlessly at each other. Then, resolutely, Basil tried to re-inter this unfortunate souvenir of the past. All that was behind him now. Perhaps he had been a little fresh, but he was making a new start. After a moment, the memory passed and with it the train and Lewis' dismal presence—the breath of the East came sweeping over him again with a vast nostalgia. A voice called him out of the fabled world; a man stood beside him with a hand on his sweater-clad shoulder.

"Lee!"

"Yes, sir."

"It all depends on you now. Understand?"

"Yes, sir."

"All right," the coach said, "go in and win."

Basil tore the sweater from his stripling form and dashed out on the field. There were two minutes to play and the score was 3 to 0 for the enemy, but at the sight of young Lee, kept out of the game all year by a malicious plan of Dan Haskins, the school bully, and Weasel Weems, his toady, a thrill of hope went over the St. Regis stand.

"33-12-16-22!" barked Midget Brown, the diminutive little quarterback.

It was his signal—

"Oh, gosh!" Basil spoke aloud, forgetting the late unpleasantness. "I wish we'd get there before tomorrow."

II

St. Regis School, Eastchester,
November 18, 19—

DEAR MOTHER: There is not much to say today, but I thought I would write you about my allowance. All the boys have a bigger allowance than me, because there are a lot of little things I have to get, such as shoe laces etc. School is still very nice and am having a fine time, but football is over and there is not much to do. I am going to New York this week to see a show. I do not know yet what it will be, but probably the Quacker Girl or little boy Blue as they are both very good. Dr. Bacon is very nice and there is a good phycission in the village. No more now as I have to study Algebra.

Your Affectionate Son,
BASIL D. LEE.

As he put the letter in its envelope, a wizened little boy came into the deserted study hall where he sat and stood staring at him.

"Hello," said Basil, frowning.

"I been looking for you," said the little boy, slowly and judicially. "I looked all over—up in your room and out in the gym, and they said you probably might of sneaked off in here."

"What do you want?" Basil demanded.

"Hold your horses, Bossy."

Basil jumped to his feet. The little boy retreated a step.

"Go on, hit me!" he chirped nervously. "Go on, hit me, cause I'm just half your size—Bossy."

Basil winced. "You call me that again and I'll spank you."

"No, you won't spank me. Brick Wales said if you ever touched any of us—"

"But I never did touch any of you."

"Didn't you chase a lot of us one day and didn't Brick Wales—"

"Oh, what do you want?" Basil cried in desperation.

"Doctor Bacon wants you. They sent me after you and somebody said maybe you sneaked in here."

Basil dropped his letter in his pocket and walked out—the little boy and his invective following him through the door. He traversed a long corridor, muggy with that odor best described as the smell of stale caramels that is so peculiar to boys' schools, ascended a stairs and knocked at an unexceptional but formidable door.

Doctor Bacon was at his desk. He was a handsome, redheaded Episcopal clergyman of fifty whose original real interest in boys was now tempered by the flustered cynicism which is the fate of all headmasters and settles on them like green mould. There were certain preliminaries before Basil was asked to sit down—gold-rimmed glasses had to be hoisted up from nowhere by a black cord and fixed on Basil to be sure that he was not an impostor; great masses of paper on the desk had to be shuffled through, not in search of anything but as a man nervously shuffles a pack of cards.

"I had a letter from your mother this morning—ah—Basil." The use of his first name had come to startle Basil. No one else in school had yet called him anything but Bossy or Lee. "She feels that your marks have been poor. I believe you have been sent here at a certain amount of—ah—sacrifice and she expects—"

Basil's spirit writhed with shame, not at his poor marks but that his financial inadequacy should be so bluntly stated. He knew that he was one of the poorest boys in a rich boys' school.

Perhaps some dormant sensibility in Doctor Bacon became aware of his discomfort; he shuffled through the papers once more and began on a new note.

"However, that was not what I sent for you about this afternoon. You applied last week for permission to go to New York on Saturday, to a matinée. Mr. Davis tells me that for almost the first time since school opened you will be off bounds tomorrow."

"Yes, sir."

"That is not a good record. However, I would allow you to go to New York if it could be arranged. Unfortunately, no masters are available this Saturday."

Basil's mouth dropped ajar. "Why, I—why, Doctor Bacon, I know two parties that are going. Couldn't I go with one of them?"

Doctor Bacon ran through all his papers very quickly. "Unfortunately, one is composed of slightly older boys and the other group made arrangements some weeks ago."

"How about the party that's going to the *Quaker Girl* with Mr. Dunn?"

"It's that party I speak of. They feel that their arrangements are complete and they have purchased seats together."

Suddenly Basil understood. At the look in his eye Doctor Bacon went on hurriedly:

"There's perhaps one thing I can do. Of course there must be several boys in the party so that the expenses of the master can be divided up among all. If you can find two other boys who would like to make up a party, and let me have their names by five o'clock, I'll send Mr. Rooney with you."

"Thank you," Basil said.

Doctor Bacon hesitated. Beneath the cynical incrustations of many years an instinct stirred to look into the unusual case of this boy and find out what made him the most detested boy in school. Among boys and masters there seemed to exist an extraordinary hostility toward him, and though Doctor Bacon had dealt with many sorts of schoolboy crimes, he had neither by himself nor with the aid of trusted sixth-formers been able to lay his hands on its underlying cause. It was probably no single thing, but a combination of things; it was most probably one of those intangible questions of personality. Yet he remembered that when he first saw Basil he had considered him unusually prepossessing.

He sighed. Sometimes these things worked themselves out. He wasn't one to rush in clumsily. "Let us have a better report to send home next month, Basil."

"Yes, sir."

Basil ran quickly downstairs to the recreation room. It was Wednesday and most of the boys had already gone into the village of Eastchester, whither Basil, who was still on bounds, was forbidden to follow. When he looked at those still scattered about the pool tables and piano, he saw that it was going to be difficult to get anyone to go with him at all. For Basil was quite conscious that he was the most unpopular boy at school.

It had begun almost immediately. One day, less than a fortnight after he came, a crowd of the smaller boys, perhaps urged on to it, gathered suddenly around him and began calling him Bossy. Within the next week he had two fights, and both times the crowd was vehemently and eloquently with the other boy. Soon after, when he was merely shoving indiscriminatively, like everyone else, to get into the dining room, Carver, the captain of the football team, turned about and, seizing him by the back of the neck, held him and dressed him down savagely. He joined a group innocently at the piano and was told, "Go on away. We don't want you around."

After a month he began to realize the full extent of his unpopularity. It shocked him. One day after a particularly bitter humiliation he went up to his room and cried. He tried to keep out of the way for a while, but it didn't help. He was accused of sneaking off here and there, as if bent on a series of nefarious errands. Puzzled and wretched, he looked at his face in the glass, trying to discover there the secret of their dislike—in the expression of his eyes, his smile.

He saw now that in certain ways he had erred at the outset—he had

boasted, he had been considered yellow at football, he had pointed out
people's mistakes to them, he had shown off his rather extraordinary fund
of general information in class. But he had tried to do better and couldn't
understand his failure to atone. It must be too late. He was queered forever.

He had, indeed, become the scapegoat, the immediate villain, the
sponge which absorbed all malice and irritability abroad—just as the most
frightened person in a party seems to absorb all the others' fear, seems to
be afraid for them all. His situation was not helped by the fact, obvious to
all, that the supreme self-confidence with which he had come to St. Regis
in September was thoroughly broken. Boys taunted him with impunity
who would not have dared raise their voices to him several months before.

This trip to New York had come to mean everything to him—surcease
from the misery of his daily life as well as a glimpse into the long-awaited
heaven of romance. Its postponement for week after week due to his sins
—he was constantly caught reading after lights, for example, driven by his
wretchedness into such vicarious escapes from reality—had deepened his
longing until it was a burning hunger. It was unbearable that he should
not go, and he told over the short list of those whom he might get to accompany him. The possibilities were Fat Gaspar, Treadway, and Bugs Brown.
A quick journey to their rooms showed that they had all availed themselves
of the Wednesday permission to go into Eastchester for the afternoon.

Basil did not hesitate. He had until five o'clock and his only chance was
to go after them. It was not the first time he had broken bounds, though
the last attempt had ended in disaster and an extension of his confinement.
In his room, he put on a heavy sweater—an overcoat was a betrayal of intent—replaced his jacket over it and hid a cap in his back pocket. Then he
went downstairs and with an elaborately careless whistle struck out across
the lawn for the gymnasium. Once there, he stood for a while as if looking
in the windows, first the one close to the walk, then one near the corner of
the building. From here he moved quickly, but not too quickly, into a
grove of lilacs. Then he dashed around the corner, down a long stretch of
lawn that was blind from all windows and, parting the strands of a wire
fence, crawled through and stood upon the grounds of a neighboring
estate. For the moment he was free. He put on his cap against the chilly
November wind, and set out along the half-mile road to town.

Eastchester was a suburban farming community, with a small shoe factory. The institutions which pandered to the factory workers were the ones
patronized by the boys—a movie house, a quick-lunch wagon on wheels
known as the Dog and the Bostonian Candy Kitchen. Basil tried the Dog
first and happened immediately upon a prospect.

This was Bugs Brown, a hysterical boy, subject to fits and strenuously
avoided. Years later he became a brilliant lawyer, but at that time he was
considered by the boys of St. Regis to be a typical lunatic because of his
peculiar series of sounds with which he assuaged his nervousness all day
long.

He consorted with boys younger than himself, who were without the prejudices of their elders, and was in the company of several when Basil came in.

"Who-ee!" he cried. "Ee-ee-ee!" He put his hand over his mouth and bounced it quickly, making a wah-wah-wah sound. "It's Bossy Lee! It's Bossy Lee! It's Boss-Boss-Boss-Boss-Bossy Lee!"

"Wait a minute, Bugs," said Basil anxiously, half afraid that Bugs would go finally crazy before he could persuade him to come to town. "Say, Bugs, listen. Don't, Bugs—wait a minute. Can you come up to New York Saturday afternoon?"

"Whe-ee-ee!" cried Bugs to Basil's distress. "Whee-ee-ee!"

"Honestly, Bugs, tell me, can you? We could go up together if you could go."

"I've got to see a doctor," said Bugs, suddenly calm. "He wants to see how crazy I am."

"Can't you have him see about it some other day?" said Basil without humor.

"Whee-ee-ee!" cried Bugs.

"All right then," said Basil hastily. "Have you seen Fat Gaspar in town?"

Bugs was lost in shrill noise, but someone had seen Fat; Basil was directed to the Bostonian Candy Kitchen.

This was a gaudy paradise of cheap sugar. Its odor, heavy and sickly and calculated to bring out a sticky sweat upon an adult's palms, hung suffocatingly over the whole vicinity and met one like a strong moral dissuasion at the door. Inside, beneath a pattern of flies, material as black point lace, a line of boys sat eating heavy dinners of banana splits, maple nut, and chocolate marshmallow nut sundaes. Basil found Fat Gaspar at a table on the side.

Fat Gaspar was at once Basil's most unlikely and most ambitious quest. He was considered a nice fellow—in fact he was so pleasant that he had been courteous to Basil and had spoken to him politely all fall. Basil realized that he was like that to everyone, yet it was just possible that Fat liked him, as people used to in the past, and he was driven desperately to take a chance. But it was undoubtedly a presumption, and as he approached the table and saw the stiffened faces which the other two boys turned toward him, Basil's hope diminished.

"Say, Fat—" he said, and hesitated. Then he burst forth suddenly. "I'm on bounds, but I ran off because I had to see you. Doctor Bacon told me I could go to New York Saturday if I could get two other boys to go. I asked Bugs Brown and he couldn't go, and I thought I'd ask you."

He broke off, furiously embarrassed, and waited. Suddenly the two boys with Fat burst into a shout of laughter.

"Bugs wasn't crazy enough!"

Fat Gaspar hesitated. He couldn't go to New York Saturday and ordinarily he would have refused without offending. He had nothing against Basil; nor, indeed, against anybody; but boys have only a certain resistance to public opinion and he was influenced by the contemptuous laughter of the others.

"I don't want to go," he said indifferently. "Why do you want to ask *me?*" Then, half in shame, he gave a deprecatory little laugh and bent over his ice cream.

"I just thought I'd ask you," said Basil.

Turning quickly away, he went to the counter and in a hollow and unfamiliar voice ordered a strawberry sundae. He ate it mechanically, hearing occasional whispers and snickers from the table behind. Still in a daze, he started to walk out without paying his check, but the clerk called him back and he was conscious of more derisive laughter.

For a moment he hesitated whether to go back to the table and hit one of those boys in the face, but he saw nothing to be gained. They would say the truth—that he had done it because he couldn't get anybody to go to New York. Clenching his fists with impotent rage, he walked from the store.

He came immediately upon his third prospect, Treadway. Treadway had entered St. Regis late in the year and had been put in to room with Basil the week before. The fact that Treadway hadn't witnessed his humiliations of the autumn encouraged Basil to behave naturally toward him, and their relations had been, if not intimate, at least tranquil.

"Hey, Treadway," he cried, still excited from the affair in the Bostonian, "can you come up to New York to a show Saturday afternoon?"

He stopped, realizing that Treadway was in the company of Brick Wales, a boy he had had a fight with and one of his bitterest enemies. Looking from one to the other, Basil saw a look of impatience in Treadway's face and a faraway expression in Brick Wales', and he realized what must have been happening. Treadway, making his way into the life of the school, had just been enlightened as to the status of his roommate. Like Fat Gaspar, rather than acknowledge himself eligible to such an intimate request, he preferred to cut their friendly relations short.

"Not on your life," he said briefly. "So long." The two walked past him into the candy kitchen.

Had these slights, so much the bitterer for their lack of passion, been visited upon Basil in September, they would have been unbearable. But since then he had developed a shell of hardness which, while it did not add to his attractiveness, spared him certain delicacies of torture. In misery enough, and despair and self-pity, he went the other way along the street for a little distance until he could control the violent contortions of his face. Then, taking a roundabout route, he started back to school.

He reached the adjoining estate, intending to go back the way he had come. Half-way through a hedge, he heard footsteps approaching along the sidewalk and stood motionless, fearing the proximity of masters. Their voices grew nearer and louder; before he knew it he was listening with horrified fascination:

"—so, after he tried Bugs Brown, the poor nut asked Fat Gaspar to go

with him and Fat said, 'What do you ask me for?' It serves him right if
he couldn't get anybody at all."

It was the dismal but triumphant voice of Lewis Crum.

III

Up in his room, Basil found a package lying on his bed. He knew its
contents and for a long time he had been eagerly expecting it, but such
was his depression that he opened it listlessly. It was a series of eight color
reproductions of Harrison Fisher girls "on glossy paper, without printing
or advertising matter and suitable for framing."

The pictures were named Dora, Marguerite, Babette, Lucille, Gretchen,
Rose, Katherine and Mina. Two of them—Marguerite and Rose—Basil
looked at, slowly tore up and dropped in the wastebasket, as one who
disposes of the inferior pups from a litter. The other six he pinned at intervals around the room. Then he lay down on his bed and regarded them.

Dora, Lucille and Katherine were blonde; Gretchen was medium;
Babette and Mina were dark. After a few minutes, he found that he was
looking oftenest at Dora and Babette and, to a lesser extent, at Gretchen,
though the latter's Dutch cap seemed unromantic and precluded the element of mystery. Babette, a dark little violet-eyed beauty in a tight-fitting
hat, attracted him most; his eyes came to rest on her at last.

"Babette," he whispered to himself—"beautiful Babette."

The sound of the word, so melancholy and suggestive, like "Velia" or
"I'm going to Maxime's" on the phonograph, softened him and, turning
over on his face, he sobbed into the pillow. He took hold of the bed rails
over his head and, sobbing and straining, began to talk to himself brok-
enly—how he hated them and whom he hated—he listed a dozen—and
what he would do to them when he was great and powerful. In previous
moments like these he had always rewarded Fat Gaspar for his kindness,
but now he was like the rest. Basil set upon him, pummeling him unmerci-
fully, or laughed sneeringly when he passed him blind and begging on
the street.

He controlled himself as he heard Treadway come in, but did not move
or speak. He listened as the other moved about the room, and after a while
became conscious that there was an unusual opening of closets and bureau
drawers. Basil turned over, his arm concealing his tear-stained face. Treadway had an armful of shirts in his hand.

"What are you doing?" Basil demanded.

His roommate looked at him stonily. "I'm moving in with Wales," he
said.

"Oh!"

Treadway went on with his packing. He carried out a suitcase full, then
another, took down some pennants and dragged his trunk into the hall.
Basil watched him bundle his toilet things into a towel and take one last
survey about the room's new barrenness to see if there was anything forgotten.

"Good-by," he said to Basil, without a ripple of expression on his face. "Good-by."

Treadway went out. Basil turned over once more and choked into the pillow.

"Oh, poor Babette!" he cried huskily. "Poor little Babette! Poor little Babette!"

Babette, svelte and piquant, looked down at him coquettishly from the wall.

IV

Doctor Bacon, sensing Basil's predicament and perhaps the extremity of his misery, arranged it that he should go into New York, after all. He went in the company of Mr. Rooney, the football coach and history teacher. At twenty Mr. Rooney had hesitated for some time between joining the police force and having his way paid through a small New England college; in fact he was a hard specimen and Doctor Bacon was planning to get rid of him at Christmas. Mr. Rooney's contempt for Basil was founded on the latter's ambiguous and unreliable conduct on the football field during the past season—he had consented to take him to New York for reasons of his own.

Basil sat meekly beside him on the train, glancing past Mr. Rooney's bulky body at the Sound and the fallow fields of Westchester County. Mr. Rooney finished his newspaper, folded it up and sank into a moody silence. He had eaten a large breakfast and the exigencies of time had not allowed him to work it off with exercise. He remembered that Basil was a fresh boy, and it was time he did something fresh and could be called to account. This reproachless silence annoyed him.

"Lee," he said suddenly, with a thinly assumed air of friendly interest, "why don't you get wise to yourself?"

"What, sir?" Basil was startled from his excited trance of this morning.

"I said why don't you get wise to yourself?" said Mr. Rooney in a somewhat violent tone. "Do you want to be the butt of the school all your time here?"

"No, I don't," Basil was chilled. Couldn't all this be left behind for just one day?

"You oughtn't to get so fresh all the time. A couple of times in history class I could just about have broken your neck." Basil could think of no appropriate answer. "Then out playing football," continued Mr. Rooney "—you didn't have any nerve. You could play better than a lot of 'em when you wanted, like that day against the Pomfret seconds, but you lost your nerve."

"I shouldn't have tried for the second team," said Basil. "I was too light. I should have stayed on the third."

"You were yellow, that was all the trouble. You ought to get wise to yourself. In class, you're always thinking of something else. If you don't study, you'll never get to college."

"I'm the youngest boy in the fifth form," Basil said rashly.

"You think you're pretty bright, don't you?" He eyed Basil ferociously. Then something seemed to occur to him that changed his attitude and they rode for a while in silence. When the train began to run through the thickly clustered communities near New York, he spoke again in a milder voice and with an air of having considered the matter for a long time:

"Lee, I'm going to trust you."

"Yes, sir."

"You go and get some lunch and then go on to your show. I've got some business of my own I got to attend to, and when I've finished I'll try to get to the show. If I can't, I'll anyhow meet you outside."

Basil's heart leaped up. "Yes, sir."

"I don't want you to open your mouth about this at school—I mean, about me doing some business of my own."

"No, sir."

"We'll see if you can keep your mouth shut for once," he said, making it fun. Then he added, on a note of moral sternness, "And no drinks, you understand that?"

"Oh, no, sir!" The idea shocked Basil. He had never tasted a drink, nor even contemplated the possibility, save the intangible and nonalcoholic champagne of his café dreams.

On the advice of Mr. Rooney he went for luncheon to the Manhattan Hotel, near the station, where he ordered a club sandwich, French fried potatoes and a chocolate parfait. Out of the corner of his eye he watched the nonchalant, debonair, blasé New Yorkers at neighboring tables, investing them with a romance by which these possible fellow citizens of his from the Middle West lost nothing. School had fallen from him like a burden; it was no more than an unheeded clamor, faint and far away. He even delayed opening the letter from the morning's mail which he found in his pocket, because it was addressed to him at school.

He wanted another chocolate parfait, but being reluctant to bother the busy waiter any more, he opened the letter and spread it before him instead. It was from his mother:

DEAR BASIL: This is written in great haste, as I didn't want to frighten you by telegraphing. Grandfather is going abroad to take the waters and he wants you and me to come too. The idea is that you'll go to school at Grenoble or Montreux for the rest of the year and learn the languages and we'll be close by. That is, if you want to. I know how you like St. Regis and playing football and baseball, and of course there would be none of that; but on the other hand, it would be a nice change, even if it postponed your entering Yale by an extra year. So, as usual, I want you to do just as you like. We will be leaving home almost as soon as you get this and will come to the Waldorf in New York, where you can come in and see us for a few days, even if you decide to stay. Think it over, dear.

With love to my dearest boy,
MOTHER.

Basil got up from his chair with a dim idea of walking over to the Waldorf and having himself locked up safely until his mother came. Then, impelled to some gesture, he raised his voice and in one of his first basso notes called boomingly and without reticence for the waiter. No more St. Regis! No more St. Regis! He was almost strangling with happiness.

"Oh, gosh!" he cried to himself. "Oh, golly! Oh, gosh! Oh, gosh!" No more Doctor Bacon and Mr. Rooney and Brick Wales and Fat Gaspar. No more Bugs Brown and on bounds and being called Bossy. He need no longer hate them, for they were impotent shadows in the stationary world that he was sliding away from, sliding past, waving his hand. "Good-by!" He pitied them. "Good-by!"

It required the din of Forty-second Street to sober his maudlin joy. With his hand on his purse to guard against the omnipresent pickpocket, he moved cautiously toward Broadway. What a day! He would tell Mr. Rooney— Why, he needn't ever go back! Or perhaps it would be better to go back and let them know what he was going to do, while they went on and on in the dismal, dreary round of school.

He found the theater and entered the lobby with its powdery feminine atmosphere of a matinée. As he took out his ticket, his gaze was caught and held by a sculptured profile a few feet away. It was that of a well-built blond young man of about twenty with a strong chin and direct gray eyes. Basil's brain spun wildly for a moment and then came to rest upon a name—more than a name—upon a legend, a sign in the sky. What a day! He had never seen the young man before, but from a thousand pictures he knew beyond the possibility of a doubt that it was Ted Fay, the Yale football captain, who had almost single-handed beaten Harvard and Princeton last fall. Basil felt a sort of exquisite pain. The profile turned away; the crowd revolved; the hero disappeared. But Basil would know all through the next hours that Ted Fay was here too.

In the rustling, whispering, sweet-smelling darkness of the theater he read the program. It was the show of all shows that he wanted to see, and until the curtain actually rose the program itself had a curious sacredness— a prototype of the thing itself. But when the curtain rose it became waste paper to be dropped carelessly to the floor.

Act I. *The Village Green of a Small Town near New York.*

It was too bright and blinding to comprehend all at once, and it went so fast that from the very first Basil felt he had missed things; he would make his mother take him again when she came—next week—tomorrow.

An hour passed. It was very sad at this point—a sort of gay sadness, but sad. The girl—the man. What kept them apart even now? Oh, those tragic errors and misconceptions. So sad. Couldn't they look into each other's eyes and *see?*

In a blaze of light and sound, of resolution, anticipation and imminent trouble, the act was over.

He went out. He looked for Ted Fay and thought he saw him leaning rather moodily on the plush wall at the rear of the theater, but he could not be sure. He bought cigarettes and lit one, but fancying at the first puff that he heard a blare of music he rushed back inside.

ACT II. *The Foyer of the Hotel Astor.*

Yes, she was, indeed, like that song—a Beautiful Rose of the Night. The waltz buoyed her up, brought her with it to a point of aching beauty and then let her slide back to life across its last bars as a leaf slants to earth across the air. The high life of New York! Who could blame her if she was carried away by the glitter of it all, vanishing into the bright morning of the amber window borders, or into distant and entrancing music as the door opened and closed that led to the ballroom? The toast of the shining town.

Half an hour passed. Her true love brought her roses like herself and she threw them scornfully at his feet. She laughed and turned to the other, and danced—danced madly, wildly. Wait! That delicate treble among the thin horns, the low curving note from the great strings. There it was again, poignant and aching, sweeping like a great gust of emotion across the stage, catching her again like a leaf helpless in the wind:

> Rose—Rose—Rose of the night,
> When the spring moon is bright you'll be fair—

A few minutes later, feeling oddly shaken and exalted, Basil drifted outside with the crowd. The first thing upon which his eyes fell was the almost forgotten and now curiously metamorphosed specter of Mr. Rooney.

Mr. Rooney had, in fact, gone a little to pieces. He was, to begin with, wearing a different and much smaller hat than when he left Basil at noon. Secondly, his face had lost its somewhat gross aspect and turned a pure and even delicate white, and he was wearing his necktie and even portions of his shirt on the outside of his unaccountably wringing-wet overcoat. How, in the short space of four hours, Mr. Rooney had got himself in such shape is explicable only by the pressure of confinement in a boys' school upon a fiery outdoor spirit. Mr. Rooney was born to toil under the clear light of heaven and, perhaps half consciously, he was headed toward his inevitable destiny.

"Lee," he said dimly, "you ought get wise to y'self. I'm going to put you wise y'self."

To avoid the ominous possibility of being put wise to himself in the lobby, Basil uneasily changed the subject.

"Aren't you coming to the show?" he asked, flattering Mr. Rooney by implying that he was in any condition to come to the show. "It's a wonderful show."

Mr. Rooney took off his hat, displaying wringing-wet matted hair. A picture of reality momentarily struggled for development in the back of his brain.

"We got to get back to school," he said in a somber and unconvinced voice.

"But there's another act," protested Basil in horror. "I've got to stay for the last act."

Swaying, Mr. Rooney looked at Basil, dimly realizing that he had put himself in the hollow of this boy's hand.

"All righ'," he admitted. "I'm going to get somethin' to eat. I'll wait for you next door."

He turned abruptly, reeled a dozen steps and curved dizzily into a bar adjoining the theater. Considerably shaken, Basil went back inside.

ACT III. *The Roof Garden of Mr. Van Astor's House. Night.*

Half an hour passed. Everything was going to be all right, after all. The comedian was at his best now, with the glad appropriateness of laughter after tears, and there was a promise of felicity in the bright tropical sky. One lovely plaintive duet, and then abruptly the long moment of incomparable beauty was over.

Basil went into the lobby and stood in thought while the crowd passed out. His mother's letter and the show had cleared his mind of bitterness and vindictiveness—he was his old self and he wanted to do the right thing. He wondered if it was the right thing to get Mr. Rooney back to school. He walked toward the saloon, slowed up as he came to it and, gingerly opening the swinging door, took a quick peer inside. He saw only that Mr. Rooney was not one of those drinking at the bar. He walked down the street a little way, came back and tried again. It was as if he thought the doors were teeth to bite him, for he had the old-fashioned Middle-Western boy's horror of the saloon. The third time he was successful. Mr. Rooney was sound asleep at a table in the back of the room.

Outside again Basil walked up and down, considering. He would give Mr. Rooney half an hour. If, at the end of that time, he had not come out, he would go back to school. After all, Mr. Rooney had laid for him ever since football season—Basil was simply washing his hands of the whole affair, as in a day or so he would wash his hands of school.

He had made several turns up and down, when, glancing up an alley that ran beside the theater his eye was caught by the sign, Stage Entrance. He could watch the actors come forth.

He waited. Women streamed by him, but those were the days before Glorification and he took these drab people for wardrobe women or something. Then suddenly a girl came out and with her a man, and Basil turned and ran a few steps up the street as if afraid they would recognize him—and ran back, breathing as if with a heart attack—for the girl, a radiant little beauty of nineteen, was Her and the young man by her side was Ted Fay.

Arm in arm, they walked past him, and irresistibly Basil followed. As they walked, she leaned toward Ted Fay in a way that gave them a fascinating air of intimacy. They crossed Broadway and turned into the Knickerbocker Hotel, and twenty feet behind them Basil followed, in time to see them go into a long room set for afternoon tea. They sat at a table for two, spoke vaguely to a waiter, and then, alone at last, bent eagerly toward each other. Basil saw that Ted Fay was holding her gloved hand.

The tea room was separated only by a hedge of potted firs from the main corridor. Basil went along this to a lounge which was almost up against their table and sat down.

Her voice was low and faltering, less certain than it had been in the play, and very sad: "Of course I do, Ted." For a long time, as their conversation continued, she repeated "Of course I do" or "But I do, Ted." Ted Fay's remarks were too low for Basil to hear.

"—— says next month, and he won't be put off any more. . . . I do in a way, Ted. It's hard to explain, but he's done everything for mother and me. . . . There's no use kidding myself. It was a fool-proof part and any girl he gave it to was made right then and there. . . . He's been awfully thoughtful. He's done everything for me."

Basil's ears were sharpened by the intensity of his emotion; now he could hear Ted Fay's voice too:

"And you say you love me."

"But don't you see I promised to marry him more than a year ago."

"Tell him the truth—that you love me. Ask him to let you off."

"This isn't musical comedy, Ted."

"That was a mean one," he said bitterly.

"I'm sorry, dear, Ted darling, but you're driving me crazy going on this way. You're making it so hard for me."

"I'm going to leave New Haven, anyhow."

"No, you're not. You're going to stay and play baseball this spring. Why, you're an ideal to all those boys! Why, if you—"

He laughed shortly. "You're a fine one to talk about ideals."

"Why not? I'm living up to my responsibility to Beltzman; you've got to make up your mind just like I have—that we can't have each other."

"Jerry! Think what you're doing! All my life, whenever I hear that waltz—"

Basil got to his feet and hurried down the corridor, through the lobby and out of the hotel. He was in a state of wild emotional confusion. He did not understand all he had heard, but from his clandestine glimpse into the privacy of these two, with all the world that his short experience could conceive of at their feet, he had gathered that life for everybody was a struggle, sometimes magnificent from a distance, but always difficult and surprisingly simple and a little sad.

They would go on. Ted Fay would go back to Yale, put her picture in his bureau drawer and knock out home runs with the bases full this spring —at 8:30 the curtain would go up and She would miss something warm and young out of her life, something she had had this afternoon.

It was dark outside and Broadway was a blazing forest fire as Basil

walked slowly along toward the point of brightest light. He looked up at
the great intersecting planes of radiance with a vague sense of approval
and possession. He would see it a lot now, lay his restless heart upon this
greater restlessness of a nation—he would come whenever he could get off
from school.

But that was all changed—he was going to Europe. Suddenly Basil realized that he wasn't going to Europe. He could not forego the molding of
his own destiny just to alleviate a few months of pain. The conquest of
the successive worlds of school, college and New York—why, that was his
true dream that he had carried from boyhood into adolescence, and because of the jeers of a few boys he had been about to abandon it and run
ignominiously up a back alley! He shivered violently, like a dog coming
out of the water, and simultaneously he was reminded of Mr. Rooney.

A few minutes later he walked into the bar, past the quizzical eyes of
the bartender and up to the table where Mr. Rooney still sat asleep. Basil
shook him gently, then firmly. Mr. Rooney stirred and perceived Basil.

"G'wise to yourself," he muttered drowsily. "G'wise to yourself an' let
me alone."

"I am wise to myself," said Basil. "Honest, I am wise to myself, Mr.
Rooney. You got to come with me into the washroom and get cleaned up,
and then you can sleep on the train again, Mr. Rooney. Come on, Mr.
Rooney, please—"

v

It was a long hard time. Basil got on bounds again in December and
wasn't free again until March. An indulgent mother had given him no
habits of work and this was almost beyond the power of anything but life
itself to remedy, but he made numberless new starts and failed and tried
again.

He made friends with a new boy named Maplewood after Christmas,
but they had a silly quarrel; and through the winter term, when a boys'
school is shut in with itself and only partly assuaged from its natural sav-
agery by indoor sports, Basil was snubbed and slighted a good deal for his
real and imaginary sins, and he was much alone. But on the other hand,
there was Ted Fay, and Rose of the Night on the phonograph—"All my
life whenever I hear that waltz"—and the remembered lights of New York,
and the thought of what he was going to do in football next autumn and
the glamorous mirage of Yale and the hope of spring in the air.

Fat Gaspar and a few others were nice to him now. Once when he and
Fat walked home together by accident from downtown they had a long
talk about actresses—a talk that Basil was wise enough not to presume
upon afterward. The smaller boys suddenly decided that they approved
of him, and a master who had hitherto disliked him put his hand on his
shoulder walking to a class one day. They would all forget eventually—
maybe during the summer. There would be new fresh boys in September;
he would have a clean start next year.

One afternoon in February, playing basketball, a great thing happened. He and Brick Wales were at forward on the second team and in the fury of the scrimmage the gymnasium echoed with sharp slapping contacts and shrill cries.

"Here yar!"

"Bill! Bill!"

Basil had dribbled the ball down the court and Brick Wales, free, was crying for it.

"Here yar! Lee! Hey! Lee-y!"

Lee-y!

Basil flushed and made a poor pass. He had been called by a nickname. It was a poor makeshift, but it was something more than the stark bareness of his surname or a term of derision. Brick Wales went on playing, unconscious that he had done anything in particular or that he had contributed to the events by which another boy was saved from the army of the bitter, the selfish, the neurasthenic and the unhappy. It isn't given to us to know those rare moments when people are wide open and the lightest touch can wither or heal. A moment too late and we can never reach them any more in this world. They will not be cured by our most efficacious drugs or slain with our sharpest swords.

Lee-y! It could scarcely be pronounced. But Basil took it to bed with him that night, and thinking of it, holding it to him happily to the last, fell easily to sleep.

QUESTIONS

1. From whose point of view is the story told?

2. Do all the boys at school have substantially the same attitude towards Basil, or are there distinctions to be observed among them? What are the attitudes of the masters, and how do they differ from or resemble those of the boys?

3. In what respects does Fitzgerald see Basil differently than the characters in the story see him? Can you point to any places in the story where irony results from the difference between the view of Basil held by one of the other characters and the view which Fitzgerald shares with the reader?

4. What is Basil's problem, and what essentially has happened to him by the end of the story?

5. There are several places in the story where we see adults and their world—the lives and habits of the masters at school, the musical comedy which Basil attends in New York, even New York itself—through Basil's eyes. Is there any difference between the way he looks at these things and the way Fitzgerald looks at them? If so, how is the difference indicated, and what does it tell us about Basil?

FRANK O'CONNOR

(1903–   )

In his entry in *Who's Who*, Frank O'Connor (pseudonym for Michael O'Donovan) describes himself as "writer and journalist," and in fact the bulk of his entry, beyond citing one or two facts of his personal history, is devoted to the long list of his books. Among these are a few critical works such as *Towards an Appreciation of Literature* (1945) and *The Modern Novel* (1956), as well as one or two books of travel, but by far the larger number of them are collections of short stories. His first volume of stories, *Guests of the Nation,* was published in 1931, and further collections have continued to appear, with the most gratifying regularity, throughout the period of almost three decades since that date.

Born in Ireland in 1903, about a generation later than James Joyce and almost two generations later than W. B. Yeats, O'Connor has been described as being "an active younger member of the Irish Literary Renaissance," and it is certainly true that his practice of the short story constitutes a consistently vigorous and delightful addition to the impressive list of works, in many forms, in which Irish writers of the past seventy or eighty years have exploited the characteristic color and interest of the Irish people, Irish problems and aspirations, Irish life. (Nor is this meant to imply that O'Connor's work is in any sense narrowly nationalistic or provincial, any more than is the work of Joyce or Yeats, of Synge or O'Casey.) At one time or another in his career, O'Connor took part in the great artistic and political movements of his country, having served on the board of The Abbey Theater and having soldiered with the Irish Republican Army. These activities are described, with the charm of understatement and anti-heroic modesty, in an interview with O'Connor published by *The Paris Review* (Autumn-Winter, 1957), from which we also learn that O'Connor now lives in the United States, in Brooklyn to be exact, and that he returns to Ireland once a year. He has taught courses in writing at various American universities, but he has found that teaching interferes with his own writing, that he becomes so involved in the work of his students that he has "nothing left over to write." And, as we have seen, he thinks of himself as being essentially and professionally a writer, and has borne out that claim in his work.

O'Connor holds very forthright views about the nature of fiction, about the way readers and writers have been led into the wilderness by the more influential and self-conscious practitioners of the art in recent generations, and about the directions which novelists and story-writers ought now to take in order to regain a vigor and essential rightness of aim which have been obscured or lost. It may be permitted to believe that, as a critic, he is more useful when he is describing what fiction can do, the positive aims which he himself has so ably achieved in his best stories, than when he is talking about the ways in which other writers have been misguided. Nevertheless, some of the points on which he insists are points which have needed to be insisted upon for some time now. Asked, in the interview already referred to, "What is the greatest essential of a story?" he answered, "You have to have a theme, a story to tell," and went on to explain what he meant by a theme—"A theme is something that is worth something to everybody. . . . You grab somebody and say, 'Look, an extraordinary thing happened to me yesterday—I met a man—he said this to me—' and that, to me, is a theme—the moment you grab somebody by the lapels and you've got something to tell, that's a real story." He also believes that the story should be told straightforwardly—"If you've got a story to tell about people and tell it in the way in which it comes chronologically, you've got the best thing you can get in fiction." These statements, and others like them in the same article, can be dangerously simplistic if they are applied hit-or-miss to writers of the recent past—James, Conrad, Joyce, for example—who have had, after all, other aims in writing their fiction than Frank O'Connor has in writing his. But such statements do constitute an insistence on certain fundamental virtues that younger writers, perhaps too eager to follow the examples of Henry James or of James Joyce, might well be encouraged to cultivate.

It will be apparent to any reader of the following story that Frank O'Connor has both a story to tell and the art to tell it. For all its air of slightness, of being completely casual, "First Confession" could easily be taken as a text for a lesson on such matters as the successful and delightful use of dramatic irony (our knowing, and sharing with the adult narrator, things that are not known to the little boy, so that the motive energy of the story is the implicit contrast between the boy's view of himself and our view of him), or the way in which an entire personality is revealed in the boy's conflict with the ill-understood forces of the adult world. Perhaps the best service one can render a reader of "First Confession," however, is to direct him to books which contain more of O'Connor's work. At present, his short stories are most conveniently obtained in two particular volumes, *The Stories of Frank O'Connor* (Knopf, 1952) and *More Stories by Frank O'Connor* (Knopf, 1954). A selection of the stories in these two volumes has been published in paper-back form by Vintage Books (1956), under the title *Stories by Frank O'Connor*.

FIRST CONFESSION

All the trouble began when my grandfather died and my grandmother— my father's mother—came to live with us. Relations in the one house are a strain at the best of times, but, to make matters worse, my grandmother was a real old countrywoman and quite unsuited to the life in town. She had a fat, wrinkled old face, and, to Mother's great indignation, went round the house in bare feet—the boots had her crippled, she said. For

REPRINTED from *The Stories of Frank O'Connor* by Frank O'Connor, by permission of Alfred A. Knopf, Inc. Copyright 1951, 1952 by Frank O'Connor.

dinner she had a jug of porter and a pot of potatoes with—sometimes—a bit of salt fish, and she poured out the potatoes on the table and ate them slowly, with great relish, using her fingers by way of a fork.

Now, girls are supposed to be fastidious, but I was the one who suffered most from this. Nora, my sister, just sucked up to the old woman for the penny she got every Friday out of the old-age pension, a thing I could not do. I was too honest, that was my trouble; and when I was playing with Bill Connell, the sergeant-major's son, and saw my grandmother steering up the path with the jug of porter sticking out from beneath her shawl I was mortified. I made excuses not to let him come into the house, because I could never be sure what she would be up to when we went in.

When Mother was at work and my grandmother made the dinner I wouldn't touch it. Nora once tried to make me, but I hid under the table from her and took the bread-knife with me for protection. Nora let on to be very indignant (she wasn't, of course, but she knew Mother saw through her, so she sided with Gran) and came after me. I lashed out at her with the bread-knife, and after that she left me alone. I stayed there till Mother came in from work and made my dinner, but when Father came in later Nora said in a shocked voice: "Oh, Dadda, do you know what Jackie did at dinnertime?" Then, of course, it all came out; Father gave me a flaking; Mother interfered, and for days after that he didn't speak to me and Mother barely spoke to Nora. And all because of that old woman! God knows, I was heart-scalded.

Then, to crown my misfortunes, I had to make my first confession and communion. It was an old woman called Ryan who prepared us for these. She was about the one age with Gran; she was well-to-do, lived in a big house on Montenotte, wore a black cloak and bonnet, and came every day to school at three o'clock when we should have been going home, and talked to us of hell. She may have mentioned the other place as well, but that could only have been by accident, for hell had the first place in her heart.

She lit a candle, took out a new half-crown, and offered it to the first boy who would hold one finger—only one finger!—in the flame for five minutes by the school clock. Being always very ambitious I was tempted to volunteer, but I thought it might look greedy. Then she asked were we afraid of holding one finger—only one finger!—in a little candle flame for five minutes and not afraid of burning all over in roasting hot furnaces for all eternity. "All eternity! Just think of that! A whole lifetime goes by and it's nothing, not even a drop in the ocean of your sufferings." The woman was really interesting about hell, but my attention was all fixed on the half-crown. At the end of the lesson she put it back in her purse. It was a great disappointment; a religious woman like that, you wouldn't think she'd bother about a thing like a half-crown.

Another day she said she knew a priest who woke one night to find a fellow he didn't recognize leaning over the end of his bed. The priest was a bit frightened—naturally enough—but he asked the fellow what he

wanted, and the fellow said in a deep, husky voice that he wanted to go
to confession. The priest said it was an awkward time and wouldn't it do
in the morning, but the fellow said that last time he went to confession,
there was one sin he kept back, being ashamed to mention it, and now it
was always on his mind. Then the priest knew it was a bad case, because
the fellow was after making a bad confession and committing a mortal
sin. He got up to dress, and just then the cock crew in the yard outside,
and—lo and behold!—when the priest looked round there was no sign of
the fellow, only a smell of burning timber, and when the priest looked at
his bed didn't he see the print of two hands burned in it? That was because the fellow had made a bad confession. This story made a shocking
impression on me.

But the worst of all was when she showed us how to examine our conscience. Did we take the name of the Lord, our God, in vain? Did we
honour our father and our mother? (I asked her did this include grandmothers and she said it did.) Did we love our neighbours as ourselves?
Did we covet our neighbour's goods? (I thought of the way I felt about
the penny that Nora got every Friday.) I decided that, between one thing
and another, I must have broken the whole ten commandments, all on
account of that old woman, and so far as I could see, so long as she remained in the house I had no hope of ever doing anything else.

I was scared to death of confession. The day the whole class went I let
on to have a toothache, hoping my absence wouldn't be noticed; but at
three o'clock, just as I was feeling safe, along comes a chap with a message from Mrs. Ryan that I was to go to confession myself on Saturday
and be at the chapel for communion with the rest. To make it worse,
Mother couldn't come with me and sent Nora instead.

Now, that girl had ways of tormenting me that Mother never knew of.
She held my hand as we went down the hill, smiling sadly and saying how
sorry she was for me, as if she were bringing me to the hospital for an
operation.

"Oh, God help us!" she moaned. "Isn't it a terrible pity you weren't
a good boy? Oh, Jackie, my heart bleeds for you! How will you ever think
of all your sins? Don't forget you have to tell him about the time you
kicked Gran on the shin."

"Lemme go!" I said, trying to drag myself free of her. "I don't want to
go to confession at all."

"But sure, you'll have to go to confession, Jackie," she replied in the
same regretful tone. "Sure, if you didn't, the parish priest would be up to
the house, looking for you. 'Tisn't, God knows, that I'm not sorry for you.
Do you remember the time you tried to kill me with the breadknife under
the table? And the language you used to me? I don't know what he'll do
with you at all, Jackie. He might have to send you up to the bishop."

I remember thinking bitterly that she didn't know the half of what I
had to tell—if I told it. I knew I couldn't tell it, and understood perfectly
why the fellow in Mrs. Ryan's story made a bad confession; it seemed to

me a great shame that people wouldn't stop criticizing him. I remember that steep hill down to the church, and the sunlit hillsides beyond the valley of the river, which I saw in the gaps between the houses like Adam's last glimpse of Paradise.

Then, when she had manoeuvred me down the long flight of steps to the chapel yard, Nora suddenly changed her tone. She became the raging malicious devil she really was.

"There you are!" she said with a yelp of triumph, hurling me through the church door. "And I hope he'll give you the penitential psalms, you dirty little caffler."

I knew then I was lost, given up to eternal justice. The door with the coloured-glass panels swung shut behind me, the sunlight went out and gave place to deep shadow, and the wind whistled outside so that the silence within seemed to crackle like ice under my feet. Nora sat in front of me by the confession box. There were a couple of old women ahead of her, and then a miserable-looking poor devil came and wedged me in at the other side, so that I couldn't escape even if I had the courage. He joined his hands and rolled his eyes in the direction of the roof, muttering aspirations in an anguished tone, and I wondered had he a grandmother too. Only a grandmother could account for a fellow behaving in that heartbroken way, but he was better off than I, for he at least could go and confess his sins; while I would make a bad confession and then die in the night and be continually coming back and burning people's furniture.

Nora's turn came, and I heard the sound of something slamming, and then her voice as if butter wouldn't melt in her mouth, and then another slam, and out she came. God, the hypocrisy of women! Her eyes were lowered, her head was bowed, and her hands were joined very low down on her stomach, and she walked up the aisle to the side altar looking like a saint. You never saw such an exhibition of devotion; and I remembered the devilish malice with which she had tormented me all the way from our door, and wondered were all religious people like that, really. It was my turn now. With the fear of damnation in my soul I went in, and the confessional door closed of itself behind me.

It was pitch-dark and I couldn't see priest or anything else. Then I really began to be frightened. In the darkness it was a matter between God and me, and He had all the odds. He knew what my intentions were before I even started; I had no chance. All I had ever been told about confession got mixed up in my mind, and I knelt to one wall and said: "Bless me, father, for I have sinned; this is my first confession." I waited for a few minutes, but nothing happened, so I tried it on the other wall. Nothing happened there either. He had me spotted all right.

It must have been then that I noticed the shelf at about one height with my head. It was really a place for grown-up people to rest their elbows, but in my distracted state I thought it was probably the place you were supposed to kneel. Of course, it was on the high side and not very deep, but I was always good at climbing and managed to get up all right. Staying up was the trouble. There was room only for my knees, and nothing you could get a grip on but a sort of wooden moulding a bit above it. I held on to the moulding and repeated the words a little louder, and this time something happened all right. A slide was slammed back; a little light entered the box, and a man's voice said: "Who's there?"

" 'Tis me, father," I said for fear he mightn't see me and go away again. I couldn't see him at all. The place the voice came from was under the moulding, about level with my knees, so I took a good grip of the moulding and swung myself down till I saw the astonished face of a young priest looking up at me. He had to put his head on one side to see me, and I had to put mine on one side to see him, so we were more or less talking to one another upside-down. It struck me as a queer way of hearing confessions, but I didn't feel it my place to criticize.

"Bless me, father, for I have sinned; this is my first confession," I rattled off all in one breath, and swung myself down the least shade more to make it easier for him.

"What are you doing up there?" he shouted in an angry voice, and the strain the politeness was putting on my hold of the moulding, and the shock of being addressed in such an uncivil tone, were too much for me. I lost my grip, tumbled, and hit the door an unmerciful wallop before I found myself flat on my back in the middle of the aisle. The people who had been waiting stood up with their mouths open. The priest opened the door of the middle box and came out, pushing his biretta back from his forehead; he looked something terrible. Then Nora came scampering down the aisle.

"Oh, you dirty little caffler!" she said. "I might have known you'd do it. I might have known you'd disgrace me. I can't leave you out of my sight for one minute."

Before I could even get to my feet to defend myself she bent down and gave me a clip across the ear. This reminded me that I was so stunned I had even forgotten to cry, so that people might think I wasn't hurt at all, when in fact I was probably maimed for life. I gave a roar out of me.

"What's all this about?" the priest hissed, getting angrier than ever and pushing Nora off me. "How dare you hit the child like that, you little vixen?"

"But I can't do my penance with him, father," Nora cried, cocking an outraged eye up at him.

"Well, go and do it, or I'll give you some more to do," he said, giving me a hand up. "Was it coming to confession you were, my poor man?" he asked me.

" 'Twas, father," said I with a sob.

"Oh," he said respectfully, "a big hefty fellow like you must have terrible sins. Is this your first?"

" 'Tis, father," said I.

"Worse and worse," he said gloomily. "The crimes of a lifetime. I don't know will I get rid of you at all today. You'd better wait now till I'm finished with these old ones. You can see by the looks of them they haven't much to tell."

"I will, father," I said with something approaching joy.

The relief of it was really enormous. Nora stuck out her tongue at me from behind his back, but I couldn't even be bothered retorting. I knew from the very moment that man opened his mouth that he was intelligent above the ordinary. When I had time to think, I saw how right I was. It only stood to reason that a fellow confessing after seven years would have more to tell than people that went every week. The crimes of a lifetime, exactly as he said. It was only what he expected, and the rest was the cackle of old women and girls with their talk of hell, the bishop, and the penitential psalms. That was all they knew. I started to make my examination of conscience, and barring the one bad business of my grandmother it didn't seem so bad.

The next time, the priest steered me into the confession box himself and left the shutter back the way I could see him get in and sit down at the further side of the grille from me.

"Well, now," he said, "what do they call you?"

"Jackie, father," said I.

"And what's a-trouble to you, Jackie?"

"Father," I said, feeling I might as well get it over while I had him in good humour, "I had it all arranged to kill my grandmother."

He seemed a bit shaken by that, all right, because he said nothing for quite a while.

"My goodness," he said at last, "that'd be a shocking thing to do. What put that into your head?"

"Father," I said, feeling very sorry for myself, "she's an awful woman."

"Is she?" he asked. "What way is she awful?"

"She takes porter, father," I said, knowing well from the way Mother talked of it that this was a mortal sin, and hoping it would make the priest take a more favourable view of my case.

"Oh, my!" he said, and I could see he was impressed.

"And snuff, father," said I.

"That's a bad case, sure enough, Jackie," he said.

"And she goes round in her bare feet, father," I went on in a rush of self-pity, "and she knows I don't like her, and she gives pennies to Nora and none to me, and my da sides with her and flakes me, and one night I was so heart-scalded I made up my mind I'd have to kill her."

"And what would you do with the body?" he asked with great interest.

"I was thinking I could chop that up and carry it away in a barrow I have," I said.

"Begor, Jackie," he said, "do you know you're a terrible child?"

"I know, father," I said, for I was just thinking the same thing myself. "I tried to kill Nora too with a bread-knife under the table, only I missed her."

"Is that the little girl that was beating you just now?" he asked.

" 'Tis, father."

"Someone will go for her with a bread-knife one day, and he won't miss her," he said rather cryptically. "You must have great courage. Between ourselves, there's a lot of people I'd like to do the same to but I'd never have the nerve. Hanging is an awful death."

"Is it, father?" I asked with the deepest interest—I was always very keen on hanging. "Did you ever see a fellow hanged?"

"Dozens of them," he said solemnly. "And they all died roaring."

"Jay!" I said.

"Oh, a horrible death!" he said with great satisfaction. "Lots of the fellows I saw killed their grandmothers too, but they all said 'twas never worth it."

He had me there for a full ten minutes talking, and then walked out the chapel yard with me. I was genuinely sorry to part with him, because he was the most entertaining character I'd ever met in the religious line. Outside, after the shadow of the church, the sunlight was like the roaring of waves on a beach; it dazzled me; and when the frozen silence melted and I heard the screech of trams on the road my heart soared. I knew now I wouldn't die in the night and come back, leaving marks on my mother's furniture. It would be a great worry to her, and the poor soul had enough.

Nora was sitting on the railing, waiting for me, and she put on a very sour puss when she saw the priest with me. She was mad jealous because a priest had never come out of the church with her.

"Well," she asked coldly, after he left me, "what did he give you?"

"Three Hail Marys," I said.

"Three Hail Marys," she repeated incredulously. "You mustn't have told him anything."

"I told him everything," I said confidently.

"About Gran and all?"

"About Gran and all."

(All she wanted was to be able to go home and say I'd made a bad confession.)

"Did you tell him you went for me with the bread-knife?" she asked with a frown.

"I did to be sure."

"And he only gave you three Hail Marys?"

"That's all."

She slowly got down from the railing with a baffled air. Clearly, this was beyond her. As we mounted the steps back to the main road she looked at me suspiciously.

"What are you sucking?" she asked.

"Bullseyes."

"Was it the priest gave them to you?"

" 'Twas."

"Lord God," she wailed bitterly, "some people have all the luck! 'Tis no advantage to anybody trying to be good. I might just as well be a sinner like you."

QUESTIONS

1. What is the point of view from which the story is told? To what extent does the reader see the other personages of the story as Jackie sees them? Are there any important respects in which the reader sees them differently?

2. In your estimation does the story make only incidental use of irony, or could irony be described as its prevailing mode? What is the connection between irony and point of view in this story?

WALTER VAN TILBURG CLARK

(1909–   )

Walter Van Tilburg Clark is well known for his three novels, *The Ox-Bow Incident* (1940), *The City of Trembling Leaves* (1945), and *The Track of The Cat* (1949), the first and the third of which have been made into movies. A volume of his short stories was published in 1950, under the title of *The Watchful Gods*, and it is from that volume that "The Indian Well" is taken. Readers of the present volume may have encountered Clark's stories in other anthologies, "The Wind and the Snow of Winter" and "The Portable Phonograph," especially, having been frequently reprinted. Without wanting all writers to be alike, and without being ungrateful for the devotion with which other writers have explored areas of subject-matter that are of secondary interest to Clark, we sometimes experience a feeling of relief when we turn from having read one account too many of the psychological and social complexities of self-conscious urban existences to one of Clark's stories about the lives and deaths of men and animals in the West. (His work is not limited to such subject-matter, as readers of *The City of Trembling Leaves* or of the title story from *The Watchful Gods* are aware.) Nor is there anything of over-simplification or escapism in his stories, which are not correctly to be seen as limited accounts of rudimentary existences. But in stories like "Hook," which tells the life-story of a hawk, or in "The Wind and the Snow of Winter," which makes an old prospector's last winter journey into town a focus for the story of his whole life and employs a particularly natural and compelling symbolism in doing so, it is as if the narrative part of the story-teller's art had come into its own again after having been too long neglected for a somewhat artificial indulgence in psychological analysis.

In "The Indian Well" there is no lack of subtlety, and by the time we come to the end of it we have been told quite a good deal about human aspirations and achievements. But one of the great reasons for its special effectiveness and power is surely the way in which it chooses a site, the Indian Well which creates a small oasis in the desert, and in a calm, non-committal way describes the doings of the many existences—the rattlesnake, the road-runner, the cliff swallows, the lizards, the coyote, the cow and her calf, the jack-rabbits, the cougar, and, for a while, the prospector and his burro—for which it forms a point of intersection and, sometimes, a point of mortal conflict. Clark has chosen the point of view of one who sees—and understands—everything that happens around The Indian Well, so that what we are given is a straight-forward chronological account of all that happens in a given segment of space within a given segment of time. (This segment of time is linked up with other times by the inscriptions on the cabin walls, and by certain more ancient inscriptions on the cliff.) His story reminds us of something we may have been inclined to forget in recent years: what a deeply absorbing thing it can be to watch, from a point of vantage, men—and animals—in action, and what a large part of what we wish to know about them can be revealed by describing their actions.

THE INDIAN WELL

In this dead land, like a vast relief model, the only allegiance was to sun. Even night was not strong enough to resist; earth stretched gratefully under it, but had no hope that day would not return. Such living things as hoarded a little juice at their cores were secret about it, and only the most ephemeral existences, the air at dawn and sunset, the amethyst shadows in the mountains, had any freedom. The Indian Well alone, of lesser creations, was in constant revolt. Sooner or later all minor, breathing rebels came to its stone basin under the spring in the cliff, and from its overflow grew a meadow delta and two columns of willows and aspens holding a tiny front against the valley. The pictograph of a starving, ancient journey, cut in rock above the basin, a sun-warped shack on the south wing of the canyon, and an abandoned mine above it, were the last minute and practically contemporary tokens of man's participation in the cycles of the well's resistance, each of which was an epitome of centuries, and perhaps of the wars of the universe.

The day before Jim Suttler came up in the early spring to take his part in one cycle was a busy day. The sun was merely lucid after four days of broken showers and one rain of an hour with a little cold wind behind it, and under the separate cloud shadows sliding down the mountain and into the valley, the canyon was alive. A rattler emerged partially from a hole in the mound on which the cabin stood, and having gorged in the darkness, rested with his head on a stone. A road-runner, stepping long and always about to sprint, came down the morning side of the mound, and his eye, quick to perceive the difference between the live and the inanimate of the same color, discovered the coffin-shaped head on the stone. At once he broke into a reaching sprint, his neck and tail stretched level, his beak agape with expectation. But his shadow arrived a step before him. The rattler recoiled, his head scarred by the sharp beak but his eye intact. The road-runner said nothing, but peered warily into the hole without stretching his neck, then walked off stiffly, leaning forward again as if about to run. When he had gone twenty feet he turned, balanced for an instant, and charged back, checking abruptly just short of the hole. The snake remained withdrawn. The road-runner paraded briefly before the hole, talking to himself, and then ran angrily up to the spring, where he drank at the overflow, sipping and stretching his neck, lifting his feet one at a time, ready to go into immediate action. The road-runner lived a dangerous and exciting life.

In the upper canyon the cliff swallows, making short harp notes, dipped and shot between the new mud under the aspens and their high community on the forehead of the cliff. Electrical bluebirds appeared to dart the length of the canyon at each low flight, but turned up tilting half way down. Lizards made similar unexpected flights and stops on the rocks, and when they stopped did rapid push-ups, like men exercising on a floor. They were variably pugnacious and timid.

Two of them arrived simultaneously upon a rock below the road-runner. One of them immediately skittered to a rock two feet off, and they faced each other, exercising. A small hawk coming down over the mountain, but shadowless under a cloud, saw the lizards. Having overfled the difficult target, he dropped to the canyon mouth swiftly and banked back into the wind. His trajectory was cleared of swallows but one of them, fluttering hastily up, dropped a pellet of mud between the lizards. The one who had retreated disappeared. The other flattened for an instant, then sprang and charged. The road-runner was on him as he struck the pellet, and galloped down the canyon in great, tense strides on his toes, the lizard lashing the air from his beak. The hawk stooped at the road-runner, thought better of it, and rose against the wind to the head of the canyon, where he turned back and coasted out over the desert, his shadow a little behind him and farther and farther below.

The swallows became the voice of the canyon again, but in moments when they were all silent the lovely smaller sounds emerged, their own feathering, the liquid overflow, the snapping and clicking of insects, a touch of wind in the new aspens. Under these lay still more delicate tones, erasing, in the most silent seconds, the difference between eye and ear, a white cloud shadow passing under the water of the well, a dark cloud shadow on the cliff, the aspen patterns on the stones. Deepest was the permanent background of the rocks, the lost on the canyon floor, and those yet strong, the thinking cliffs. When the swallows began again it was impossible to understand the cliffs, who could afford to wait.

At noon a red and white range cow with one new calf, shining and curled, came slowly up from the desert, stopping often to let the calf rest. At each stop the calf would try vigorously to feed, but the cow would go on. When they reached the well the cow drank slowly for a long time; then she continued to wrinkle the water with her muzzle, drinking a little and blowing, as if she found it hard to leave. The calf worked under her with spasmodic nudgings. When she was done playing with the water, she nosed and licked him out from under her and up to the well. He shied from the surprising coolness and she put him back. When he stayed, she drank again. He put his nose into the water also, and bucked up as if bitten. She continued to pretend, and he returned, got water up his nostrils and took three jumps away. The cow was content and moved off toward the canyon wall, tonguing grass tufts from among the rocks. Against the cliff she rubbed gently and continuously with a mild voluptuous look, occasionally lapping her nose with a serpent tongue. The loose winter shag came off in tufts on the rock. The calf lost her, became panicked and made desperate noises which stopped prematurely, and when he discovered her, complicated her toilet. Finally she led him down to the meadow where, moving slowly, they both fed until he was full and went to sleep in a ball in the sun. At sunset they returned to the well, where the cow drank again and gave him a second lesson. After this they went back into the brush and northward into the dusk. The cow's size and relative immunity to sudden death left an aftermath of peace, rendered gently humorous by the calf.

Also at sunset, there was a resurgence of life among the swallows. The thin golden air at the cliff tops, in which there were now no clouds so that the eastern mountains and the valley were flooded with unbroken light, was full of their cries and quick maneuvers among a dancing myriad of insects. The direct sun gave them, when they perched in rows upon the cliff, a dramatic significance like that of men upon an immensely higher promontory. As dusk rose out of the canyon, while the eastern peaks were still lighted, the swallows gradually became silent creatures with slightly altered flight, until, at twilight, the air was full of velvet, swooping bats.

In the night jack-rabbits multiplied spontaneously out of the brush of the valley, drank in the rivulet, their noses and great ears continuously searching the dark, electrical air, and played in fits and starts on the meadow, the many young hopping like rubber, or made thumping love among the aspens and the willows.

A coyote came down canyon on his belly and lay in the brush with his nose between his paws. He took a young rabbit in a quiet spring and snap, and went into the brush again to eat it. At the slight rending of his meal the meadow cleared of leaping shadows and lay empty in the starlight. The rabbits, however, encouraged by newcomers, returned soon, and the coyote killed again and went off heavily, the jack's great hind legs dragging.

In the dry-wash below the meadow an old coyote, without family, profited by the second panic, which came over him. He ate what his loose teeth could tear, leaving the open remnant in the sand, drank at the basin and, carefully circling the meadow, disappeared into the dry wilderness.

Shortly before dawn, when the stars had lost luster and there was no sound in the canyon but the rivulet and the faint, separate clickings of mice in the gravel, nine antelope in loose file, with three silently flagging fawns, came on trigger toe up the meadow and drank at the well, heads often up, muzzles dripping, broad ears turning. In the meadow they grazed and the fawns nursed. When there was as much gray as darkness in the air, and new wind in the canyon, they departed, the file weaving into the brush, merging into the desert, to nothing, and the swallows resumed the talkative day shift.

Jim Suttler and his burro came up into the meadow a little after noon, very slowly, though there was only a spring-fever warmth. Suttler walked pigeon-toed, like an old climber, but carefully and stiffly, not with the loose walk natural to such a long-legged man. He stopped in the middle of the meadow, took off his old black sombrero, and stared up at the veil of water shining over the edge of the basin.

"We're none too early, Jenny," he said to the burro.

The burro had felt water for miles, but could show no excitement. She stood with her head down and her four legs spread unnaturally, as if to postpone a collapse. Her pack reared higher than Suttler's head, and was hung with casks, pails, canteens, a pick, two shovels, a crowbar and a rifle in a sheath. Suttler had the cautious uncertainty of his trade. His other burro had died two days before in the mountains east of Beatty, and Jenny and he bore its load.

Suttler shifted his old six shooter from his rump to his thigh, and studied the well, the meadow, the cabin and the mouth of the mine as if he might choose not to stay. He was not a cinema prospector. If he looked like one of the probably mistaken conceptions of Christ, with his red beard and red hair to his shoulders, it was because he had been long away from barbers and without spare water for shaving. He was unlike Christ in some other ways also.

"It's kinda run down," he told Jenny, "but we'll take it."

He put his sombrero back on, let his pack fall slowly to the ground, showing the sweat patch in his bleached brown shirt, and began to unload Jenny carefully, like a collector handling rare vases, and put everything into one neat pile.

"Now," he said, "we'll have a drink." His tongue and lips were so swollen that the words were unclear, but he spoke casually, like a clubman sealing a minor deal. One learns to do business slowly with deserts and mountains. He picked up a bucket and started for the well. At the upper edge of the meadow he looked back. Jenny was still standing with her head down and her legs apart. He did not particularly notice her extreme thinness for he had seen it coming on gradually. He was thinner himself, and tall, and so round-shouldered that when he stood his straightest he seemed to be peering ahead with his chin out.

"Come on, you old fool," he said. "It's off you now."

Jenny came, stumbling in the rocks above the meadow, and stopping often as if to decide why this annoyance recurred. When she became interested, Suttler would not let her get to the basin, but for ten minutes gave her water from his cupped hands, a few licks at a time. Then he drove her off and she stood in the shade of the canyon wall watching him. He began on his thirst in the same way, a gulp at a time, resting between gulps. After ten gulps he sat on a rock by the spring and looked at the little meadow and the big desert, and might have been considering the courses of the water through his body, but noticed also the antelope tracks in the mud.

After a time he drank another half dozen gulps, gave Jenny half a pailful, and drove her down to the meadow, where he spread a dirty blanket in the striped sun and shadow under the willows. He sat on the edge of the blanket, rolled a cigarette and smoked it while he watched Jenny. When she began to graze with her rump to the canyon, he flicked his cigarette onto the grass, rolled over with his back to the sun and slept until it became chilly after sunset. Then he woke, ate a can of beans, threw the can into the willows and led Jenny up to the well, where they drank together from the basin for a long time. While she resumed her grazing, he took another blanket and his rifle from the pile, removed his heel-worn boots, stood his rifle against a fork, and, rolling up in both blankets, slept again.

In the night many rabbits played in the meadow in spite of the strong sweat and tobacco smell of Jim Suttler lying under the willows, but the antelope, when they came in the dead dark before dawn, were nervous, drank less, and did not graze but minced quickly back across the meadow and began to run at the head of the dry wash. Jenny slept with her head hanging, and did not hear them come or go.

Suttler woke lazy and still red-eyed, and spent the morning drinking at the well, eating and dozing on his blanket. In the afternoon, slowly, a few things at a time, he carried his pile to the cabin. He had a bachelor's obsession with order, though he did not mind dirt, and puttered until sundown making a brush bed and arranging his gear. Much of this time, however, was spent studying the records, on the cabin walls, of the recent human life of the well. He had to be careful, because among the still legible names and dates, after Frank Davis, 1893, Willard Harbinger, 1893, London, England, John Mason, June 13, 1887, Bucksport, Maine, Matthew Kenling, from Glasgow, 1891, Penelope and Martin Reave, God Guide Us, 1885, was written Frank Hayward, 1492, feeling my age. There were other wits too. John Barr had written, Giv it back to the injuns, and Kenneth Thatcher, two years later, had written under that, Pity the noble redskin, while another man, whose second name was Evans, had written what was already a familiar libel, since it was not strictly true: Fifty miles from water, a hundred miles from wood, a million miles from God, three feet from hell. Someone unnamed had felt differently, saying, God is kind. We may make it now. Shot an antelope here July 10, 188— and the last number blurred. Arthur Smith, 1881, had recorded, Here berried my beloved wife Semantha, age 22, and my soul. God let me keep the child. J.M. said cryptically, Good luck, John, and Bill said, Ralph, if you come this way, am trying to get to Los Angeles. B. Westover said he had recovered from his wound there in 1884, and Galt said, enigmatically and without date, Bart and Miller burned to death in the Yellow Jacket. I don't care now. There were poets too, of both parties. What could still be read of Byron Cotter's verses, written in 1902, said,

. . . here alone
Each shining dawn I greet,
The Lord's wind on my forehead
And where he set his feet
One mark of heel remaining
Each day filled up anew,
To keep my soul from burning,
With clear, celestial dew.
Here in His Grace abiding
The mortal years and few
I shall . . . but you can't tell what he intended, while J.A. had printed,
My brother came out in '49
I came in '51
At first we thought we liked it fine
But now, by God, we're done.

Suttler studied these records without smiling, like someone reading a funny paper, and finally, with a heavy blue pencil, registered, Jim and Jenny Suttler, damn dried out, March—and paused, but had no way of discovering the day—1940.

In the evening he sat on the steps watching the swallows in the golden upper canyon turn bats in the dusk, and thought about the antelope. He had seen the new tracks also, and it alarmed him a little that the antelope could have passed twice in the dark without waking him.

Before false dawn he was lying in the willows with his carbine at ready. Rabbits ran from the meadow when he came down, and after that there was no movement. He wanted to smoke. When he did see them at the lower edge of the meadow, he was startled, yet made no quick movement, but slowly pivoted to cover them. They made poor targets in that light and backed by the pale desert, appearing and disappearing before his eyes. He couldn't keep any one of them steadily visible, and decided to wait until they made contrast against the meadow. But his presence was strong. One of the antelope advanced onto the green, but then threw its head up, spun, and ran back past the flank of the herd, which swung after him. Suttler rose quickly and raised the rifle, but let it down without firing. He could hear the light rattle of their flight in the wash, but had only a belief that he could see them. He had few cartridges, and the report and ponderous echo under the cliffs would scare them off for weeks.

His energies, however, were awakened by the frustrated hunt. While there was still more light than heat in the canyon, he climbed to the abandoned mine tunnel at the top of the alluvial wing of the cliff. He looked at the broken rock in the dump, kicked up its pack with a boot toe, and went into the tunnel, peering closely at its sides, in places black with old smoke smudges. At the back he struck two matches and looked at the jagged dead end and the fragments on the floor, then returned to the shallow beginning of a side tunnel. At the second match here he knelt quickly, scrutinized a portion of the rock, and when the match went out at once lit another. He lit six matches, and pulled at the rock with his hand. It was firm.

"The poor chump," he said aloud.

He got a loose rock from the tunnel and hammered at the projection with it. It came finally, and he carried it into the sun on the dump.

"Yessir," he said aloud, after a minute.

He knocked his sample into three pieces and examined each minutely.

"Yessir, yessir," he said with malicious glee, and, grinning at the tunnel, "The poor chump."

Then he looked again at the dump, like the mound before a gigantic gopher hole. "Still, that's a lot of digging," he said.

He put sample chips into his shirt pocket, keeping a small, black, heavy one that had fallen neatly from a hole like a borer's, to play with in his hand. After trouble he found the claim pile on the side hill south of the tunnel, its top rocks tumbled into the shale. Under the remaining rocks he found what he wanted, a ragged piece of yellowed paper between two boards. The writing was in pencil, and not diplomatic. "I hereby clame this whole damn side hill as far as I can shoot north and south and as far as I can dig in. I am a good shot. Keep off. John Barr, April 11, 1897."

Jim Suttler grinned. "Tough guy, eh?" he said.

He made a small ceremony of burning the paper upon a stone from the cairn. The black tinsel of ash blew off and broke into flakes.

"O.K., John Barr?" he asked.

"O.K., Suttler," he answered himself.

In blue pencil, on soiled paper from his pocket, he slowly printed, "Becus of the lamented desease of the late clament, John Barr, I now clame these diggins for myself and partner Jenny. I can shoot too." And wrote rather than printed, "James T. Suttler, March—" and paused.

"Make it an even month," he said, and wrote, "11, 1940." Underneath he wrote, "Jenny Suttler, her mark," and drew a skull with long ears.

"There," he said, and folded the paper, put it between the two boards, and rebuilt the cairn into a neat pyramid above it.

In high spirit he was driven to cleanliness. With scissors, soap and razor he climbed to the spring. Jenny was there, drinking.

"When you're done," he said, and when she lifted her head, pulled her ears and scratched her.

"Maybe we've got something here, Jenny," he said.

Jenny observed him soberly and returned to the meadow.

"She doesn't believe me," he said, and began to perfect himself. He sheared off his red tresses in long hanks, then cut closer, and went over yet a third time, until there remained a brush, of varying density, of stiff red bristles, through which his scalp shone whitely. He sheared the beard likewise, then knelt to the well for mirror and shaved painfully. He also shaved his neck and about his ears. He arose younger and less impressive, with jaws as pale as his scalp, so that his sunburn was a red domino. He burned tresses and beard ceremoniously upon a sage bush, and announced, "It is spring."

He began to empty the pockets of his shirt and breeches onto a flat stone, yelling, "In the spring a young man's fancy," to a kind of tune, and paused, struck by the facts.

"Oh yeah?" he said. "Fat chance."

"Fat," he repeated with obscene consideration. "Oh, well," he said, and finished piling upon the rock notebooks, pencil stubs, cartridges, tobacco, knife, stump pipe, matches, chalk, samples, and three wrinkled photographs. One of the photographs he observed at length before weighting it down with a .45 cartridge. It showed a round, blonde girl with a big smile on a stupid face, in a patterned calico house dress, in front of a blossoming rhododendron bush.

He added to this deposit his belt and holster with the big .45.

Then he stripped himself, washed and rinsed his garments in the spring, and spread them upon stones and brush, and carefully arranged four flat stones into a platform beside the trough. Standing there he scooped water over himself, gasping, made it a lather, and at last, face and copper bristles also foaming, gropingly entered the basin, and submerged, flooding the water over in a thin and soapy sheet. His head emerged at once. "My God," he whispered. He remained under, however, till he was soapless, and goose pimpled as a file, when he climbed out cautiously onto the rock platform and performed a dance of small, revolving patterns with a great deal of up and down.

At one point in his dance he observed the pictograph journey upon the cliff, and danced nearer to examine it.

"Ignorant," he pronounced. "Like a little kid," he said.

He was intrigued, however, by more recent records, names smoked and cut upon the lower rock. One of these, in script, like a gigantic handwriting deeply cut, said ALVAREZ BLANCO DE TOLEDO, Anno Di 1624. A very neat, upright cross was chiseled beneath it.

Suttler grinned. "Oh, yeah?" he asked, with his head upon one side. "Nuts," he said, looking at it squarely.

But it inspired him, and with his jack-knife he began scraping beneath the possibly Spanish inscription. His knife, however, made scratches, not incisions. He completed a bad Jim and Jenny and quit, saying, "I should kill myself over a phony wop."

Thereafter, for weeks, while the canyon became increasingly like a furnace in the daytime and the rocks stayed warm at night, he drove his tunnel farther into the mountain and piled the dump farther into the gully, making, at one side of the entrance, a heap of ore to be worked, and occasionally adding a peculiarly heavy pebble to the others in his small leather bag with a draw string. He and Jenny thrived upon this fixed and well-watered life. The hollows disappeared from his face and he became less stringy, while Jenny grew round, her battleship-gray pelt even lustrous and its black markings distinct and ornamental. The burro found time from her grazing to come to the cabin door in the evenings and attend solemnly to Suttler playing with his samples and explaining their future.

"Then, old lady," Suttler said, "you will carry only small children, one at a time, for never more than half an hour. You will have a bedroom with French windows and a mattress, and I will paint your feet gold.

"The children," he said, "will probably be red-headed, but maybe blonde. Anyway, they will be beautiful.

"After we've had a holiday, of course," he added. "For one hundred and thirty-three nights," he said dreamily. "Also," he said, "just one hundred and thirty-three quarts. I'm no drunken bum.

"For you, though," he said, "for one hundred and thirty-three nights a quiet hotel with other old ladies. I should drag my own mother in the gutter." He pulled her head down by the ears and kissed her loudly upon the nose. They were very happy together.

Nor did they greatly alter most of the life of the canyon. The antelope did not return, it is true, the rabbits were fewer and less playful because he sometimes snared them for meat, the little, clean mice and desert rats avoided the cabin they had used, and the road-runner did not come in daylight after Suttler, for fun, narrowly missed him with a piece of ore from the tunnel mouth. Suttler's violence was disproportionate perhaps, when he used his .45 to blow apart a creamy rat who did invade the cabin, but the loss was insignificant to the pattern of the well, and more than compensated when he one day caught the rattler extended at the foot of the dump in a drunken stupor from rare young rabbit, and before it could recoil held it aloft by the tail and snapped its head off, leaving the heavy body to turn slowly for a long time among the rocks. The dominant voices went undisturbed, save when he sang badly at his work or said beautiful things to Jenny in a loud voice.

There were, however, two more noticeable changes, one of which, at least, was important to Suttler himself. The first was the execution of the range cow's calf in the late fall, when he began to suggest a bull. Suttler felt a little guilty about this because the calf might have belonged to somebody, because the cow remained near the meadow bawling for two nights, and because the calf had come to meet the gun with more curiosity than challenge. But when he had the flayed carcass hung in the mine tunnel in a wet canvas, the sensation of providence overcame any qualms.

The other change was more serious. It occurred at the beginning of such winter as the well had, when there was sometimes a light rime on the rocks at dawn, and the aspens held only a few yellow leaves. Suttler thought often of leaving. The nights were cold, the fresh meat was eaten, his hopes had diminished as he still found only occasional nuggets, and his dreams of women, if less violent, were more nostalgic. The canyon held him with a feeling he would have called lonesome but at home, yet he probably would have gone except for this second change.

In the higher mountains to the west, where there was already snow, and at dawn a green winter sky, hunger stirred a buried memory in a cougar. He had twice killed antelope at the well, and felt there had been time enough again. He came down from the dwarfed trees and crossed the narrow valley under the stars, sometimes stopping abruptly to stare intently about, like a house-cat in a strange room. After each stop he would at once resume a quick, noiseless trot. From the top of the mountain above the spring he came down very slowly on his belly, but there was nothing at the well. He relaxed, and leaning on the rim of the basin, drank, listening between laps. His nose was clean with fasting, and he knew of the man in the cabin and Jenny in the meadow, but they were strange, not what he remembered about the place. But neither had his past made him fearful. It was only habitual hunting caution which made him go down into the willows carefully, and lie there head up, watching Jenny, but still waiting for antelope, which he had killed before near dawn. The strange smells were confusing and therefore irritating. After an hour he rose and went silently to the cabin, from which the strangest smell came strongly, a carnivorous smell which did not arouse appetite, but made him bristle nervously. The tobacco in it was like pins in his nostrils. He circled the cabin, stopping frequently. At the open door the scent was violent. He stood with his front paws up on the step, moving his head in serpent motions, the end of his heavy tail furling and unfurling constantly. In a dream Suttler turned over without waking, and muttered. The cougar crouched, his eyes intent, his ruff lifting. Then he swung away from the door, growling a little, and after one pause, crept back down to the meadow again and lay in the willows, but where he could watch the cabin also.

When the sky was alarmingly pale and the antelope had not come, he crawled a few feet at a time, behind the willows, to a point nearer Jenny. There he crouched, working his hind legs slowly under him until he was set, and sprang, raced the three or four jumps to the drowsy burro, and struck. The beginning of her mortal scream was severed, but having made an imperfect leap, and from no height, the cat did not at once break her neck, but drove her to earth, where her small hooves churned futilely in the sod, and chewed and worried until she lay still.

Jim Suttler was nearly awakened by the fragment of scream, but heard nothing after it, and sank again.

The cat wrestled Jenny's body into the willows, fed with uncertain relish, drank long at the well, and went slowly over the crest, stopping often to look back. In spite of the light and the beginning talk of the swallows, the old coyote also fed and was gone before Suttler woke.

When Suttler found Jenny, many double columns of regimented ants were already at work, streaming in and out of the interior and mounting like bridge workers upon the ribs. Suttler stood and looked down. He desired to hold the small muzzle in the hollow of his hand, feeling that this familiar gesture would get through to Jenny, but couldn't bring himself to it because of what had happened to that side of her head. He squatted and lifted one hoof on its stiff leg and held that. Ants emerged hurriedly from the fetlock, their lines of communication broken. Two of them made disorganized excursions on the back of his hand. He rose, shook them off, and stood staring again. He didn't say anything because he spoke easily only when cheerful or excited, but a determination was beginning in him. He followed the drag to the spot torn by the small hoofs. Among the willows again, he found the tracks of both the cougar and the coyote, and the cat's tracks again at the well and by the cabin doorstep. He left Jenny in the willows with a canvas over her during the day, and did not eat.

At sunset he sat on the doorstep, cleaning his rifle and oiling it until he could spring the lever almost without sound. He filled the clip, pressed it home, and sat with the gun across his knees until dark, when he put on his sheepskin, stuffed a scarf into the pocket, and went down to Jenny. He removed the canvas from her, rolled it up and held it under his arm.

"I'm sorry, old woman," he said. "Just tonight."

There was a little cold wind in the willows. It rattled the upper branches lightly.

Suttler selected a spot thirty yards down wind, from which he could see Jenny, spread the canvas and lay down upon it, facing toward her. After an hour he was afraid of falling asleep and sat up against a willow clump. He sat there all night. A little after midnight the old coyote came into the dry-wash below him. At the top of the wash he sat down, and when the mingled scents gave him a clear picture of the strategy, let his tongue loll out, looked at the stars for a moment with his mouth silently open, rose and trotted back into the desert.

At the beginning of daylight the younger coyote trotted in from the north, and turned up toward the spring, but saw Jenny. He sat down and looked at her for a long time. Then he moved to the west and sat down again. In the wind was only winter, and the water, and faintly the acrid bat dung in the cliffs. He completed the circle, but not widely enough, walking slowly through the willows, down the edge of the meadow and in again not ten yards in front of the following muzzle of the carbine. Like Jenny, he felt his danger too late. The heavy slug caught him at the base of the skull in the middle of the first jump, so that it was amazingly accelerated for a fraction of a second. The coyote began it alive, and ended it quite dead, but with a tense muscular movement conceived which resulted in a grotesque final leap and twist of the hindquarters alone, leaving them propped high against a willow clump while the head was half buried in the sand, red welling up along the lips of the distended jaws. The cottony underpelt of the tail and rump stirred gleefully in the wind.

When Suttler kicked the body and it did not move, he suddenly dropped his gun, grasped it by the upright hind legs, and hurled it out into the sage-brush. His face appeared slightly insane with fury for that instant. Then he picked up his gun and went back to the cabin, where he ate, and drank half of one of his last three bottles of whiskey.

In the middle of the morning he came down with his pick and shovel, dragged Jenny's much lightened body down into the dry-wash, and dug in the rock and sand for two hours. When she was covered, he erected a small cairn of stone, like the claim post, above her.

"If it takes a year," he said, and licked the salt sweat on his lips.

That day he finished the half bottle and drank all of a second one, and became very drunk, so that he fell asleep during his vigil in the willows, sprawled wide on the dry turf and snoring. He was not disturbed. There was a difference in his smell after that day which prevented even the rabbits from coming into the meadow. He waited five nights in the willows. Then he transferred his watch to a niche in the cliff, across from and just below the spring.

All winter, while the day wind blew long veils of dust across the desert, regularly repeated, like waves or the smoke of line artillery fire, and the rocks shrank under the cold glitter of night, he did not miss a watch. He learned to go to sleep at sundown, wake within a few minutes of midnight, go up to his post, and become at once clear headed and watchful. He talked to himself in the mine and the cabin, but never in the niche. His supplies ran low, and he ate less, but would not risk a startling shot. He rationed his tobacco, and when it was gone worked up to a vomiting sickness every three days for nine days, but did not miss a night in the niche. All winter he did not remove his clothes, bathe, shave, cut his hair or sing. He worked the dead mine only to be busy, and became thin again, with sunken eyes which yet were not the eyes he had come with the spring before. It was April, his food almost gone, when he got his chance.

There was a half moon that night, which made the canyon walls black, and occasionally gleamed on wrinkles of the overflow. The cat came down so quietly that Suttler did not see him until he was beside the basin. The animal was suspicious. He took the wind, and twice started to drink, and didn't, but crouched. On Suttler's face there was a set grin which exposed his teeth.

"Not even a drink, you bastard," he thought.

The cat drank a little though, and dropped again, softly, trying to get the scent from the meadow. Suttler drew slowly upon his soul in the trigger. When it gave, the report was magnified impressively in the canyon. The cougar sprang straight into the air and screamed outrageously. The back of Suttler's neck was cold and his hands trembled, but he shucked the lever and fired again. This shot ricocheted from the basin and whined away thinly. The first, however, had struck near enough, the cat began to scramble rapidly on the loose stone, at first without voice, then screaming repeatedly. It doubled upon itself snarling and chewing in a small furious circle, fell and began to throw itself in short, leaping spasms upon the stones, struck across the rim of the tank and lay half in the water, its head and shoulders raised in one corner and resting against the cliff. Suttler could hear it breathing hoarsely and snarling very faintly. The soprano chorus of swallows gradually became silent.

Suttler had risen to fire again, but lowered the carbine and advanced, stopping at every step to peer intently and listen for the hoarse breathing, which continued. Even when he was within five feet of the tank the cougar did not move, except to gasp so that the water again splashed from the basin. Suttler was calmed by the certainty of accomplishment. He drew the heavy revolver from his holster, aimed carefully at the rattling head, and fired again. The canyon boomed, and the east responded faintly and a little behind, but Suttler did not hear them, for the cat thrashed heavily in the tank, splashing him as with a bucket, and then lay still on its side over the edge, its muzzle and forepaws hanging. The water was settling quietly in the tank, but Suttler stirred it again, shooting five more times with great deliberation into the heavy body, which did not move except at the impact of the slugs.

The rest of the night, even after the moon was gone, he worked fiercely, slitting and tearing with his knife. In the morning, under the swallows, he dragged the marbled carcass, still bleeding a little in places, onto the rocks on the side away from the spring, and dropped it. Dragging the ragged hide by the neck, he went unsteadily down the canyon to the cabin, where he slept like a drunkard, although his whiskey had been gone for two months.

In the afternoon, with dreaming eyes, he bore the pelt to Jenny's grave, took down the stones with his hands, shoveled the earth from her, covered her with the skin, and again with earth and the cairn.

He looked at this monument. "There," he said.

That night, for the first time since her death, he slept through.

In the morning, at the well, he repeated his cleansing ritual of a year before, save that they were rags he stretched to dry, even to the dance upon the rock platform while drying. Squatting naked and clean, shaven and clipped, he looked for a long time at the grinning countenance, now very dirty, of the plump girl in front of the blossoming rhododendrons, and in the resumption of his dance he made singing noises accompanied by the words, "Spring, spring, beautiful spring." He was a starved but revived and volatile spirit.

An hour later he went south, his boot soles held on by canvas strips, and did not once look back.

The disturbed life of the spring resumed. In the second night the rabbits loved in the willows, and at the end of a week the rats played in the cabin again. The old coyote and a vulture cleaned the cougar, and his bones fell apart in the shale. The road-runner came up one day, tentatively, and in front of the tunnel snatched up a horned toad and ran with it around the corner, but no farther. After a month the antelope returned. The well brimmed, and in the gentle sunlight the new aspen leaves made a tiny music of shadows.

QUESTIONS

1. How consistently, and to how large an extent, are such creatures as the road-runner, the hawk, the lizards described in terms of their actions? From what areas of life does the writer draw the metaphors he occasionally uses in describing these actions?

2. What is the effect, for meaning, of setting down the inscriptions on the cabin walls one after another with no attempt to isolate each one by quotation marks?

3. To what extent, and in what specific ways, is Jim Suttler presented as different from the other "minor, breathing rebels" whose existences come into the pattern of the story? Is it suggested, either in the story as a whole or at particular points in it, that his actions and impulses are evenly comparable to theirs?

4. What comparison (and contrast) do you find between this story and "The Circular Valley" as regards the placing of present-day individual lives against a background of other cycles and other modes of existence?

PAUL BOWLES

(1910–   )

Among the writers of fiction who have achieved prominence since the end of World War II, it is hard to think of any who have done so on the basis of a more original and consistent vision or a more assured artistic control than Paul Bowles. In a note contributed to Kunitz's *Twentieth Century Authors*, Bowles has described how in his last year in high school he had sent some poems to *transition*, the avant-garde literary magazine published in Paris between the two wars, and, when they were accepted, had continued to send poems to the little magazines and, in fact, had begun to think of himself as a poet. In this view of himself he was discouraged by Gertrude Stein, whom he visited in France in the summer of 1931. But her advice was not all negative. She suggested that he visit Tangier, he says, "which I did, at the same time determined never to write again. However, from there I posted her a short story I had written a year earlier, and she wrote me an approving letter, saying 'I take back all the harsh things I said about your writing. It makes a picture and that is always good. But it is alright to learn to play Bach in writing too.' "

But although Gertrude Stein had provided him both with approval and with the suggestion that led him to visit a part of the world that has since been of central importance to his fiction and the vision it embodies, it was to be some time before any of this took effect. For fifteen years, as Bowles points out in the autobiographical sketch already referred to, he devoted himself entirely to music (he has a very considerable reputation as a composer, and several of his works are available on records) and music criticism. Then, after translating a one-act play by Sartre, he began to write short stories, which were accepted by magazines as diverse as *Harper's Bazaar* and *Partisan Review*. An advance from a publisher enabled him to go to Tangier to write his first novel, *The Sheltering Sky*, eventually to be published (1949) not by the publisher who had given the advance but by New Directions. From this point on, he has evidently led the life of independence and detachment, in carefully chosen, exotic places, which aspiring writers hold up to themselves as the very hallmark and reward of success in the profession. He has told how, in 1952, he was finally able to buy an island off the south coast of Ceylon which had pleased him when he first saw it on a visit to India and Ceylon in 1949, and how he now "hopes to live between Ceylon and Morocco, since both are good places in which to work."

Up to the present, he has published two novels besides the first one mentioned above: *Let It Come Down* (1952) and *The Spider's House* (1955). All three of his novels have North African settings. The short stories in *The Delicate Prey* (1950) are for the most part set in North Africa, though some of them are set in Mexico, the United States, or the Caribbean. At least one edition of these stories bears on the verso of the title-page the dedication: "For my mother, who first read me the stories of Poe." This indication of a literary ancestry is significant (Bowles says he went to the University of Virginia because Poe had gone there). Certain of the stories offer the most direct similarity of aim with stories of Poe: "You Are Not I," for instance, which can challenge "The Fall of the House of Usher" or "Ligeia" for the breath-taking matter-of-factness with which a state of psychotic derangement is presented from the inside out. And Bowles' writing is always comparable to Poe's for the superb, pure, imperturbable style in which it chronicles outrage, violence, or hallucination.

Yet he usually produces his sense of horror by a more direct exploitation of actuality than we find in Poe, and this he is able to do with a special and individual effectiveness because of his knowledge of Morocco and Mexico. One of his characteristic methods is to place his American protagonist in direct, cruel contact with representatives of a civilization to whom the American's codes of behavior, to say nothing of his view of his own importance, have no meaning or validity whatever. A professor of linguistics, in Morocco, wanders too far off the beaten track, is kidnapped and sold into slavery with a nomad tribe, suffering innumerable indignities and injuries, including the cutting out of his tongue, before he escapes and makes his way back, a maniacal, clown-like figure, to the civilization from which he had so dangerously veered off ("A Distant Episode"). Or a Protestant missionary in Mexico fails to gain control of the Indians among whom he has come to work, so that they dictate more and more completely and grotesquely the conditions of his existence among them, conditions which are blandly, innocently, and diametrically opposed to any doctrine he might have hoped to bring them ("Pastor Dowe at Tacaté"). Sometimes the scope of a story is divided between the two modes of fantasy and realism, as in "The Circular Valley," reprinted here: or better say, a typical twentieth-century situation is seen, by means of fantasy, from a point of view to which all times and all modes of life are as one.

"Horror," "terror," and "suspense" are words which are used easily in our time, by the producers of movies and television shows as well as by the publishers of fiction. Nevertheless, they have a valid applicability to Bowles' stories. He has no facile didactic purpose, no direct lesson to offer about the conduct of world affairs or the shape of things to come. But he has seen, and makes us see in terms of dramatic incidents in individual lives, that there are many places in the world where the tenets and modes of Western European civilization have neither meaning nor power, and this truth gives a foundation of stark actuality to the incidents with which he confronts us. The men and women he sends wandering in these places are, more often than not, decadent and weak, drawing whatever strength they have from a civilization which they take for granted and to which they contribute nothing. Out of its protective orbit, they are whirled about by a wind of which it is difficult to say whether it is hostile or indifferently cruel: yet the sound of its rising is such as to be heard with uneasiness by keener ears than theirs.

THE CIRCULAR VALLEY

The abandoned monastery stood on a slight eminence of land in the middle of a vast clearing. On all sides the ground sloped gently downward toward the tangled, hairy jungle that filled the circular valley, ringed about by sheer, black cliffs. There were a few trees in some of the court-yards, and the birds used them as meeting-places when they flew out of the rooms and corridors where they had their nests. Long ago bandits had taken whatever was removable out of the building. Soldiers had used it once as headquarters, had, like the bandits, built fires in the great windy rooms so that afterward they looked like ancient kitchens. And now that everything was gone from within, it seemed that never again would any-one come near the monastery. The vegetation had thrown up a protecting wall; the first story was soon quite hidden from view by small trees which dripped vines to lasso the cornices of the windows. The meadows round-about grew dank and lush; there was no path through them.

At the higher end of the circular valley a river fell off the cliffs into a great cauldron of vapor and thunder below; after this it slid along the base of the cliffs until it found a gap at the other end of the valley, where it hurried discreetly through with no rapids, no cascades—a great thick black rope of water moving swiftly downhill between the polished flanks of the canyon. Beyond the gap the land opened out and became smiling; a village nestled on the side hill just outside. In the days of the monastery it was there that the friars had got their provisions, since the Indians would not enter the circular valley. Centuries ago when the building had been constructed the Church had imported the workmen from another part of the country. These were traditional enemies of the tribes there-abouts, and had another language; there was no danger that the in-habitants would communicate with them as they worked at setting up the mighty walls. Indeed, the construction had taken so long that before the east wing was completed the workmen had all died, one by one. Thus it was the friars themselves who had closed off the end of the wing with blank walls, leaving it that way, unfinished and blind-looking, facing the black cliffs.

Generation after generation, the friars came, fresh-cheeked boys who grew thin and gray, and finally died, to be buried in the garden beyond the courtyard with the fountain. One day not long ago they had all left the monastery; no one knew where they had gone, and no one thought to ask. It was shortly after this that the bandits, and then the soldiers had come. And now, since the Indians do not change, still no one from the village went up through the gap to visit the monastery. The Atlájala lived there; the friars had not been able to kill it, had given up at last and gone away. No one was surprised, but the Atlájala gained in prestige by their departure. During the centuries the friars had been there in the monastery, the Indians had wondered why it allowed them to stay. Now, at last, it had driven them out. It always had lived there, they said, and would go on living there because the valley was its home, and it could never leave.

In the early morning the restless Atlájala would move through the halls of the monastery. The dark rooms sped past, one after the other. In a small patio, where eager young trees had pushed up the paving stones to reach the sun, it paused. The air was full of small sounds: the movement of butterflies, the falling to the ground of bits of leaves and flowers, the air following its myriad courses around the edges of things, the ants pursuing their endless labors in the hot dust. In the sun it waited, conscious of each gradation in sound and light and smell, living in the awareness of the slow, constant disintegration that attacked the morning and transformed it into afternoon. When evening came, it often slipped above the monastery roof and surveyed the darkening sky: the waterfall would roar distantly. Night after night, along the procession of years, it had hovered here above the valley, darting down to become a bat, a leopard, a moth for a few minutes or hours, returning to rest immobile in the center of the space enclosed by the cliffs. When the monastery had been built, it had taken to frequenting the rooms, where it had observed for the first time the meaningless gestures of human life.

And then one evening it had aimlessly become one of the young friars. This was a new sensation, strangely rich and complex, and at the same time unbearably stifling, as though every other possibility besides that of being enclosed in a tiny, isolated world of cause and effect had been removed forever. As the friar, it had gone and stood in the window, looking out at the sky, seeing for the first time, not the stars, but the space between and beyond them. Even at that moment it had felt the urge to leave, to step outside the little shell of anguish where it lodged for the moment, but a faint curiosity had impelled it to remain a little longer and partake a little further of the unaccustomed sensation. It held on; the friar raised his arms to the sky in an imploring gesture. For the first time the Atlájala sensed opposition, the thrill of a struggle. It was delicious to feel the young man striving to free himself of its presence, and it was immeasurably sweet to remain there. Then with a cry the friar had rushed to the other side of the room and seized a heavy leather whip hanging on the wall. Tearing off his clothing he had begun to carry out a ferocious self-beating. At the first blow of the lash the Atlájala had been on the point of letting go, but then it realized that the immediacy of that intriguing inner pain was only made more manifest by the impact of the blows from without, and so it stayed and felt the young man grow weak under his own lashing. When he had finished and said a prayer, he crawled to his pallet and fell asleep weeping, while the Atlájala slipped out obliquely and entered into a bird which passed the night sitting in a great tree on the edge of the jungle, listening intently to the night sounds, and uttering a scream from time to time.

Thereafter the Atlájala found it impossible to resist sliding inside the bodies of the friars; it visited one after the other, finding an astonishing variety of sensation in the process. Each was a separate world, a separate existence, because each had different reactions when he became conscious of the other being within him. One would sit and read or pray, one would go for a long troubled walk in the meadows, around and around the building, one would find a comrade and engage in an absurd but bitter quarrel, a few wept, some flagellated themselves or sought a friend to wield the lash for them. Always there was a rich profusion of perceptions for the Atlájala to enjoy, so that it no longer occurred to it to frequent the bodies of insects, birds and furred animals, nor even to leave the monastery and move in the air above. Once it almost got into difficulties when an old friar it was occupying suddenly fell back dead. That was a hazard it ran in the frequenting of men: they seemed not to know when they were doomed, or if they did know, they pretended with such strength not to know, that it amounted to the same thing. The other beings knew beforehand, save when it was a question of being seized unawares and devoured. And that the Atlájala was able to prevent: a bird in which it was staying was always avoided by the hawks and eagles.

When the friars left the monastery, and, following the government's orders, doffed their robes, dispersed and became workmen, the Atlájala was at a loss to know how to pass its days and nights. Now everything was as it had been before their arrival: there was no one but the creatures that always had lived in the circular valley. It tried a giant serpent, a deer, a bee: nothing had the savor it had grown to love. Everything was the same as before, but not for the Atlájala; it had known the existence of man, and now there were no men in the valley—only the abandoned building with its empty rooms to make man's absence more poignant.

Then one year bandits came, several hundreds of them in one stormy afternoon. In delight it tried many of them as they sprawled about cleaning their guns and cursing, and it discovered still other facets of sensation: the hatred they felt for the world, the fear they had of the soldiers who were pursuing them, the strange gusts of desire that swept through them as they sprawled together drunk by the fire that smoldered in the center of the floor, and the insufferable pain of jealousy which the nightly orgies seemed to awaken in some of them. But the bandits did not stay long. When they had left, the soldiers came in their wake. It felt very much the same way to be a soldier as to be a bandit. Missing were the strong fear and the hatred, but the rest was almost identical. Neither the bandits nor the soldiers appeared to be at all conscious of its presence in them; it could slip from one man to another without causing any change in their behavior. This surprised it, since its effect on the friars had been so definite, and it felt a certain disappointment at the impossibility of making its existence known to them.

Nevertheless, the Atlájala enjoyed both bandits and soldiers immensely, and was even more desolate when it was left alone once again. It would

become one of the swallows that made their nests in the rocks beside the
top of the waterfall. In the burning sunlight it would plunge again and
again into the curtain of mist that rose from far below, sometimes uttering
exultant cries. It would spend a day as a plant louse, crawling slowly
along the under side of the leaves, living quietly in the huge green world
down there which is forever hidden from the sky. Or at night, in the velvet
body of a panther, it would know the pleasure of the kill. Once for a year
it lived in an eel at the bottom of the pool below the waterfall, feeling the
mud give slowly before it as it pushed ahead with its flat nose; that was a
restful period, but afterward the desire to know again the mysterious life
of man had returned—an obsession of which it was useless to try to rid
itself. And now it moved restlessly through the ruined rooms, a mute
presence, alone, and thirsting to be incarnate once again, but in man's
flesh only. And with the building of highways through the country it was
inevitable that people should come once again to the circular valley.

A man and a woman drove their automobile as far as a village down in
a lower valley; hearing about the ruined monastery and the waterfall that
dropped over the cliffs into the great amphitheatre, they determined to
see these things. They came on burros as far as the village outside the gap,
but there the Indians they had hired to accompany them refused to go any
farther, and so they continued alone, upward through the canyon and
into the precinct of the Atlájala.

It was noon when they rode into the valley; the black ribs of the cliffs
glistened like glass in the sun's blistering downward rays. They stopped
the burros by a cluster of boulders at the edge of the sloping meadows.
The man got down first, and reached up to help the woman off. She
leaned forward, putting her hands on his face, and for a long moment they
kissed. Then he lifted her to the ground and they climbed hand in hand
up over the rocks. The Atlájala hovered near them, watching the woman
closely: she was the first ever to have come into the valley. The two sat
beneath a small tree on the grass, looking at one another, smiling. Out of
habit, the Atlájala entered into the man. Immediately, instead of existing
in the midst of the sunlit air, the bird calls and the plant odors, it was
conscious only of the woman's beauty and her terrible imminence. The
waterfall, the earth, and the sky itself receded, rushed into nothingness, and
there were only the woman's smile and her arms and her odor. It was a
world more suffocating and painful than the Atlájala had thought possible.
Still, while the man spoke and the woman answered, it remained within.

"Leave him. He doesn't love you."

"He would kill me."

"But I love you. I need you with me."

"I can't. I'm afraid of him."

The man reached out to pull her to him; she drew back slightly, but
her eyes grew large.

"We have today," she murmured, turning her face toward the yellow
walls of the monastery.

The man embraced her fiercely, crushing her against him as though the act would save his life. "No, no, no. It can't go on like this," he said. "No."

The pain of his suffering was too intense; gently the Atlájala left the man and slipped into the woman. And now it would have believed itself to be housed in nothing, to be in its own spaceless self, so completely was it aware of the wandering wind, the small flutterings of the leaves, and the bright air that surrounded it. Yet there was a difference: each element was magnified in intensity, the whole sphere of being was immense, limitless. Now it understood what the man sought in the woman, and it knew that he suffered because he never would attain that sense of completion he sought. But the Atlájala, being one with the woman, had attained it, and being aware of possessing it, trembled with delight. The woman shuddered as her lips met those of the man. There on the grass in the shade of the tree their joy reached new heights; the Atlájala, knowing them both, formed a single channel between the secret springs of their desires. Throughout, it remained within the woman, and began vaguely to devise ways of keeping her, if not inside the valley, at least nearby, so that she might return.

In the afternoon, with dreamlike motions, they walked to the burros and mounted them, driving them through the deep meadow grass to the monastery. Inside the great courtyard they halted, looking hesitantly at the ancient arches in the sunlight, and at the darkness inside the doorways.

"Shall we go in?" said the woman.

"We must get back."

"I want to go in," she said. (The Atlájala exulted.) A thin gray snake slid along the ground into the bushes. They did not see it.

The man looked at her perplexedly. "It's late," he said.

But she jumped down from her burro by herself and walked beneath the arches into the long corridor within. (Never had the rooms seemed so real as now when the Atlájala was seeing them through her eyes.)

They explored all the rooms. Then the woman wanted to climb up into the tower, but the man took a determined stand.

"We must go back now," he said firmly, putting his hand on her shoulder.

"This is our only day together, and you think of nothing but getting back."

"But the time . . ."

"There is a moon. We won't lose the way."

He would not change his mind. "No."

"As you like," she said. "I'm going up. You can go back alone if you like."

The man laughed uneasily. "You're mad." He tried to kiss her.

She turned away and did not answer for a moment. Then she said: "You want me to leave my husband for you. You ask everything from me, but what do you do for me in return? You refuse even to climb up into a little tower with me to see the view. Go back alone. Go!"

She sobbed and rushed toward the dark stairwell. Calling after her, he followed, but stumbled somewhere behind her. She was as sure of foot as if she had climbed the many stone steps a thousand times before, hurrying up through the darkness, around and around.

In the end she came out at the top and peered through the small apertures in the cracking walls. The beams which had supported the bell had rotted and fallen; the heavy bell lay on its side in the rubble, like a dead animal. The waterfall's sound was louder up here; the valley was nearly full of shadow. Below, the man called her name repeatedly. She did not answer. As she stood watching the shadow of the cliffs slowly overtake the farthest recesses of the valley and begin to climb the naked rocks to the east, an idea formed in her mind. It was not the kind of idea which she would have expected of herself, but it was there, growing and inescapable. When she felt it complete there inside her, she turned and went lightly back down. The man was sitting in the dark near the bottom of the stairs, groaning a little.

"What is it?" she said.

"I hurt my leg. Now are you ready to go or not?"

"Yes," she said simply. "I'm sorry you fell."

Without saying anything he rose and limped after her out into the courtyard where the burros stood. The cold mountain air was beginning to flow down from the tops of the cliffs. As they rode through the meadow she began to think of how she would broach the subject to him. (It must be done before they reached the gap. The Atlájala trembled.)

"Do you forgive me?" she asked him.

"Of course," he laughed.

"Do you love me?"

"More than anything in the world."

"Is that true?"

He glanced at her in the failing light, sitting erect on the jogging animal.

"You know it is," he said softly.

She hesitated.

"There is only one way, then," she said finally.

"But what?"

"I'm afraid of him. I won't go back to him. You go back. I'll stay in the village here." (Being that near, she would come each day to the monastery.) "When it is done, you will come and get me. Then we can go somewhere else. No one will find us."

The man's voice sounded strange. "I don't understand."

"You do understand. And that is the only way. Do it or not, as you like. It is the only way."

They trotted along for a while in silence. The canyon loomed ahead, black against the evening sky.

Then the man said, very clearly: "Never."

A moment later the trail led out into an open space high above the swift water below. The hollow sound of the river reached them faintly. The light in the sky was almost gone; in the dusk the landscape had taken on false contours. Everything was gray—the rocks, the bushes, the trail—and nothing had distance or scale. They slowed their pace.

His word still echoed in her ears.

"I won't go back to him!" she cried with sudden vehemence. "You can go back and play cards with him as usual. Be his good friend the same as always. I won't go. I can't go on with both of you in the town." (The plan was not working; the Atlájala saw it had lost her, yet still it could help her.)

"You're very tired," he said softly.

He was right. Almost as he said the words, that unaccustomed exhilaration and lightness she had felt ever since noon seemed to leave her; she hung her head wearily, and said: "Yes, I am."

At the same moment the man uttered a sharp, terrible cry; she looked up in time to see his burro plunge from the edge of the trail into the grayness below. There was a silence, and then the faraway sound of many stones sliding downward. She could not move or stop her burro; she sat dumbly, letting it carry her along, an inert weight on its back.

For one final instant, as she reached the pass which was the edge of its realm, the Atlájala alighted tremulously within her. She raised her head and a tiny exultant shiver passed through her; then she let it fall forward once again.

Hanging in the dim air above the trail, the Atlájala watched her indistinct figure grow invisible in the gathering night. (If it had not been able to hold her there, still it had been able to help her.)

A moment later it was in the tower, listening to the spiders mend the webs that she had damaged. It would be a long, long time before it would bestir itself to enter into another being's awareness. A long, long time—perhaps forever.

QUESTIONS

1. What is the Atlájala? What are its chief properties and characteristics?

2. Do you find any special pattern of significance in the varieties of existence which the Atlájala has experienced? Is any implicit comment offered by the *order* in which one phase of its experience follows another, or does it seem to you that the order has been chosen at random?

3. At what point does recognizable present-day reality enter the story?

4. What is the effect, what advantages has the writer gained by juxtaposing fantasy and reality in the same story? Is there any essential relationship between all that the Atlájala has lived through previously and what it lives through during the story's immediate action?

SHIRLEY ANN GRAU

(1932–   )

"It is all colored people here, and it is the poorest part of the smallest and worst county in the state. The place at the end of the dirt road leading from the state highway, the place where Luther's Store and Willie's Café stand, does not even have a name in the county records." These are the opening sentences of "The Black Prince," the story which gives its title to the volume from which "Joshua" is taken, and they accurately suggest the milieu and the subject matter of some of Miss Grau's most distinguished and individual stories. But her stories are not confined in their settings to any one locale—though as far as one can tell they all take place in the Delta States—and four of the nine which make up the volume take place in the white parts of town, where the Negro comes only as a servant and where air-conditioning units, or at least electric fans, put up some kind of opposition to the summer heat. With one or two exceptions, such as "Joshua," with its cold winter rain, the atmosphere of her stories is summer heat, when "even the dew is hot."

There might be more than one opinion as to which of Miss Grau's stories show her at her best, but it is certain that "The Black Prince," "Miss Yellow Eyes," "The Way of a Man," and "Joshua," stories which deal with the lives of colored people, present a highly distinctive array of qualities. They are not mere exercises in regionalism, nor are they confined in their aim to the reiteration of hard sociological truths. Perhaps only the inhabitants of a region are fully equipped to judge whether a writer has been faithful in his rendering of it, but we have an unmistakable sense in reading *The Black Prince* that we are seeing the lives Miss Grau has chosen to show us—especially the lives in abandoned places—in full, true focus. These are lives in which every human impulse is subject to the distortion, greater or less, of an enormous social problem, of a fundamental deprivation. Yet in describing them, Miss Grau has written stories, not sociological tracts or propaganda. She does not deny or sentimentalize the conditions under which her Negro characters live, but she has been faithful to her vocation as a story-teller and presents us in each instance with characters who interest us as individuals and about whom she has a real story to tell, a story of aspirations, longings, or endeavour which we follow eagerly to the end. As a consequence, the truth comes out far more compellingly than it ever does in works conceived as propaganda, both the individual human truth of the foreground and the somber social truth of the background.

Miss Grau, whose stories have appeared in *The New Yorker, New World Writing,* and *The New Mexico Quarterly,* belongs to the youngest generation of Southern writers. At present, not so very long after the publication of her first volume, it is too early to attempt exact critical formulations of her achievement or to predict what her development is likely to be. It is enough for the moment to recognize that her skill as a story-teller, her warmth of sympathy, and her imaginative power entitle her to a place beside such distinguished Southern writers of the immediately preceding generation as Eudora Welty and Carson McCullers.

(Since the above note was written, Miss Grau's first novel, *The Hard Blue Sky,* has been published by Alfred A. Knopf, New York.)

JOSHUA

South of New Orleans, down along the stretch that is called the Lower Coast, the land trails off to a narrow strip between river and marsh. Solid ground here is maybe only a couple of hundred feet across, and there is a dirt road that runs along the foot of the green, carefully sodded levee. It once had state highway markers, but people used the white painted signs for shotgun targets, until they were so riddled they crumbled away. The highway commission has never got around to replacing them. Maybe it doesn't even know the signs are gone; highway inspectors hardly ever come down this way. To the east is the expanse of shifting swamp grass, and beyond that is the little, sheltered Bay Cardoux, and farther still, beyond the string of protecting islands, is the Gulf. To the west is the Mississippi, broad and slow and yellow.

At intervals along the road there are towns—scattered collections of rough, unpainted board houses with tin roofs, stores that are like the houses except that they have crooked painted signs, and long, flat, windowless warehouses to store the skins of the muskrats that are taken every year from the marsh. Each building perches on stilts two or three feet high; in the spring the bayous rise. The waters always reach up to the roadbed and sometimes even cover it with a couple of inches of water.

There is no winter to speak of. Sometimes there is a little scum of ice on the pools and backwaters of the bayous and a thin coating over the ruts in the road. But the temperature never stays below freezing more than a day or two, and the little gray film of ice soon disappears under the rain.

For it rains almost constantly from October to March. Not hard; not a storm; there is never any lightning. There is just a steady, cold rain.

The river is high. The trees that grow out on the *batture*—on the land between the river's usual bed and the levee, on the land that all summer and fall has been dry and fertile—are half-covered with water.

The inside walls of the houses drip moisture in tiny beads like sweat, and bread turns moldy in a single day. Roofs begin to leak, and the pans

ORIGINALLY published in *The New Yorker*, and reprinted from *The Black Prince and Other Stories* by Shirley Ann Grau, by permission of Alfred A. Knopf, Inc. Copyright 1954 by Shirley Ann Grau.

put under the leaks have to be emptied twice a day. From the bayous and the swamps to the east come heavy, choking odors of musk and rotting grasses.

It is mostly all colored people here in the lower reaches. Poor people, who live on what they find in the river and the swamps and the Gulf beyond them.

Joshua Samuel Watkin sat at the kitchen table in one of the dozen-odd houses that make up Bon Secour, Good Hope, the farthest of the towns along the dirt highway, which ends there, and the nearest town to the river's mouth.

Joshua Samuel Watkin leaned both elbows on the table and watched the way his mother used her hands when she talked. She swung them from her wrist, limply, while the fingers twisted and poked, way off by themselves.

His small, quick, black eyes shifted from her hands to her lips, which were moving rapidly. Joshua stared at them for a moment and then went back to the hands. He had the ability to shut out sounds he did not wish to hear. His mother's flaming, noisy temper he could shut out easily now; it had taken the practice of most of his eleven years.

He glanced at the doorway, where his father was standing. He had just come in. The shoulders of his light-gray jacket were stained black by the rain, and the tan of his cap had turned almost brown. Joshua glanced briefly down at his father's hands. They were empty; he would have dropped the string of fish outside on the porch. Pretty soon, Joshua knew, one of his parents was going to remember those fish and send him outside to clean them for supper. It was a job he had never liked. No reason, really. He would have to squat outside, working carefully, so that most of the mess fell over the side into the yard, where the cats could fight for it.

His father yanked one of the wooden chairs from under the table and sat down on it heavily. He was answering now, Joshua noticed, and his face was beginning to get the straight-down-the-cheek lines of anger. He tilted his chair back against the wall and jammed both hands down deep into his pockets.

From the way things were beginning to look, Josh thought, it might be just as well if he got out for a while. But he'd better stay long enough to see if there was going to be any supper. He still hadn't bothered to listen to them, to either of them; he knew what they were saying. He balanced his spoon across the top of his coffee cup and then tapped it with his finger gently, swinging it. He miscalculated, and the spoon hit the oilcloth with a sharp crack.

His father's chair crashed down and with an extra rattle one of the rungs came loose. "Christ Almighty," his father said. "Ain't I told you a million times not to do nothing like that?"

"He ain't done nothing," his mother said, and, reaching out her limp black hand, balanced the spoon across the cup again.

Joshua smiled to himself, though his face did not move. It was one sure way to get his mother on his side—just let his father say a word against him. It worked the other way, too; let his mother fuss at him and his father would be sure to take his part. It was as if they couldn't ever be together.

His father let his breath out with a high-pitched hiss.

"He ain't done nothing," his mother repeated. "Just drop his spoon a little."

His father kept on staring at her, his head bent a little, the dark eyes in his dark face glaring.

"Leastways he ain't just sitting around the house on his tail end, scared to stick his nose outside."

"Woman," his father said, "iffen you ain't the naggingest—"

"Scared." His mother stuck out her underlip. "You just plain scared."

"I ain't scared of nothing a man ain't got cause to be scared of."

"I hear you talking," his mother said. "Only I plain don't see you moving nohow."

"Nagging bitch," his father said, almost gently, under his breath.

His mother's underlip stuck out even farther, and she whistled sharply, derisively, through her teeth.

His father bent forward, slapping a hand down, one on each knee. "Sure I scared!" he shouted in her face. She did not even blink. "Everybody scared!"

Joshua turned his eyes toward the window. All he could see was gray sky. Raining, solid, gray sky in all four directions—east over the swamps and west over the river and north to the city and south to the Gulf, where the fishing boats went, and the U-boats were hiding.

His father was saying: "Like Jesse Baxter, you want me to plain get blown to bits."

Joshua did not take his eyes off the square of gray sky, but he was seeing something else. The fishing boats from Bon Secour, three of them, had come on the two U-boats, surfaced in the fog and together, exchanging supplies. And one of the ships had lobbed a couple of shots from its deck gun square into Baxter's boat. There wasn't anything but pieces left, and the two other fishing boats hadn't even time to look for them, they were so busy running. All they'd heard, just for a second or so, was the men around the gun laughing. The two surviving boats had not gone out again. Nobody would take them out.

Joshua had heard the story and he had dreamed about it often enough. He would wake up sweating even in the cold and shaking with fear. He couldn't quite imagine a U-boat, so its outline and shape changed with each dream. But the action was always the same—the gun pointing at him and the laughing.

With a little shudder, Joshua turned his eyes back to his parents. "That been a week and a half," his mother was saying, "and how you think we gonna eat? How you think we gonna eat iffen you don't find a boat?"

"We been eating." His father had his chin pressed down against the rolled collar of his gray wool sweatshirt. "Ain't we been eating?"

His mother snorted. "Why, sure," she said. "You man enough to go sneaking out in the little old back bayous and catch us a couple of fish."

"Fish ain't bad," his father said. "Ask *him* iffen he going hungry."

Joshua felt their eyes focused on him, and he squirmed.

"Don't go putting words in the boy's mouth," his mother said.

"Just you ask him."

"Ask him iffen there ain't things you got to have money to buy. Ask him iffen he don't got no coat to wear with the cold. Ask him iffen he don't need a new coat." She turned to Joshua. "You tell him what you want. You tell him what you plain got to have." Her voice ended in a kind of ragged shriek.

"I get him a coat," his father said.

"When that gonna be? He plain gonna freeze first."

"Ain't no son of mine gonna freeze," his father said.

"You plain scared," his mother taunted. "You just plain scared."

Joshua got to his feet and slipped around the edge of the table and outside. On the porch he found a square of black canvas and wrapped it around himself, letting it make a cowl above his head. It had been used to cover an engine, and it smelled of grease and was slippery to the touch, but it would keep him dry and very warm.

He noticed the string of fish that his father had brought home. With the toe of one blue canvas sneaker, he kicked the string down into the yard. It hit the soggy ground with a little splash. The cats would be coming around at dark.

He walked down the road, stepping carefully, watching for the biggest puddles, keeping to the levee side, where the ground was highest. The rain was falling noisily on his square of tarpaulin. With the steady, quick, clicking sound of drops all around him, falling on his head but not touching him, tapping on his shoulders but not really being there, after a while he wouldn't be sure of his balance any more, or his direction, there would be such an echo in his head. He kept blinking to steady himself, but that didn't seem to do much good. He had heard men say they would rather get drenched to the skin and maybe get the fever than spend hours under a tarpaulin with a slow, steady winter rain falling.

The wind blew in swirling eddies—like puffs of smoke, almost, the drops were so fine. Joshua rubbed the wet from his eyes. Over the noise of the rain he heard the faint sound of the river against the levee, a sound that went on day and night, winter and spring, until you got so used to it you had to make a special effort to hear it. Squinting, he looked up. The tops of water aspens on the other side of the levee shuddered under the rain, showing the frightened white underside of their leaves.

Joshua hunched the tarpaulin higher over his head and walked faster. Over to the right now he could see the landings where Goose Bayou swung in close and deep. And there were the boats, moored and wet under the rain, and empty, just where they'd been for the last week or more, and, at the far end of one of the landings, the empty space where Jesse Baxter's boat belonged.

Joshua stopped and stared at the empty space, at the muddy, rain-specked water and Baxter's mooring posts with the ropes still around them but dragging down into the water. Like it was in his dream, he thought, when, cold and sweating, he saw the shape of a ship in the fog and heard the sound of a deck gun.

He reached the shelter of the overhang of a building and let the tarpaulin drop from his head. He still kept it wrapped around his shoulders, because he was shivering. In the middle of the board platform in front of the building, a yellow dog with black-marked flanks was scratching behind one ear, slowly, limply, and overhead a doubleboard sign hung upside down at a sharp angle. On one side of it was painted, in white letters: "Bourgeois Store." Years ago the wind had lifted it and turned it on its hook, and it had jammed that way, with only the blank side showing. Nobody ever seemed to notice. Maybe because nobody ever looked up.

Joshua peeped in through the window. A single electric-light bulb way up against the ceiling in the center of the room was burning, because the day was so dark. It was a little bulb and almost worn out—you could see the red, glowing coils of wire inside it; and it wasn't much brighter inside the store than out.

Joshua rubbed his fingers against the glass and stared harder. There were two tables set together lengthwise across the front of the room, and behind them two more. They were covered with clothes in neat little piles, according to size and color. There were wall shelves, too, filled with a clutter of hardware. There were so many things in the room that you couldn't find any single object quickly, even if the thing you were looking for was as big as a man.

Joshua finally located Claude Bourgeois at the side of the room, over by the stove, almost hidden behind small crab nets that were hanging by long cords from the ceiling. There were two men sitting with him. Joshua could have known he would be there; he hardly ever moved from that spot during the winter, his bones ached so. Now that he was old, he'd stopped fighting the rain and the cold; he just let them have their way outside the store. He didn't move outside at all. His wife, Kastka, who was part Indian, rubbed his arms and legs with liniment and kept the fire going full away in the silver-painted potbellied stove.

Joshua opened the door. Just inside he let his tarpaulin fall in a heap. Claude and the two men with him turned, and looked, and Claude said: "Close that there door quick, boy," and they went back to their talking.

Joshua recognized the two other men: Oscar Lavie and Stanley Phillips. Lavie ran Claude's fishing boat for him now that he was too old to go out, and Phillips was never very far away from Lavie. They always worked together; it had been that way since they were kids.

Joshua walked over to the small glass case that stood against the left wall, the case that was filled with knives. He stood looking down at them, at one in particular, one in the middle of the case. It had a blade at least six inches long, and its handle was of some white stuff, white and iridescent and shining as the inside of an oyster shell that is wet and fresh. Someday, he told himself, when he had money of his own, he would buy that. If just nobody got to it first.

Not that he needed a knife; his father had bought him one a month or less ago, with the money from the last haul the men had made. He remembered how angry his mother had been. "God Almighty," she'd said. "Iffen you ain't plain crazy, you. Buying that there trash when the boy needs a coat."

His father had just winked at him and said: "You don't hear him complaining none."

"Maybe he ain't got no more sense than you," his mother had said, "but he gonna be mighty cold this winter without no coat."

"Woman," his father had said, "ain't you got but one idea in you head?"

Little Henry Bourgeois came and stood alongside of Joshua. He was Claude's son, the son of his old age, the son of the woman who was part Indian. Henry had the round Negro features of his father and the skin color of his mother, a glowing red, deep and far down, so deep that it wasn't so much a skin color as a color under that. It was almost like seeing the blood.

"You heard the news?" Henry asked. His father had a radio in the store, a small one in a square green case. It was the only radio in Bon Secour.

"No," Joshua said.

"They come almost up the river," Henry said. "They sink one of the freighter ships again."

The war and the shooting and the submarines. And just a little way off. Joshua felt his breath catch in the middle of his chest, catch on the lump that was so big and cold that it hurt. And he remembered all his dreams: the fog, and the other ship, and himself in the gray, rain-speckled water, dying, in a million pieces for the fish to chew. His face did not change. He kept on looking at the knife. "That right?" he said.

"Josh," old Claude Bourgeois called to him. "You come over here."

He turned and crossed through the maze of tables and ducked under the hanging skeins of nets.

"Boy," Claude Bourgeois said, "iffen you don't quit leaning on that there glass it gonna crack through, sure as anything."

Joshua looked down at his feet in the blue canvas sneakers, blue stained darker by the water he had been walking through. He wiggled his toes, and they made little bumps on the outside of the canvas.

"You papa home?" Claude Bourgeois asked.

Joshua nodded.

"He wanting to go out fishing?"

"I reckon—if Ma wanting him to go out."

Oscar Lavie shifted in his chair, lifted one bare foot, and hooked it between his cupped hands. "Iffen you want you boat out," he told Claude Bourgeois, "I reckon you plain better take it out yourself."

Claude opened his mouth, and then, thinking better of whatever he was about to say, closed it again.

"I seen that there ship popping up out of the fog," Oscar went on, "and it ain't nobody's fault it ain't blown me up, place of Jesse Baxter."

Stanley Phillips nodded his head slowly. He stuttered badly, and when he talked people hardly ever understood him. So he let others do the talking. But his lack of speech had given him an air of confidence. Sometimes when he stood leaning against the corner of a building, his hands jammed down in his pockets, his slight body arched back and braced for balance, he seemed to own everything he looked at—the streets and the houses and the people. All the women liked him; some of them got a dreamy look in their eyes when he passed. "He don't have to talk, him," they would say. Only last year Stanley Phillips had married—all proper, in the church over at Petit Bayou—a wife, by far the prettiest colored girl anywhere along the river. And when he'd been out fishing, gone for maybe a couple of days or a week, he'd always head straight home, and when he got within fifty yards of his house, he'd stop and give a long, loud whistle and then walk on slowly, counting his steps, and every fifth step giving another whistle, so his wife would have time to get ready for what was coming.

"Iffen you was in the army," Claude Bourgeois said softly, "you wouldn't have no chance to say no."

Neither Stanley nor Oscar had bothered registering for the army. They just disappeared whenever any stranger came around asking questions, which wasn't very often.

"You figure on anything there?" Oscar asked, his eyes resting on the fat, lumpy body of the old man.

"Not me," Claude Bourgeois said hastily. "Not me."

"That real fine of you," Oscar said. "Then I reckon I ain't gonna have to slice up all you fat and feed it to the gators."

"Me?" Claude rolled his eyes around so that they almost disappeared. "I ain't gonna do nothing like that."

"That nice of you," Oscar said.

"Why, man," Claude said, changing the subject quickly, "you plain got to go out eventually."

"That ain't yet," Oscar said, and Stanley nodded. "It ain't worth nothing going out to get blown to pieces."

"How they gonna find you in all that water out there?"

"It ain't worth the chance," Oscar said.

Joshua stared over at the pot of coffee on the stove top, where it always stood to keep warm. Nobody offered him any, so he looked away.

"Why, man"—Claude was holding his hand outspread in front of him—"you can't go on living on bayou fish forever; there other things you got to have money for." He nodded at Joshua. "This here boy need a coat, only his daddy ain't working to give him none."

"Leastways his daddy ain't lying in pieces all over the bottom of the Gulf, with the fishes eating on him," Oscar said. "Leastways, iffen you are so concerned, you plain can give him a coat. Just you give him one on credit now."

"You gonna do that?" Joshua asked.

Claude coughed. "There ain't no cause to do nothing like that," he said. "This here a matter of business, and this ain't good business, any way you looks at it. There all sort of money waiting for his daddy out there, iffen you wasn't too scared to go get it."

Joshua drifted away toward the door. He picked up the tarpaulin, studied it for a minute, then flipped it around himself and went outside. Little Henry Bourgeois followed right behind him. The low gray sky was thickening with the evening. In the branches of a chinaberry tree a hawk and a catbird were fighting. "Where you going?" Henry asked.

Joshua went down the steps and out into the road. The mud was soft and gummy, and stuck to the bottom of his shoes in heavy cakes. Each step was a sucking sound.

"Damn gumbo mud," he said. He could hear Henry's steps behind him.

They walked about a block, with their heads bent way down, so they really couldn't see where they were going. Henry gave a quick little squishing skip and came abreast of Joshua. "Where you going?" he asked again. "You going there?"

Joshua nodded.

They came to the warehouse. The fur-trading company had put it up maybe ten years ago, when they first discovered all the muskrat around here. There'd been need for extra space then. But things had changed; a couple of hurricanes had drowned out the animals, and they were coming back slowly. It hardly paid for a man to set his traps during the season, since he had to take the skins up to Petit Bayou now to sell them.

But the old warehouse still stood, at the north end of the string of houses. It was a rough building with plain, unpainted wood sides that time and rain and fogs had stained to an almost uniform black. On the far side, behind some low bushes—barberry bushes, with thick thorns and pronged leaves—Joshua had discovered a loose board. It had taken him nearly three hours to work it loose.

The two boys wiggled through the bushes, pried down the board, and slipped inside. They shook themselves like wet puppies and kicked off their shoes. The building was unheated, but somehow it always seemed warm, maybe only because it was dry. The floor boards were double thickness and carefully waterproofed with tar. It was a single room, big and almost empty. There were no windows, and when Henry put the board back in place, the only light came from the thin cracks between the boards. The two boys had been here so often that they knew their way around the room; they did not need to see.

They both walked straight out into the center of the room, until their bare feet felt the familiar rough texture of burlap. There had been a big heap of old bags in the warehouse, and the boys had carefully piled them in a circle, leaving a clear place about four feet across in the middle. When they sat there, the bags were higher than their heads and kept off drafts and cold. In the corners of the warehouse they had found a few furs— tattered, mangy things, too poor to be sold—and they used these as seats or beds, for sometimes they slept here, too. Their families did not miss them; after all, a boy should be able to look out for himself.

Joshua and Henry settled themselves, and Joshua lit the kerosene lantern he had brought a couple of days before. His mother had stomped and raged for a whole day after she discovered it was missing. Joshua did not even have to lie about it; before she had thought to ask him, his father came home and her anger turned on him, and they argued long and hard, and ended as they always did, going in their room to make love.

"I done brought something this time," Henry said. He pulled a paper-wrapped package from under his jacket. The greasy stains of food were already smearing the brown paper. "This here is our supper."

They divided the cold fried fish and the bread, and then Joshua put out the lamp—it was hard to get kerosene for it—and they ate in the darkness, with just the sound of rain on the tar-paper roof and the sound of their own chewing and the occasional scurry of a rat or maybe a lizard or a big roach.

"Man," Joshua said slowly. "This is fine, no?"

"Sure," Henry agreed, with his mouth full. "Sure is."

"Look like they gonna be a fog tonight."

"Sure do," Henry said. "It a good night to be right in here. It a fine night to be in here."

Joshua's fingers brushed the surface of one of the moldy-smelling pelts with a faint scratching sound. "You might even could make a coat outa these here, iffen you had enough," he said.

"No," Henry said scornfully.

Joshua did not argue.

They fell asleep then, because it was dark and warm and they weren't hungry any longer. And Joshua dreamed the same dream he dreamed almost every night. There was a thing that he knew was a submarine. Even the way its shape kept changing—from long, like a racing boat only a hundred times bigger, to narrow and tall, like the picture postcards of the buildings in New Orleans. But it was always fog-colored. At times it slipped back into the fog, and when it came out again, it was a different shape. And he was always there, too, in a boat sometimes, a pirogue or a skiff, hunched down, trying not to be seen, or on foot in the marsh, in knee-high water, crouched down behind some few, almost transparent grasses. Hiding where he knew there was no hiding place.

Joshua shook himself, turned over, bent his other arm and pillowed his head on it, and went back to the dream. He did not wake again, but from time to time he whimpered.

That night one of the submarines was destroyed. The patrol boats found it almost a quarter mile inside the pass, heading for the shipping upriver. The heavy, cold, raining night exploded and then exploded again. Joshua woke up and couldn't be sure he wasn't still in his dream, for the waking was like a dream. Alongside him, Henry was whispering: "Sweet Jesus. Sweet Jesus." With fumbling fingers and a quick sharp scratch of matches, Joshua lit the lantern. The light raced to the roof and stayed there, holding back the darkness. Quickly, afraid, he glanced around the room. He was almost surprised to find it empty.

"What that?" Henry asked. His eyes caught the light and reflected it—bright, flat animal eyes.

Joshua did not answer. His throat was quivering too much. He looked around the empty room again and shook his head slowly.

"What that?" Henry repeated.

Joshua turned up the wick high as it would go. The top of the glass chimney began to cloud with smoke, but he did not lower the flame.

Henry jiggled his elbow persistently. "What that go up out there?" he asked.

"Ain't nothing."

Outside, people were yelling, their voices frightened and sleepy. Their words were muffled and garbled by the walls.

"You reckon maybe we ought to go out and see?" Henry asked.

"I reckon not," Joshua said, and there was a flat note of decision in his voice. "I reckon we best stay right here."

A plane flew by, close overhead. The building shook and the lamp flame wavered.

"I reckon the war come plain close," Joshua said.

"It quiet now," Henry said, and even managed to smile.

Joshua moved his lips but no sound came out. His tongue fluttered around in his throat.

The shouting outside was stopping. There were now just two voices, calling back and forth to each other, slower and slower, like a clock running down. Finally they stopped, too.

Henry said: "It smoking some."

Joshua turned the lamp wick down. The circle of light around them contracted. He watched it out of the corner of his eye and quickly turned the wick back up again.

"Ain't you better put that out?" Henry said. "We ain't got all that much kerosene."

"We got enough," Joshua said.

"You scared."

"Me?" Joshua said. "Me? No." Even he did not believe this. He tried hard to stay awake, knowing that just as soon as he fell asleep, just as soon as he stepped over that line, the indistinct shape, gray like the fog, would be waiting to kill him.

Suddenly it was broad daylight. The lamp had burned out; its chimney was solid black. Henry pointed to it. Joshua nodded. "You left the lamp burning till it run out of oil," Henry said.

Joshua walked slowly across the room. "Me?" he said. "No."

"I heard you talking in you sleep."

"I don't talk in my sleep, me." Joshua put his shoulder to the loose board and pushed. He felt the cold, damp air in his face. He blinked and looked out at the gray day.

"You was crying," Henry said. "You was crying and saying 'Don't.' That what you was doing."

Joshua wriggled through the opening without answering.

Henry stuck his head out after him. "You was scared," he shouted.

Joshua kept going steadily. He could feel a trembling behind his knees, and he had to concentrate with all his might to keep his walk straight.

As he went up the splintered wooden steps of his house, he could hear his father singing:

> "*Mo parle Simon, Simon, Simon,*
> *Li parle Ramon, Ramon, Ramon,*
> *Li parle Didine,*
> *Li tombe dans chagrin.*"

Sober, his father wouldn't even admit to understanding the downriver version of French. He'd near killed a man once who'd called him a Cajun. Drunk, he would remember that he knew hundreds of Cajun songs.

Joshua opened the door and went inside. His father and Oscar Lavie were in the kitchen, sitting at opposite ends of the table. Stanley Phillips was not around; he wasn't ever one for leaving his wife before afternoon.

In the middle of the green-checked oilcloth table cover were two gallon jugs of light-colored orange wine. One was already half empty. And on the table, too, next to the big wine bottles, was the small, round bottle of white lightning. Just in case they should need it.

They were so busy with their song they did not notice Joshua. He looked at them, wondering where his mother was. Then he went looking for his food. He found some beans on a plate at the back of the stove, and a piece of bread in the wall cupboard. He ate them, standing up in a corner.

Slowly his father swung his head around to him and said: "Look who come in."

Oscar Lavie said: "We celebrating way they blow up everything last night."

"You ma gone rushing out of here like the devils of hell hanging on her petticoat."

"I ain't done nothing of the kind." His mother popped her head in through the narrow little door that led to the lean-to at the back of the house. "I just went to get some kindling wood, so you crazy fool drunks ain't gonna freeze to death."

Oscar began singing, almost to himself:

> *"Cher, mo l'aime toi.*
> *Oui, mo l'aime toi.*
> *Vec tou mo cœur*
> *Comme cochon l'aime la bou."*

"Ain't I told you to get out?" his father said softly to his mother. "Ain't I told you I sick and tired of looking at you?"

Joshua finished eating silently. Oscar gave a deep sigh. "Us all gonna starve to death," he said. "Us all."

His father poured himself another glass of the wine. Joshua's mother did not move. She stood in the doorway holding the kindling in her arms.

His father's heavy-lidded eyes focused on Joshua and lifted a little. "What you gonna eat tonight?" his father asked.

The boy turned and put the dish back where he had found it, on the stove. "I don't know, me," he said.

His father began to laugh. He laughed so hard that he had to put his head down on the tabletop, and the table shook, and the wine in the bottles swished back and forth. When he spoke, it was from under his arms. "You hear him Oscar, man," he said. "He don't know what he going to eat. He don't know."

Oscar did not even smile as he stared off into space. The black of his skin seemed almost blue under the morning light.

"He don't know what he going to eat. I don't know either, me."

Joshua stood watching them.

"I ain't going out today, me, to look for nothing," his father said. "I plain sick of catching a couple of fish or shrimp with a hand net."

"Han Oliver, he got a pig," Lavie said, with a dreamy look on his face.

"Man," Joshua's father said, "Han plain swears he gonna kill anybody what tried to touch his pig, and he been sitting guard on it."

"I seen a dog out front there."

"I just ain't that hungry yet."

Lavie sighed deeply. "It ain't gonna hurt us none not to eat for one day."

"No," his father said, and was silent for so long that Joshua began walking toward the door. He had no clear idea what he would do outside; he only felt he had to leave. His father's head jerked up. "Unless *he* go out."

Joshua stopped short. "Me?" he said.

Oscar looked at him. His eyes faltered, focused again, and held. "He a fine little boy," he said. "He can go run my lines."

"No," Joshua said.

"He ain't gonna do that," his mother said. She came into the room now and dumped her armload of kindling alongside the stove.

"That kindling plain all wet," Oscar said vaguely, scowling.

"You ain't never found nothing dry in winter," his mother snapped.

"It gonna smoke," Oscar said plaintively.

"No skin off my nose," his mother said.

"Ain't I told you to get out?" his father said.

"You done told me a lot of things," his mother said.

"I tired of hearing you—"

"You ain't sending that little old boy out where you scared to go."

"Ain't scared," Oscar corrected. "Drunk."

"Woman," his father said, "I plain gonna twist you head around till you sees where you been."

He stood up, a little uncertain on his feet, and his chair fell over. His mother turned and ran out. They could see her through the window, scurrying over to the Delattes' house, next door. She was yelling something over her shoulder; they couldn't make out what.

His father looked at Joshua, his eyes traveling up and down every inch of his body. "You going out," he said.

"I ain't," Josh whispered.

"You going out and save you poor old papa some work," his father said. "Or I gonna twist up every bone in you body till you feels just like a shrimp."

Joshua edged his way carefully to the door.

"You know I mean what I done said."

Joshua ducked out the door. Behind him he heard his father laugh.

Henry was down at the landing, leaning against one of the black tar-coated pilings and teasing a big yellow tomcat with a long piece of rope. Joshua walked past without a word, and righted his father's pirogue and pushed it into the water.

"You going out?" Henry asked, and his voice quivered with interest.

"Reckon so." Josh bent down to tie the lace of one of his sneakers.

"Why you going out?"

"Reckon somebody got to see about getting something to eat."

"Oh," Henry said.

"My papa, he gonna stay drunk today."

"I heard."

"I reckon I could let you come along."

"That okay. We ain't needing no fish at my house."

"You afraid." Joshua looked at him and lifted his eyebrows. "You plain afraid."

"No-o-o," Henry said, and scowled.

"Why ain't you come along with me, then?"

"I ain't said I ain't coming." Henry tossed the piece of rope away. The cat pounced on it in spitting fury. "I ain't said nothing like that."

"Let's get started, then."

"I tell you what," Henry said. "I gonna go borrow my daddy's shotgun. Maybe we see something worth shooting at. I seen a couple of ducks yesterday or so."

Joshua nodded. It would feel better, having a shotgun with them.

Wasn't much good, maybe, but it was something. In his nightmares, he'd wished often enough that he had one with him.

While he waited, he got down in the pirogue and took his place in the stern. Carefully he wrapped the grease-stained black tarpaulin around him. "It cold, all right, man," he said aloud. The yellow tomcat turned his head and watched him. For a minute Joshua stared into the bright yellow eyes and at the straggling broken tufts of whiskers.

Joshua made the sign of the cross quickly. "If you a evil spirit, you can't touch me now," he said. The cat continued to look at him, its black pupils widening slightly and then contracting. Joshua began to wonder if maybe this wasn't one of his nightmares, if this wasn't all part of something he was dreaming. Maybe when he woke up he'd just be back in his bed, and maybe his mother would be shaking him and telling him to stop yelling and his father would be laughing at him for a coward. He took one of his fingers, cracked and almost blue with the cold, between his teeth. He bit it so hard the tears came to his eyes. But he'd done that before in dreams and still he hadn't waked up. No matter how scared he was, he had to finish it out, right to the end.

He held the lightly moving pirogue in place with his paddle and waited for Henry, impatiently, humming a little tune under his breath—the one he'd heard his father singing:

> Mo parle Simon, Simon, Simon,
> Li parle Ramon, Ramon, Ramon . . .

and told himself that the cold in his stomach was the weather outside.

He noticed something different. He lifted his head, sniffing the air; it had stopped raining. The sky had not cleared or lifted, and the air was still so heavy you could feel it brushing your face. Everything was soaked through; the whole world was floating, drenched, on water. But for a little while there was not the sound of rain.

And he missed that sound. He felt lonesome without it, the way he always did in spring—suspended and floating. For there isn't any real spring here—just a couple of weeks of hesitation and indecision between the rainy winter and the long, dry summer. There are always more fights and knifings then.

Henry came running back, a shotgun in one hand and four or five shells in the other. "I done got it," he said.

"Don't you point that there thing at me," Joshua said, and jerked his head aside.

"Us can go now," Henry said. He laid the gun in the bottom of the boat and then quickly got in the bow and wrapped a narrow blanket around his shoulders and knees. "I feel better with that along, me."

Joshua shrugged. "It don't matter to me."

They paddled out, following the curve of Goose Bayou, grinning to themselves with the fine feel of the pirogue—the tight, delicate, nervous quiver of the wood shell, the feel of walking across the water the way a long-legged fly does.

A couple of hundred yards down Goose Bayou they turned south, into a smaller bayou, which, for all anybody knew, had no name. It circled on the edge of a thick swamp, which nobody had bothered to name, either, though most people at one time or other had gone exploring in the tangle of old cypress and vines and water aspens and sudden bright hibiscus plants. Way back in the center somewhere, so that people hardly ever saw them, some cats lived—plain house cats gone wild and grown to almost the size of a panther, living up in the tangled branches of the trees, breeding there. Some nights you could hear their screaming—pleasure or maybe pain; you couldn't tell.

Nobody had ever had the courage to go all the way through the swamp. It wasn't all that big; people simply went around it. Except for one man, and that was an old story, maybe true, maybe not. Anyhow, it had been on to fifty years past. There'd been a white man with yellow hair, the story said, and he'd jumped ship out there in the river. He'd had a long swim in from the channel to the levee, but by the time he climbed up the muddy *batture*, he wasn't as tired as he should have been. Maybe he was hopped up on dope of some sort. Anyhow, when he came walking out of the river, just a little above Bon Secour, his clothes dripping and sticking to his body, his yellow hair all matted and hanging down over his face, there was a girl walking on the levee top. She stopped, watched him stumbling and slipping on the wet, slimy river mud, waved to the people she was with to wait a little, and went down to help him, making her way carefully through the tangle of aspens and hackberries, so that her dress wouldn't get torn.

It was torn clear off her, almost, when they found her half an hour later—those people she'd been walking with. They'd finally got tired waiting for her and gone down to see. They'd have killed him, white man or not, if they'd found him. For nearly two days the men hunted for him while the women went ahead with the funeral. They trailed him at last to the small stretch of swamp, and then they stopped, because none of them wanted to go in there themselves and they couldn't ever have found him in there, in a stretch about four miles long and maybe a mile wide. They did look in the outer fringes—in the part they knew. They could see the signs of where he'd been; they could see that he was heading right straight for the middle of the swamp. Nobody ever saw him again. Maybe he fought his way out and went on like he intended to, though the way he went crashing around, he didn't seem to know where he was going. Or maybe he kept on living in there; it wouldn't have been hard. He had a knife; he'd killed the girl with it. Or maybe he just died, and the fish and the ants and the little animals cleaned his bones until they were left shining white and the shreds of his hair shining yellow.

Joshua and Henry paddled past the thick swamp and remembered the story, and listened for the screaming of the cats, but since it was daylight, they heard nothing.

"It good to get out, man," Joshua said.

Henry did not answer, but then nobody talked much in the swamps. People got suddenly embarrassed and shy of their words and spoke only in whispers when they said anything at all, because the swamp was like a person listening. The grasses and bushes and trees and water were like a person holding his breath, listening, and ready to laugh at whatever you said.

Joshua and Henry found the trotlines that Oscar Lavie had set out the day before across a little cove that the bayou made in the swampy island. Oscar had tied a red strip of handkerchief to the end of a vine to mark the place. Henry reached up and unknotted the cloth. "Man," he said, "this wet through." He squeezed the rag over the side of the pirogue.

"It been raining," Joshua said. He gave the pirogue a quick shove up among the cypress knees to the one the line was tied to. "Iffen you loose that, we see what all we got." A sudden swinging vine hit his cheek. He jumped slightly, then grinned.

They worked their way back across the little cove, checking each of the seven single lines. The first three were empty, the bait gone. The next two held only the heads of catfish; the bodies were eaten clean away. "That plain must have been a gar," Henry said, and Joshua nodded.

They could tell by the drag of the lines that the last two were full. Joshua coaxed the lines slowly to the surface—two catfish with dripping whiskers, and gigs, and sharp and pointed and set.

"Watch 'em," Josh said. "They slice you up good."

"You ain't gonna worry about me," Henry said. "You just bring 'em up where I can get at 'em." He picked up the steel-pointed gaff from the bottom of the boat and jabbed it through the whiskered bottom jaw of one of the fish. While Joshua steadied the boat, Henry held the fish until its convulsive movements had all but stopped.

When they had finished, Joshua coiled up the trotline and dropped it in the center of the boat with the fish. "Granddaddies, them, all right," he said.

Henry nodded, breathless from exertion.

Joshua turned the pirogue back out into the bayou and paddled rapidly. Soon they passed the swampy island and were in the salt marshes, miles of grasses rustling lightly and stretching off flat on both sides, with just a few *chênières*—shell ridges with dwarfed, twisted water oaks—scattered on the trembling, shifting surface.

"Man, it cold!" Joshua said. "Sure wish I had me a big old heavy coat."

"Look there," Henry said. From a *chênière* away to the left, four or five shapes pumping heavily up into the air.

"Too far away to do us no good."

"Leastways they still got some duck around."

"That a bunch of pintails," Joshua said.

"How you tell?"

"I just plain know, man. I just plain can tell, that all."

Henry was staring over where the indistinct shapes had faded into the low sky. "It mighty late for them to be around."

Joshua dug his paddle deeper in the water. The pirogue shuddered and shot ahead.

"You can't tell what they are from way over here," Henry said.

"I plain can."

Henry turned his head and studied him. "What the matter with you?"

"I hope to God that that there moccasin chew out you wagging tongue," Joshua said.

Henry jerked around; the pirogue swayed wildly. "Where a moccasin?"

"There." Joshua pointed to a long, dark form that was disappearing among the reeds and the Spanish-fern bushes. "And, man, you plain better stop jumping or you have us in this here water."

"I ain't liked snakes."

"You plain scared," Joshua said softly.

"Maybe we get in shooting range of some ducks," Henry said.

Joshua snorted.

Henry said: "Wonder why they all afraid to come out. Ain't nothing out here."

After a moment Joshua said: "I aim to have a look at where all the trouble was. I aim to keep on going till I can plain see the river." He had been afraid last night; and Henry had seen him. Now there was something he had to prove.

For a while Henry was quiet. Then he said: "Man, I'm colding stiff. Let's go back."

"Ain't no use to yet," Josh said.

"I'm freezing up."

"Me, too," Josh said. "But there ain't no use to turn back yet."

They moved steadily south, in a twisting line through the narrow water-ways, following the pattern of a curve that would bring them to the river, far down where it met the Gulf.

In about an hour they were there, in a narrow passage of water sheltered by a curve of reeds from the full force of the river, but where they could see into the broad stream and across to the faint, low line of grasses on the other side. Here the river was just a yellow-brown pass flowing between banks of sifting mud and reeds and tough, tangled bushes and twisted, dead trees brought down years ago and left far up out of the usual channel by the flood waters.

The wind was high. The grasses all around bent with a small screaming sound. The water was swift and almost rough. The pirogue shuddered and bounced. They let their bodies move with it, balancing gently. "Watch that old alligator grass there," Henry said as the craft swung over near the tall reeds. "They plain cut you up like a knife."

Joshua turned the pirogue crosswise in the channel. Behind them a pair of ducks rose, hung for a minute, and then began a quick climb up the strips of wind.

"God Almighty!" Henry said. "There more duck!"

Joshua stood up in the pirogue, following the sweep of their flight. They disappeared almost at once in the low sky. He sat down.

"You reckon we ever gonna get close enough for a shot?" Henry said.

Joshua did not answer. Out of the corner of his eye he had seen something—something blue-colored. And that was one color you did not see down here in the marsh, ever. There were browns and greens and yellows, but never blue—not even the sky in winter. Still, when he had stood up in the pirogue, so that he was taller than the surrounding reeds, and had followed the flight of the ducks, his eyes had passed over a bright blue. He stood up again, balancing himself gently in the moving boat, and let his eyes swing back—carefully this time.

He found it. Down a way, on the other side of the stretch of reeds, right by the open stream of river. There must be a little shell mound there, he thought, a little solid ground, because bushes grew there, and there was one bare, twisted, dead chinaberry tree. The river was always throwing up little heaps like that and then in a couple of years lifting them away. His eyes found the spot of blue color again. "Look there," he said.

Henry got to his feet slowly, carefully. The wooden shell rocked and then steadied. Henry squinted along the line of the pointing finger. "Sweet Jesus God!" he whispered. "That a man there!"

They were still for a long time. The pirogue drifted over to one side of the channel and nudged gently against the reeds. They took hold of the tops of the grasses, steadying themselves. The water got too rough; they had to sit down quickly.

Joshua found a small channel opening through the grass. He pushed the pirogue through it until there was only a dozen yards or so of low oyster grass ahead of them. The river there was full of driftwood, turning and washing down with the slow force of a truck.

"We plain can't get around the other side," Joshua said.

"Ain't no need to get closer," Henry said.

"I plain wonder who he is."

They could see so clearly now: bright-blue pants and a leather jacket.

They were bent forward, staring. "He got yellow hair," Henry said. The water made a sucking sound against the hull, and he looked down at it with a quick, nervous movement. "Water sound like it talking, times," he said.

"I plain wonder who he is."

"Ain't been here long, that for sure," Henry said. "Ain't puffed up none."

"That right," Joshua said.

"Remember the way it was with the people after the hurricane? And they only out two days?" Henry's voice trailed off to a whisper.

"I remember," Joshua said.

The man had been washed up high into the tough grasses. He was lying face down. He would stay here until the spring floods lifted him away—if there was anything left then.

"He got his hands stuck out up over his head," Henry said. They could not see the hands, but the brown, leatherclad arms were lifted straight ahead and pointing into the tangle of hackberries.

"His fingers is hanging down so the fishes nibble on them," Joshua said, and felt his shoulders twitch.

"I done felt fish nibble on my fingers," Henry said.

"Not when you was dead."

They were quiet again. All around them the sound of the miles of moving water was like breathing.

Suddenly Henry remembered. "I bet I know who he is."

"Who?" Joshua did not turn his eyes.

"I bet he off that there submarine that got sunk out in the river."

"Maybe," Joshua said.

"Or maybe he off one of the ships that got sunk."

"It don't make no difference, none."

"It ain't no use to hang around here," Henry said finally. "What we hanging around here for?"

Joshua did not answer. Henry turned and looked at him. Joshua was rubbing his chin slowly. "He got a mighty nice jacket there," he said.

"Ain't no use hanging around admiring a dead man's clothes, none."

"I might could like that jacket, me," Joshua said.

Henry stared back over his shoulder.

"You think I scared," Joshua said.

"No," Henry said. "I ain't thinking that."

"I ain't scared of going over there and getting that coat that I like," Joshua bragged.

Henry shook his head.

"Him there—he ain't gonna need it no more," Joshua said.

"You ain't gonna do that."

"You think I afraid. I reckon I just gonna do that."

"You plain could get killed going on that riverside, with all the driftwood coming down."

"Ain't going on that side," Joshua said. "I gonna climb over from this here side."

"Iffen you ain't drown yourself," Henry said, "you gonna get cut to pieces by swordgrass or get bit by one of them snakes we seen a little while ago."

"I ain't afraid," Joshua said.

He handed Henry the paddle. "You steady it now, man," he said. He got to his feet, and the pirogue did not even tremble with his movement. He took a firm grasp on the top of the toughest grasses and jumped over the side. The boat dipped heavily and the yellow, cold water splashed in.

"God Almighty," Henry said. "You like to upset us for sure."

Joshua fought his way through the twenty feet or so of matted oyster grass and waist-high water until he reached the little shell mound. The water was shallower there; it came only a little above his ankles. He began to move slowly along through the tangle of bushes, working his way across to the riverside. A heavy branch snapped away from his shoulders and clipped him in the face. He jerked his head back and clapped his hand to the cut spot.

"What that?" Henry called. "A snake ain't got you?"

"No," Joshua said. "I ain't afraid of no snakes when I sees something I want, me."

He could feel a quivering deep down inside himself. But he said aloud: "That just the cold, just the cold water, boy. I can just think how warm and fine it gonna be with a nice coat, me."

He took his hand away and looked at it. There was blood all over the palm. The branch must have cut his cheek deeply.

"It beginning to rain again," Henry called.

"I ain't afraid of no little rain," Joshua called back.

The ground under his feet must have been covered with moss, for it was slippery walking. He lost his balance once and almost fell. He felt the water splash cold up to his shoulders.

"That a gator got you?" Henry's voice was thin and ragged.

"I ain't afraid of no gators," Joshua called back. He had reached the man now. He bent down and touched the soft brown leather of the jacket. From the feel, he knew that it was buttoned across the chest. He'd have to turn the body over. He tugged at one shoulder, but the arms were caught somehow.

"You come help me," he told Henry, and, getting no answer, he looked around quickly. "Iffen you got any ideas of getting scared and running off, I just gonna peel you hide off."

He spread his legs and braced himself and pulled harder and harder. The body turned over stiffly, with a swish of water. Joshua did not look at the face. He stared at the. two buttons, and then his cold fingers fumbled with them. They would not loosen.

"What you doing?" Henry called.

Joshua took out his knife, the one his father had given him, and cut off the buttons. One fell in the water. The other he caught between two fingers and dropped in his own pocket.

"Ain't you near got it?"

Joshua looked up and over at Henry when he pulled the jacket off.

"Come on," Henry said, and waved the paddle in the air.

Joshua, still without looking down, turned and worked his way back, dragging the jacket from one hand, in the water.

By the time they got home, it was almost dark and the rain was falling heavily. All the color had washed out of the country, leaving it gray and streaked and blurry, like the clouds overhead. The marshes off a little way looked just like the lower part of the sky.

Joshua picked up the fish with one hand, and with the other he tossed the jacket over his right shoulder.

He could feel the leather pressing cold against his neck. It had a smell, too. He crinkled his nose. A slight smell, one you wouldn't notice unless you were taking particular notice of such things. Faint, but distinct, too—like the way the swamp smelled, because it had so many dead things in it.

There was a cold wind coming up with the night; you could hear its angry murmuring out in the marshes. Wet as he was, and shivering, Joshua stopped for just one moment and turned and looked back the way they had come, down Goose Bayou, across the gray grasses, and he blinked and shook his head, because he couldn't quite see clear. It had gotten that dark.

QUESTIONS

1. At what time of year does the story take place, and at approximately what point in history?

2. In what way are the season and the background of world events made integral to the story? That is, what other aspects of the story would have to be changed if the season were changed? If the story took place a few years earlier or later?

3. Does the author seem to have focussed her interest primarily on the experience of adults or on that of children? What seems to you to be the exact relationship between these two kinds of experience in the story?

4. What seems to you to be the emotion which is given most consistent thematic treatment in the story? How many variations on the theme can you find, distributed among the various characters?

FLANNERY O'CONNOR

(1925–   )

In the last few decades the South has produced a remarkable and brilliant array of writers of fiction. If we think of such writers as William Faulkner and Thomas Wolfe, or of Eudora Welty, Carson McCullers, and Truman Capote, we realize that while they resemble one another in that they write about the South, they differ from each other in almost every other respect. Like Shirley Ann Grau, Flannery O'Connor belongs to the latest generation of writers who are carrying on this tradition. And these two writers, like those mentioned above, resemble one another only in that they find their subject matter in the South and that they treat it with the most assured creative power and with alert attention to the demands and possibilities of the art of fiction. In most other respects they are quite unlike. The "tradition" of twentieth-century Southern fiction has been capable of constituting itself as a tradition within which there has been ample room for the free play of individuality.

Flannery O'Connor, her publishers tell us, was born in Georgia, graduated from Georgia State College for Women, and studied writing at the State University of Iowa. She is the author of a novel, *Wise Blood*, and of a volume of short stories, *A Good Man Is Hard to Find*, from which "The Displaced Person" is taken. In *A Good Man Is Hard to Find*, she takes a very sharp look indeed at life, customs, and moral values of the present day. Her vision is uniquely compounded of such elements as an intelligent moral earnestness, a sardonic despair at the ubiquity of foolishness and selfishness, and a sense of the sometimes comic and sometimes ugly ridiculousness of much that passes before her eyes. Her stories can be funny and painful at the same time; she has a great comic gift, but it is employed in the service of a responsible and consistent view of the ways in which people spoil life, for themselves and for one another. Often, this spectacle is fittingly presented in terms of the grotesque.

"The Displaced Person" is the longest story in *A Good Man Is Hard to Find*. It has many excellences, not the least of which is its force as a parable demonstrating that prejudice, the evil from which so many have suffered so bitterly in our time, has its parentage in greed and ignorant fear of losing what greed would hold.

THE DISPLACED PERSON

The peacock was following Mrs. Shortley up the road to the hill where she meant to stand. Moving one behind the other, they looked like a complete procession. Her arms were folded and as she mounted the prominence, she might have been the giant wife of the countryside, come out at some sign of danger to see what the trouble was. She stood on two tremendous legs, with the grand self-confidence of a mountain, and rose, up narrowing bulges of granite, to two icy blue points of light that pierced forward, surveying everything. She ignored the white afternoon sun which was creeping behind a ragged wall of cloud as if it pretended to be an intruder and cast her gaze down the red clay road that turned off from the highway.

The peacock stopped just behind her, his tail—glittering green-gold and blue in the sunlight—lifted just enough so that it would not touch the ground. It flowed out on either side like a floating train and his head on the long blue reed-like neck was drawn back as if his attention were fixed in the distance on something no one else could see.

Mrs. Shortley was watching a black car turn through the gate from the highway. Over by the toolshed, about fifteen feet away, the two Negroes, Astor and Sulk, had stopped work to watch. They were hidden by a mulberry tree but Mrs. Shortley knew they were there.

Mrs. McIntyre was coming down the steps of her house to meet the car. She had on her largest smile but Mrs. Shortley, even from her distance, could detect a nervous slide in it. These people who were coming were only hired help, like the Shortleys themselves or the Negroes. Yet here was the owner of the place out to welcome them. Here she was, wearing her best clothes and a string of beads, and now bounding forward with her mouth stretched.

The car stopped at the walk just as she did and the priest was the first to get out. He was a long-legged black-suited old man with a white hat on and a collar that he wore backwards, which, Mrs. Shortley knew, was what priests did who wanted to be known as priests. It was this priest who had arranged for these people to come here. He opened the back door of the car and out jumped two children, a boy and a girl, and then, stepping more slowly, a woman in brown, shaped like a peanut. Then the front door opened and out stepped the man, the Displaced Person. He was short and a little sway-backed and wore gold-rimmed spectacles.

Mrs. Shortley's vision narrowed on him and then widened to include the woman and the two children in a group picture. The first thing that struck her as very peculiar was that they looked like other people. Every time she had seen them in her imagination, the image she had got was of the three bears, walking single file, with wooden shoes on like Dutchmen and sailor hats and bright coats with a lot of buttons. But the woman had on a dress she might have worn herself and the children were dressed like anybody from around. The man had on khaki pants and a blue shirt. Suddenly, as Mrs. McIntyre held out her hand to him, he bobbed down from the waist and kissed it.

Mrs. Shortley jerked her own hand up toward her mouth and then after a second brought it down and rubbed it vigorously on her seat. If Mr. Shortley had tried to kiss her hand, Mrs. McIntyre would have knocked him into the middle of next week, but then Mr. Shortley wouldn't have kissed her hand anyway. He didn't have time to mess around.

She looked closer, squinting. The boy was in the center of the group, talking. He was supposed to speak the most English because he had learned some in Poland and so he was to listen to his father's Polish and say it in English and then listen to Mrs. McIntyre's English and say that in Polish. The priest had told Mrs. McIntyre his name was Rudolph and he was twelve and the girl's name was Sledgewig and she was nine. Sledgewig sounded to Mrs. Shortley like something you would name a bug, or vice versa, as if you named a boy Bollweevil. All of them's last name was something that only they themselves and the priest could pronounce. All she could make out of it was Gobblehook. She and Mrs. McIntyre had been calling them the Gobblehooks all week while they got ready for them.

There had been a great deal to do to get ready for them because they didn't have anything of their own, not a stick of furniture or a sheet or a dish, and everything had had to be scraped together out of things that Mrs. McIntyre couldn't use any more herself. They had collected a piece of odd furniture here and a piece there and they had taken some flowered chicken feed sacks and made curtains for the windows, two red and one green, because they had not had enough of the red sacks to go around. Mrs. McIntyre said she was not made of money and she could not afford to buy curtains. "They can't talk," Mrs. Shortley said. "You reckon they'll know what colors even is?" and Mrs. McIntyre had said that after what those people had been through, they should be grateful for anything they could get. She said to think how lucky they were to escape from over there and come to a place like this.

Mrs. Shortley recalled a newsreel she had seen once of a small room piled high with bodies of dead naked people all in a heap, their arms and legs tangled together, a head thrust in here, a head there, a foot, a knee, a part that should have been covered up sticking out, a hand raised clutching nothing. Before you could realize that it was real and take it into your head, the picture changed and a hollow-sounding voice was saying, "Time marches on!" This was the kind of thing that was happening every day in Europe where they had not advanced as in this country, and watching from her vantage point, Mrs. Shortley had the sudden intuition that the Gobblehooks, like rats with typhoid fleas, could have carried all those murderous ways over the water with them directly to this place. If they had come from where that kind of thing was done to them, who was to say they were not the kind that would also do it to others? The width and breadth of this question nearly shook her. Her stomach trembled as if there had been a slight quake in the heart of the mountains and automatically she moved down from her elevation and went forward to be introduced to them, as if she meant to find out at once what they were capable of.

She approached, stomach foremost, head back, arms folded, boots flopping gently against her large legs. About fifteen feet from the gesticulating group, she stopped and made her presence felt by training her gaze on the back of Mrs. McIntyre's neck. Mrs. McIntyre was a small woman of sixty with a round wrinkled face and red bangs that came almost down to two high orange-colored penciled eyebrows. She had a little doll's mouth and eyes that were a soft blue when she opened them wide but more like steel or granite when she narrowed them to inspect a milk can. She had buried one husband and divorced two and Mrs. Shortley respected her as a person nobody had put anything over on yet—except, ha, ha, perhaps the Shortleys. She held out her arm in Mrs. Shortley's direction and said to the Rudolph boy, "And this is Mrs. Shortley. Mr. Shortley is my dairyman. Where's Mr. Shortley?" she asked as his wife began to approach again, her arms still folded. "I want him to meet the Guizacs."

Now it was Guizac. She wasn't calling them Gobblehook to their face. "Chancey's at the barn," Mrs. Shortley said. "He don't have time to rest himself in the bushes like them niggers over there."

Her look first grazed the tops of the displaced people's heads and then revolved downwards slowly, the way a buzzard glides and drops in the air until it alights on the carcass. She stood far enough away so that the man would not be able to kiss her hand. He looked directly at her with little green eyes and gave her a broad grin that was toothless on one side. Mrs. Shortley, without smiling, turned her attention to the little girl who stood by the mother, swinging her shoulders from side to side. She had long braided hair in two looped pigtails and there was no denying she was a pretty child even if she did have a bug's name. She was better looking than either Annie Maude or Sarah Mae, Mrs. Shortley's two girls going on fifteen and seventeen but Annie Maude had never got her growth and Sarah Mae had a cast in her eye. She compared the foreign boy to her son, H. C., and H. C. came out far ahead. H. C. was twenty years old with her build and eyeglasses. He was going to Bible School now and when he finished he was going to start him a church. He had a strong sweet voice for hymns and could sell anything. Mrs. Shortley looked at the priest and was reminded that these people did not have an advanced religion. There was no telling what all they believed since none of the foolishness had been reformed out of it. Again she saw the room piled high with bodies.

The priest spoke in a foreign way himself, English but as if he had a throatful of hay. He had a big nose and a bald rectangular face and head. While she was observing him, his large mouth dropped open and with a stare behind her, he said, "Arrrrrr!" and pointed.

Mrs. Shortley spun around. The peacock was standing a few feet behind her, with his head slightly cocked.

"What a beauti-ful birdrrrd!" the priest murmured.

"Another mouth to feed," Mrs. McIntyre said, glancing in the peafowl's direction.

"And when does he raise his splendid tail?" asked the priest.

"Just when it suits him," she said. "There used to be twenty or thirty of those things on the place but I've let them die off. I don't like to hear them scream in the middle of the night."

"So beauti-ful," the priest said. "A tail full of suns," and he crept forward on tiptoe and looked down on the bird's back where the polished gold and green design began. The peacock stood still as if he had just come down from some sun-drenched height to be a vision for them all. The priest's homely red face hung over him, glowing with pleasure.

Mrs. Shortley's mouth had drawn acidly to one side. "Nothing but a peachicken," she muttered.

Mrs. McIntyre raised her orange eyebrows and exchanged a look with her to indicate that the old man was in his second childhood. "Well, we must show the Guizacs their new home," she said impatiently and she herded them into the car again. The peacock stepped off toward the mulberry tree where the two Negroes were hiding and the priest turned his absorbed face away and got in the car and drove the displaced people down to the shack they were to occupy.

Mrs. Shortley waited until the car was out of sight and then she made her way circuitously to the mulberry tree and stood about ten feet behind the two Negroes, one an old man holding a bucket half full of calf feed and the other a yellowish boy with a short woodchuck-like head pushed into a rounded felt hat. "Well," she said slowly, "yawl have looked long enough. What you think about them?"

The old man, Astor, raised himself. "We been watching," he said as if this would be news to her. "Who they now?"

"They come from over the water," Mrs. Shortley said with a wave of her arm. "They're what is called Displaced Persons."

"Displaced Persons," he said. "Well now. I declare. What do that mean?"

"It means they ain't where they were born at and there's nowhere for them to go—like if you was run out of here and wouldn't nobody have you."

"It seems like they here, though," the old man said in a reflective voice. "If they here, they somewhere."

"Sho is," the other agreed. "They here."

The illogic of Negro-thinking always irked Mrs. Shortley. "They ain't where they belong to be at," she said. "They belong to be back over yonder where everything is still like they been used to. Over here it's more advanced than where they come from. But yawl better look out now," she said and nodded her head. "There's about ten million billion more just like them and I know what Mrs. McIntyre said."

"Say what?" the young one asked.

"Places are not easy to get nowadays, for white or black, but I reckon I heard what she stated to me," she said in a sing-song voice.

"You liable to hear most anything," the old man remarked, leaning forward as if he were about to walk off but holding himself suspended.

"I heard her say, 'This is going to put the Fear of the Lord into those shiftless niggers!'" Mrs. Shortley said in a ringing voice.

The old man started off. "She say something like that every now and then," he said. "Ha. Ha. Yes indeed."

"You better get on in that barn and help Mr. Shortley," she said to the other one. "What you reckon she pays you for?"

"He the one sont me out," the Negro muttered. "He the one gimme something else to do."

"Well you better get to doing it then," she said and stood there until he moved off. Then she stood a while longer, reflecting, her unseeing eyes directly in front of the peacock's tail. He had jumped into the tree and his tail hung in front of her, full of fierce planets with eyes that were each ringed in green and set against a sun that was gold in one second's light and salmon-colored in the next. She might have been looking at a map of the universe but she didn't notice it any more than she did the spots of sky that cracked the dull green of the tree. She was having an inner vision instead. She was seeing the ten million billion of them pushing their way into new places over here and herself, a giant angel with wings as wide as a house, telling the Negroes that they would have to find another place. She turned herself in the direction of the barn, musing on this, her expression lofty and satisfied.

She approached the barn from an oblique angle that allowed her a look in the door before she could be seen herself. Mr. Chancey Shortley was adjusting the last milking machine on a large black and white spotted cow near the entrance, squatting at her heels. There was about a half-inch of cigarette adhering to the center of his lower lip. Mrs. Shortley observed it minutely for half a second. "If she seen or heard of you smoking in this barn, she would blow a fuse," she said.

Mr. Shortley raised a sharply rutted face containing a washout under each cheek and two long crevices eaten down both sides of his blistered mouth. "You gonter be the one to tell her?" he asked.

"She's got a nose of her own," Mrs. Shortley said.

Mr. Shortley, without appearing to give the feat any consideration, lifted the cigarette stub with the sharp end of his tongue, drew it into his mouth, closed his lips tightly, rose, stepped out, gave his wife a good round appreciative stare, and spit the smoldering butt into the grass.

"Aw Chancey," she said, "haw haw," and she dug a little hole for it with her toe and covered it up. This trick of Mr. Shortley's was actually his way of making love to her. When he had done his courting, he had not brought a guitar to strum or anything pretty for her to keep, but had sat on her porch steps, not saying a word, imitating a paralyzed man propped up to enjoy a cigarette. When the cigarette got the proper size, he would turn his eyes to her and open his mouth and draw in the butt and then sit there as if he had swallowed it, looking at her with the most loving look anybody could imagine. It nearly drove her wild and every time he did it, she wanted to pull his hat down over his eyes and hug him to death.

"Well," she said, going into the barn after him, "the Gobblehooks have come and she wants you to meet them, says, 'Where's Mr. Shortley?' and I says, 'He don't have time . . .'"

"Tote up them weights," Mr. Shortley said, squatting to the cow again.

"You reckon he can drive a tractor when he don't know English?" she asked. "I don't think she's going to get her money's worth out of them. That boy can talk but he looks delicate. The one can work can't talk and the one can talk can't work. She ain't any better off than if she had more niggers."

"I rather have a nigger if it was me," Mr. Shortley said.

"She says it's ten million more like them, Displaced Persons, she says that there priest can get her all she wants."

"She better quit messin with that there priest," Mr. Shortley said.

"He don't look smart," Mrs. Shortley said, "—kind of foolish."

"I ain't going to have the Pope of Rome tell me how to run no dairy," Mr. Shortley said.

"They ain't Eye-talians, they're Poles," she said. "From Poland where all them bodies were stacked up at. You remember all them bodies?"

"I give them three weeks here," Mr. Shortley said.

Three weeks later Mrs. McIntyre and Mrs. Shortley drove to the cane bottom to see Mr. Guizac start to operate the silage cutter, a new machine that Mrs. McIntyre had just bought because she said, for the first time, she had somebody who could operate it. Mr. Guizac could drive a tractor, use the rotary hay-baler, the silage cutter, the combine, the letz mill, or any other machine she had on the place. He was an expert mechanic, a carpenter, and a mason. He was thrifty and energetic. Mrs. McIntyre said she figured he would save her twenty dollars a month on repair bills alone. She said getting him was the best day's work she had ever done in her life. He could work milking machines and he was scrupulously clean. He did not smoke.

She parked her car on the edge of the cane field and they got out. Sulk, the young Negro, was attaching the wagon to the cutter and Mr. Guizac was attaching the cutter to the tractor. He finished first and pushed the colored boy out of the way and attached the wagon to the cutter himself, gesticulating with a bright angry face when he wanted the hammer or the screwdriver. Nothing was done quick enough to suit him. The Negroes made him nervous.

The week before, he had come upon Sulk at the dinner hour, sneaking with a croker sack into the pen where the young turkeys were. He had watched him take a frying-size turkey from the lot and thrust it in the sack and put the sack under his coat. Then he had followed him around the barn, jumped on him, dragged him to Mrs. McIntyre's back door and had acted out the entire scene for her, while the Negro muttered and grumbled and said God might strike him dead if he had been stealing any turkey, he had only been taking it to put some black shoe polish on its head because it had the sorehead. God might strike him dead if that was not the truth before Jesus. Mrs. McIntyre told him to go put the turkey back and then she was a long time explaining to the Pole that all Negroes would steal. She finally had to call Rudolph and tell him in English and have him tell his father in Polish, and Mr. Guizac had gone off with a startled disappointed face.

Mrs. Shortley stood by hoping there would be trouble with the silage machine but there was none. All of Mr. Guizac's motions were quick and accurate. He jumped on the tractor like a monkey and maneuvered the big orange cutter into the cane; in a second the silage was squirting in a green jet out of the pipe into the wagon. He went jolting down the row until he disappeared from sight and the noise became remote.

Mrs. McIntyre sighed with pleasure. "At last," she said, "I've got somebody I can depend on. For years I've been fooling with sorry people. Sorry people. Poor white trash and niggers," she muttered. "They've drained me dry. Before you all came I had Ringfields and Collins and Jarrells and Perkins and Pinkins and Herrins and God knows what all else and not a one of them left without taking something off this place that didn't belong to them. Not a one!"

Mrs. Shortley could listen to this with composure because she knew that if Mrs. McIntyre had considered her trash, they couldn't have talked about trashy people together. Neither of them approved of trash. Mrs. McIntyre continued with the monologue that Mrs. Shortley had heard oftentimes before. "I've been running this place for thirty years," she said, looking with a deep frown out over the field, "and always just barely making it. People think you're made of money. I have the taxes to pay. I have the insurance to keep up. I have the repair bills. I have the feed bills." It all gathered up and she stood with her chest lifted and her small hands gripped around her elbows. "Ever since the Judge died," she said, "I've barely been making ends meet and they all take something when they leave. The niggers don't leave—they stay and steal. A nigger thinks anybody is rich he can steal from and that white trash thinks anybody is rich who can afford to hire people as sorry as they are. And all I've got is the dirt under my feet!"

You hire and fire, Mrs. Shortley thought, but she didn't always say what she thought. She stood by and let Mrs. McIntyre say it all out to the end but this time it didn't end as usual. "But at last I'm saved!" Mrs. McIntyre said. "One fellow's misery is the other fellow's gain. That man there," and she pointed where the Displaced Person had disappeared, "—he has to work! He wants to work!" She turned to Mrs. Shortley with her bright wrinkled face. "That man is my salvation!" she said.

Mrs. Shortley looked straight ahead as if her vision penetrated the cane and the hill and pierced through to the other side. "I would suspicion salvation got from the devil," she said in a slow detached way.

"Now what do you mean by that?" Mrs. McIntyre asked, looking at her sharply.

Mrs. Shortley wagged her head but would not say anything else. The fact was she had nothing else to say for this intuition had only at that instant come to her. She had never given much thought to the devil for she felt that religion was essentially for those people who didn't have the brains to avoid evil without it. For people like herself, for people of gumption, it was a social occasion providing the opportunity to sing; but if she had ever given it much thought, she would have considered the devil the head of it and God the hanger-on. With the coming of these displaced people, she was obliged to give new thought to a good many things.

"I know what Sledgewig told Annie Maude," she said, and when Mrs. McIntyre carefully did not ask her what but reached down and broke off a sprig of sassafras to chew, she continued in a way to indicate she was not telling all, "that they wouldn't be able to live long, the four of them, on seventy dollars a month."

"He's worth raising," Mrs. McIntyre said. "He saves me money."

This was as much as to say that Chancey had never saved her money. Chancey got up at four in the morning to milk her cows, in winter wind and summer heat, and he had been doing it for the last two years. They had been with her the longest she had ever had anybody. The gratitude they got was these hints that she hadn't been saved any money.

"Is Mr. Shortley feeling better today?" Mrs. McIntyre asked.

Mrs. Shortley thought it was about time she was asking that question. Mr. Shortley had been in bed two days with an attack. Mr. Guizac had taken his place in the dairy in addition to doing his own work. "No he ain't," she said. "The doctor said he was suffering from over-exhaustion."

"If Mr. Shortley is over-exhausted," Mrs. McIntyre said, "then he must have a second job on the side," and she looked at Mrs. Shortley with almost closed eyes as if she were examining the bottom of a milk can.

Mrs. Shortley did not say a word but her dark suspicion grew like a black thunder cloud. The fact was that Mr. Shortley did have a second job on the side and that, in a free country, this was none of Mrs. McIntyre's business. Mr. Shortley made whiskey. He had a small still back in the farthest reaches of the place, on Mrs. McIntyre's land to be sure, but on land that she only owned and did not cultivate, on idle land that was not doing anybody any good. Mr. Shortley was not afraid of work. He got up at four in the morning and milked her cows and in the middle of the day when he was supposed to be resting, he was off attending to his still. Not every man would work like that. The Negroes knew about his still but he knew about theirs so there had never been any disagreeableness between them. But with foreigners on the place, with people who were all eyes and no understanding, who had come from a place continually fighting, where the religion had not been reformed—with this kind of people, you had to be on the lookout every minute. She thought there ought to be a law against them. There was no reason they couldn't stay over there and take the places of some of the people who had been killed in their wars and butcherings.

"What's furthermore," she said suddenly, "Sledgewig said as soon as her papa saved the money, he was going to buy him a used car. Once they get them a used car, they'll leave you."

"I can't pay him enough for him to save money," Mrs. McIntyre said. "I'm not worrying about that. Of course," she said then, "if Mr. Shortley got incapacitated, I would have to use Mr. Guizac in the dairy all the time and I would have to pay him more. He doesn't smoke," she said, and it was the fifth time within the week that she had pointed this out.

"It is no man," Mrs. Shortley said emphatically, "that works as hard as

Chancey, or is as easy with a cow, or is more of a Christian," and she folded her arms and her gaze pierced the distance. The noise of the tractor and cutter increased and Mr. Guizac appeared coming around the other side of the cane row. "Which can not be said about everybody," she muttered. She wondered whether, if the Pole found Chancey's still, he would know what it was. The trouble with these people was, you couldn't tell what they knew. Every time Mr. Guizac smiled, Europe stretched out in Mrs. Shortley's imagination, mysterious and evil, the devil's experiment station.

The tractor, the cutter, the wagon passed, rattling and rumbling and grinding before them. "Think how long that would have taken with men and mules to do it," Mrs. McIntyre shouted. "We'll get this whole bottom cut within two days at this rate."

"Maybe," Mrs. Shortley muttered, "if don't no terrible accident occur." She thought how the tractor had made mules worthless. Nowadays you couldn't give away a mule. The next thing to go, she reminded herself, will be niggers.

In the afternoon she explained what was going to happen to them to Astor and Sulk who were in the cow lot, filling the manure spreader. She sat down next to the block of salt under a small shed, her stomach in her lap, her arms on top of it. "All you colored people better look out," she said. "You know how much you can get for a mule."

"Nothing, no indeed," the old man said, "not one thing."

"Before it was a tractor," she said, "it could be a mule. And before it was a Displaced Person, it could be a nigger. The time is going to come," she prophesied, "when it won't be no more occasion to speak of a nigger."

The old man laughed politely. "Yes indeed," he said. "Ha, ha."

The young one didn't say anything. He only looked sullen but when she had gone in the house, he said, "Big Belly act like she know everything."

"Never mind," the old man said, "your place too low for anybody to dispute with you for it."

She didn't tell her fears about the still to Mr. Shortley until he was back on the job in the dairy. Then one night after they were in bed, she said, "That man prowls."

Mr. Shortley folded his hands on his bony chest and pretended he was a corpse.

"Prowls," she continued and gave him a sharp kick in the side with her knee. "Who's to say what they know and don't know? Who's to say if he found it he wouldn't go right to her and tell? How you know they don't make liquor in Europe? They drive tractors. They got them all kinds of machinery. Answer me."

"Don't worry me now," Mr. Shortley said. "I'm a dead man."

"It's them little eyes of his that's foreign," she muttered. "And that way he's got of shrugging." She drew her shoulders up and shrugged several times. "Howcome he's got anything to shrug about?" she asked.

"If everybody was as dead as I am, nobody would have no trouble," Mr. Shortley said.

"That priest," she muttered and was silent for a minute. Then she said, "In Europe they probably got some different way to make liquor but I reckon they know all the ways. They're full of crooked ways. They never have advanced or reformed. They got the same religion as a thousand years ago. It could only be the devil responsible for that. Always fighting amongst each other. Disputing. And then get us into it. Ain't they got us into it twict already and we ain't got no more sense than to go over there and settle it for them and then they come on back over here and snoop around and find your still and go straight to her. And liable to kiss her hand any minute. Do you hear me?"

"No," Mr. Shortley said.

"And I'll tell you another thing," she said. "I wouldn't be a tall surprised if he don't know everything you say, whether it be in English or not."

"I don't speak no other language," Mr. Shortley murmured.

"I suspect," she said, "that before long there won't be no more niggers on this place. And I tell you what. I'd rather have niggers than them Poles. And what's furthermore, I aim to take up for the niggers when the time comes. When Gobblehook first come here, you recollect how he shook their hands, like he didn't know the difference, like he might have been as black as them, but when it come to finding out Sulk was taking turkeys, he gone on and told her. I know he was taking turkeys. I could have told her myself."

Mr. Shortley was breathing softly as if he were asleep.

"A nigger don't know when he has a friend," she said. "And I'll tell you another thing. I get a heap out of Sledgewig. Sledgewig said that in Poland they lived in a brick house and one night a man come and told them to get out of it before daylight. Do you believe they ever lived in a brick house?

"Airs," she said. "That's just airs. A wooden house is good enough for me. Chancey," she said, "turn thisaway. I hate to see niggers mistreated and run out. I have a heap of pity for niggers and poor folks. Ain't I always had?" she asked. "I say ain't I always been a friend to niggers and poor folks?

"When the times comes," she said, "I'll stand up for the niggers and that's that. I ain't going to see that priest drive out all the niggers."

Mrs. McIntyre bought a new drag harrow and a tractor with a power lift because she said, for the first time, she had someone who could handle machinery. She and Mrs. Shortley had driven to the back field to inspect what he had harrowed the day before. "That's been done beautifully!" Mrs. McIntyre said, looking out over the red undulating ground.

Mrs. McIntyre had changed since the Displaced Person had been working for her and Mrs. Shortley had observed the change very closely: she had begun to act like somebody who was getting rich secretly and she didn't confide in Mrs. Shortley the way she used to. Mrs. Shortley suspected that the priest was at the bottom of the change. They were very slick. First he would get her into his Church and then he would get his hand in her pocketbook. Well, Mrs. Shortley thought, the more fool she! Mrs. Shortley had a secret herself. She knew something the Displaced Person was doing that would floor Mrs. McIntyre. "I still say he ain't going to work forever for seventy dollars a month," she murmured. She intended to keep her secret to herself and Mr. Shortley.

"Well," Mrs. McIntyre said, "I may have to get rid of some of this other help so I can pay him more."

Mrs. Shortley nodded to indicate she had known this for some time. "I'm not saying those niggers ain't had it coming," she said. "But they do the best they know how. You can always tell a nigger what to do and stand by until he does it."

"That's what the Judge said," Mrs. McIntyre said and looked at her with approval. The Judge was her first husband, the one who had left the place. Mrs. Shortley had heard that she had married him when she was thirty and he was seventy-five, thinking she would be rich as soon as he died, but the old man was a scoundrel and when his estate was settled, they found he didn't have a nickel. All he left her were the fifty acres and the house. But she always spoke of him in a reverent way and quoted his sayings, such as, "One fellow's misery is the other fellow's gain," and "The devil you know is better than the devil you don't."

"However," Mrs. Shortley remarked, "the devil you know is better than the devil you don't," and she had to turn away so that Mrs. McIntyre would not see her smile. She had found out what the Displaced Person was up to through the old man, Astor, and she had not told anybody but Mr. Shortley. Mr. Shortley had risen straight up in bed like Lazarus from the tomb.

"Shut your mouth!" he had said.

"Yes," she had said.

"Naw!" Mr. Shortley had said.

"Yes," she had said.

Mr. Shortley had fallen back flat.

"The Pole don't know any better," Mrs. Shortley had said. "I reckon that priest is putting him up to it is all. I blame the priest."

The priest came frequently to see the Guizacs and he would always stop in and visit Mrs. McIntyre too and they would walk around the place and she would point out her improvements and listen to his rattling talk. It suddenly came to Mrs. Shortley that he was trying to persuade her to bring another Polish family onto the place. With two of them here, there would be almost nothing spoken but Polish! The Negroes would be gone and there would be the two families against Mr. Shortley and herself! She began to imagine a war of words, to see the Polish words and the English words coming at each other, stalking forward, not sentences, just words, gabble gabble gabble, flung out high and shrill and stalking forward and then grappling with each other. She saw the Polish words, dirty and all-knowing and unreformed, flinging mud on the clean English words until everything was equally dirty. She saw them all piled up in a room, all the dead dirty words, theirs and hers too, piled up like the naked bodies in the newsreel. God save me! she cried silently, from the stinking power of Satan! And she started from that day to read her Bible with a new attention. She poured over the Apocalypse and began to quote from the Prophets and before long she had come to a deeper understanding of her existence. She saw plainly that the meaning of the world was a mystery that had been planned and she was not surprised to suspect that she had a special part in the plan because she was strong. She saw that the Lord God Almighty had created the strong people to do what had to be done and she felt that she would be ready when she was called. Right now she felt that her business was to watch the priest.

His visits irked her more and more. On the last one, he went about picking up feathers off the ground. He found two peacock feathers and four or five turkey feathers and an old brown hen feather and took them off with him like a bouquet. This foolish-acting did not deceive Mrs. Shortley any. Here he was, leading foreigners over in hoards to places that were not theirs, to cause disputes, to uproot niggers, to plant the Whore of Babylon in the midst of the righteous! Whenever he came on the place, she hid herself behind something and watched until he left.

It was on a Sunday afternoon that she had her vision. She had gone to drive in the cows for Mr. Shortley who had a pain in his knee and she was walking slowly through the pasture, her arms folded, her eyes on the distant low-lying clouds that looked like rows and rows of white fish washed up on a great blue beach. She paused after an incline to heave a sigh of exhaustion for she had an immense weight to carry around and she was not as young as she used to be. At times she could feel her heart, like a child's fist, clenching and unclenching inside her chest, and when the feeling came, it stopped her thought altogether and she would go about like a large hull of herself, moving for no reason; but she gained this incline without a tremor and stood at the top of it, pleased with herself. Suddenly while she watched, the sky folded back in two pieces like the curtain to a stage and a gigantic figure stood facing her. It was the color of the sun in the early afternoon, white-gold. It was of no definite shape but there were fiery wheels with fierce dark eyes in them, spinning rapidly all around it. She was not able to tell if the figure was going forward or backward because its magnificence was so great. She shut her eyes in order to look at it and it turned blood-red and the wheels turned white. A voice, very resonant, said the one word, "Prophesy!"

She stood there, tottering slightly but still upright, her eyes shut tight and her fists clenched and her straw sun hat low on her forehead. "The children of wicked nations will be butchered," she said in a loud voice. "Legs where arms should be, foot to face, ear in the palm of hand. Who will remain whole? Who will remain whole? Who?"

Presently she opened her eyes. The sky was full of white fish carried lazily on their sides by some invisible current and pieces of the sun, submerged some distance beyond them, appeared from time to time as if they were being washed in the opposite direction. Woodenly she planted one foot in front of the other until she had crossed the pasture and reached the lot. She walked through the barn like one in a daze and did not speak to Mr. Shortley. She continued up the road until she saw the priest's car parked in front of Mrs. McIntyre's house. "Here again," she muttered. "Come to destroy."

Mrs. McIntyre and the priest were walking in the yard. In order not to meet them face to face, she turned to the left and entered the feed house, a single-room shack piled on one side with flowered sacks of scratch feed. There were spilled oyster shells in one corner and a few old dirty calendars on the wall, advertising calf feed and various patent medicine remedies. One showed a bearded gentleman in a frock coat, holding up a bottle, and beneath his feet was the inscription, "I have been made regular by this marvelous discovery!" Mrs. Shortley had always felt close to this man as if he were some distinguished person she was acquainted with but now her mind was on nothing but the dangerous presence of the priest. She stationed herself at a crack between two boards where she could look out and see him and Mrs. McIntyre strolling toward the turkey brooder, which was placed just outside the feed house.

"Arrrrr!" he said as they approached the brooder. "Look at the little biddies!" and he stooped and squinted through the wire.

Mrs. Shortley's mouth twisted.

"Do you think the Guizacs will want to leave me?" Mrs. McIntyre asked. "Do you think they'll go to Chicago or some place like that?"

"And why should they do that now?" asked the priest, wiggling his finger at a turkey, his big nose close to the wire.

"Money," Mrs. McIntyre said.

"Arrrr, give them some morrre then," he said indifferently. "They have to get along."

"So do I," Mrs. McIntyre muttered. "It means I'm going to have to get rid of some of these others."

"And arrre the Shortleys satisfactory?" he inquired, paying more attention to the turkeys than to her.

"Five times in the last month I've found Mr. Shortley smoking in the barn," Mrs. McIntyre said. "Five times."

"And arrre the Negroes any better?"

"They lie and steal and have to be watched all the time," she said.

"Tsk, tsk," he said. "Which will you discharge?"

"I've decided to give Mr. Shortley his month's notice tomorrow," Mrs. McIntyre said.

The priest scarcely seemed to hear her he was so busy wiggling his finger inside the wire. Mrs. Shortley sat down on an open sack of laying mash with a dead thump that sent feed dust clouding up around her.

She found herself looking straight ahead at the opposite wall where the gentleman on the calendar was holding up his marvelous discovery but she didn't see him. She looked ahead as if she saw nothing whatsoever. Then she rose and ran to her house. Her face was an almost volcanic red.

She opened all the drawers and dragged out boxes and old battered suitcases from under the bed. She began to unload the drawers into the boxes, all the time without pause, without taking off the sun hat she had on her head. She set the two girls to doing the same. When Mr. Shortley came in, she did not even look at him but merely pointed one arm at him while she packed with the other. "Bring the car around to the back door," she said. "You ain't waiting to be fired!"

Mr. Shortley had never in his life doubted her omniscience. He perceived the entire situation in half a second and, with only a sour scowl, retreated out the door and went to drive the automobile around to the back.

They tied the two iron beds to the top of the car and the two rocking chairs inside the beds and rolled the two mattresses up between the rocking chairs. On top of this they tied a crate of chickens. They loaded the inside of the car with the old suitcases and boxes, leaving a small space for Annie Maude and Sarah Mae. It took them the rest of the afternoon and half the night to do this but Mrs. Shortley was determined that they would leave before four o'clock in the morning, that Mr. Shortley should not adjust another milking machine on this place. All the time she had been working, her face was changing rapidly from red to white and back again.

Just before dawn, as it began to drizzle rain, they were ready to leave. They all got in the car and sat there cramped up between boxes and bundles and rolls of bedding. The square black automobile moved off with more than its customary grinding noises as if it were protesting the load. In the back, the two long bony yellow-haired girls were sitting on a pile of boxes and there was a beagle hound puppy and a cat with two kittens somewhere under the blankets. The car moved slowly, like some overfreighted leaking ark, away from their shack and past the white house where Mrs. McIntyre was sleeping soundly—hardly guessing that her cows would not be milked by Mr. Shortley that morning—and past the Pole's shack on top of the hill and on down the road to the gate where the two Negroes were walking, one behind the other, on their way to help with the milking. They looked straight at the car and its occupants but even as the dim yellow headlights lit up their faces, they politely did not seem to see anything, or anyhow, to attach significance to what was there. The loaded car might have been passing mist in the early morning half-light. They continued up the road at the same even pace without looking back.

A dark yellow sun was beginning to rise in a sky that was the same slick dark gray as the highway. The fields stretched away, stiff and weedy, on either side. "Where we goin?" Mr. Shortley asked for the first time.

Mrs. Shortley sat with one foot on a packing box so that her knee was pushed into her stomach. Mr. Shortley's elbow was almost under her nose and Sarah Mae's bare left foot was sticking over the front seat, touching her ear.

"Where we goin?" Mr. Shortley repeated and when she didn't answer again, he turned and looked at her.

Fierce heat seemed to be swelling slowly and fully into her face as if it were welling up now for a final assault. She was sitting in an erect way in spite of the fact that one leg was twisted under her and one knee was almost into her neck, but there was a peculiar lack of light in her icy blue eyes. All the vision in them might have been turned around, looking inside her. She suddenly grabbed Mr. Shortley's elbow and Sarah Mae's foot at the same time and began to tug and pull on them as if she were trying to fit the two extra limbs onto herself.

Mr. Shortley began to curse and quickly stopped the car and Sarah Mae yelled to quit but Mrs. Shortley apparently intended to rearrange the whole car at once. She thrashed forward and backward, clutching at everything she could get her hands on and hugging it to herself, Mr. Shortley's head, Sarah Mae's leg, the cat, a wad of white bedding, her own big moon-like knee; then all at once her fierce expression faded into a look of astonishment and her grip on what she had loosened. One of her eyes drew near to the other and seemed to collapse quietly and she was still.

The two girls, who didn't know what had happened to her, began to say, "Where we goin, Ma? Where we goin?" They thought she was playing a joke and that their father, staring straight ahead at her, was imitating a dead man. They didn't know that she had had a great experience or ever been displaced in the world from all that belonged to her. They were frightened by the gray slick road before them and they kept repeating in higher and higher voices, "Where we goin, Ma? Where we goin?" while their mother, her huge body rolled back still against the seat and her eyes like blue-painted glass, seemed to contemplate for the first time the tremendous frontiers of her true country.

II

"Well," Mrs. McIntyre said to the old Negro, "we can get along without them. We've seen them come and seen them go—black and white." She was standing in the calf barn while he cleaned it and she held a rake in her hand and now and then pulled a corn cob from a corner or pointed to a soggy spot that he had missed. When she discovered the Shortleys were gone, she was delighted as it meant she wouldn't have to fire them. The people she hired always left her—because they were that kind of people. Of all the families she had had, the Shortleys were the best if she didn't count the Displaced Person. They had been not quite trash; Mrs. Shortley was a good woman, and she would miss her but as the Judge used to say, you couldn't have your pie and eat it too, and she was satisfied with the D. P. "We've seen them come and seen them go," she repeated with satisfaction.

"And me and you," the old man said, stooping to drag his hoe under a feed rack, "is still here."

She caught exactly what he meant her to catch in his tone. Bars of sunlight fell from the cracked ceiling across his back and cut him in three distinct parts. She watched his long hands clenched around the hoe and his crooked old profile pushed close to them. You might have been here *before* I was, she said to herself, but it's mighty likely I'll be here when you're gone. "I've spent half my life fooling with worthless people," she said in a severe voice, "but now I'm through."

"Black and white," he said, "is the same."

"I am through," she repeated and gave her dark smock that she had thrown over her shoulders like a cape a quick snatch at the neck. She had on a broad-brimmed black straw hat that had cost her twenty dollars twenty years ago and that she used now for a sun hat. "Money is the root of all evil," she said. "The Judge said so every day. He said he deplored money. He said the reason you niggers were so uppity was because there was so much money in circulation."

The old Negro had known the Judge. "Judge say he long for the day when he be too poor to pay a nigger to work," he said. "Say when that day come, the world be back on its feet."

She leaned forward, her hands on her hips and her neck stretched and said, "Well that day has almost come around here and I'm telling each and every one of you: you better look sharp. I don't have to put up with foolishness any more. I have somebody now who *has* to work!"

The old man knew when to answer and when not. At length he said, "We seen them come and we seen them go."

"However, the Shortleys were not the worst by far," she said. "I well remember those Garrits."

"They were before them Collinses," he said.

"No, before the Ringfields."

"Sweet Lord, them Ringfields!" he murmured.

"None of that kind *want* to work," she said.

"We seen them come and we seen them go," he said as if this were a refrain. "But we ain't never had one before," he said, bending himself up until he faced her, "like what we got now." He was cinnamon-colored with eyes that were so blurred with age that they seemed to be hung behind cobwebs.

She gave him an intense stare and held it until, lowering his hands on the hoe, he bent down again and dragged a pile of shavings alongside the wheelbarrow. She said stiffly, "He can wash out that barn in the time it took Mr. Shortley to make up his mind he had to do it."

"He from Pole," the old man muttered.

"From Poland."

"In Pole it ain't like it is here," he said. "They got different ways of doing," and he began to mumble unintelligibly.

"What are you saying?" she said. "If you have anything to say about him, say it and say it aloud."

He was silent, bending his knees precariously and edging the rake along the underside of the trough.

"If you know anything he's done that he shouldn't, I expect you to report it to me," she said.

"It warn't like it was what he should ought or oughtn't," he muttered. "It was like what nobody else don't do."

"You don't have anything against him," she said shortly, "and he's here to stay."

"We ain't never had one like him before is all," he murmured and gave his polite laugh.

"Times are changing," she said. "Do you know what's happening to this world? It's swelling up. It's getting so full of people that only the smart thrifty energetic ones are going to survive," and she tapped the words, smart, thrifty, and energetic out on the palm of her hand. Through the far end of the stall she could see down the road to where the Displaced Person was standing in the open barn door with the green hose in his hand. There was a certain stiffness about his figure that seemed to make it necessary for her to approach him slowly, even in her thoughts. She had decided this was because she couldn't hold an easy conversation with him. Whenever she said anything to him, she found herself shouting and nodding extravagantly and she would be conscious that one of the Negroes was leaning behind the nearest shed, watching.

"No indeed!" she said, sitting down on one of the feed racks and folding her arms, "I've made up my mind that I've had enough trashy people on this place to last me a lifetime and I'm not going to spend my last years fooling with Shortleys and Ringfields and Collins when the world is full of people who *have* to work."

"Howcome they so many extra?" he asked.

"People are selfish," she said. "They have too many children. There's no sense in it any more."

He had picked up the wheelbarrow handles and was backing out the door and he paused, half in the sunlight and half out, and stood there chewing his gums as if he had forgotten which direction he wanted to move in.

"What you colored people don't realize," she said, "is that I'm the one around here who holds all the strings together. If you don't work, I don't make any money and I can't pay you. You're all dependent on me but you each and every one act like the shoe is on the other foot."

It was not possible to tell from his face if he heard her. Finally he backed out with the wheelbarrow. "Judge say the devil he know is better than the devil he don't," he said in a clear mutter and turned and trundled off.

She got up and followed him, a deep vertical pit appearing suddenly in the center of her forehead, just under the red bangs. "The Judge has long since ceased to pay the bills around here," she called in a piercing voice.

He was the only one of her Negroes who had known the Judge and he thought this gave him title. He had had a low opinion of Mr. Crooms and Mr. McIntyre, her other husbands, and in his veiled polite way, he had congratulated her after each of her divorces. When he thought it necessary, he would work under a window where he knew she was sitting and talk to himself, a careful roundabout discussion, question and answer and then refrain. Once she had got up silently and slammed the window down so hard that he had fallen backwards off his feet. Or occasionally he spoke with the peacock. The cock would follow him around the place, his steady eye on the ear of corn that stuck up from the old man's back pocket or he would sit near him and pick himself. Once from the open kitchen door, she had heard him say to the bird, "I remember when it was twenty of you walking about this place and now it's only you and two hens. Crooms it was twelve. McIntyre it was five. You and two hens now."

And that time she had stepped out of the door onto the porch and said, "MISTER Crooms and MISTER McIntyre! And I don't want to hear you call either of them anything else again. And you can understand this: when that peachicken dies there won't be any replacements."

She kept the peacock only out of a superstitious fear of annoying the Judge in his grave. He had liked to see them walking around the place for he said they made him feel rich. Of her three husbands, the Judge was the one most present to her although he was the only one she had buried. He was in the family graveyard, a little space fenced in the middle of the back cornfield, with his mother and father and grandfather and three great aunts and two infant cousins. Mr. Crooms, her second, was forty miles away in the state asylum and Mr. McIntyre, her last, was intoxicated, she supposed, in some hotel room in Florida. But the Judge, sunk in the cornfield with his family, was always at home.

She had married him when he was an old man and because of his money but there had been another reason that she would not admit then, even to herself: she had liked him. He was a dirty snuff-dipping Court House figure, famous all over the country for being rich, who wore high-top shoes, a string tie, a gray suit with a black stripe in it, and a yellowed panama hat, winter and summer. His teeth and hair were tobacco-colored and his face a clay pink pitted and tracked with mysterious prehistoric-looking marks as if he had been unearthed among fossils. There had been a peculiar odor about him of sweaty fondled bills but he never carried money on him or had a nickel to show. She was his secretary for a few months and the old man with his sharp eye had seen at once that here was a woman who admired him for himself. The three years that he lived after they married were the happiest and most prosperous of Mrs. McIntyre's life, but when he died his estate proved to be bankrupt. He left her a mortgaged house and fifty acres that he had managed to cut the timber off before he died. It was as if, as the final triumph of a successful life, he had been able to take everything with him.

But she had survived. She had survived a succession of tenant farmers and dairymen that the old man himself would have found hard to outdo, and she had been able to meet the constant drain of a tribe of moody unpredictable Negroes, and she had even managed to hold her own against the incidental bloodsuckers, the cattle dealers and lumber men and the buyers and sellers of anything who drove up in pieced-together trucks and honked in the yard.

She stood slightly reared back with her arms folded under her smock and a satisfied expression on her face as she watched the Displaced Person turn off the hose and disappear inside the barn. She was sorry that the poor man had been chased out of Poland and run across Europe and had had to take up in a tenant shack in a strange country, but she had not been responsible for any of this. She had had a hard time herself. She knew what it was to struggle. People ought to have to struggle. Mr. Guizac had probably had everything given to him all the way across Europe and over here. He had probably not had to struggle enough. She had given him a job. She didn't know if he was grateful or not. She didn't know anything about him except that he did the work. The truth was that he was not very real to her yet. He was a kind of miracle that she had seen happen and that she talked about but that she didn't believe.

She watched as he came out of the barn and motioned to Sulk, who was coming around the back of the lot. He gesticulated and then took something out of his pocket and the two of them stood looking at it. She started down the lane toward them. The Negro's figure was slack and tall and he was craning his round head forward in his usual idiotic way. He was a little better than half-witted but when they were like that they were always good workers. The Judge had said always hire you a half-witted nigger because they don't have sense enough to stop working. The Pole was gesticulating rapidly. He left something with the colored boy and then walked off and before she rounded the turn in the lane, she heard the tractor crank up. He was on his way to the field. The Negro was still hanging there, gaping at whatever he had in his hand.

She entered the lot and walked through the barn, looking with approval at the wet spotless concrete floor. It was only nine-thirty and Mr. Shortley had never got anything washed until eleven. As she came out at the other end, she saw the Negro moving very slowly in a diagonal path across the road in front of her, his eyes still on what Mr. Guizac had given him. He didn't see her and he paused and dipped his knees and leaned over his hand, his tongue describing little circles. He had a photograph. He lifted one finger and traced it lightly over the surface of the picture. Then he looked up and saw her and seemed to freeze, his mouth in a half-grin, his finger lifted.

"Why haven't you gone to the field?" she asked.

He raised one foot and opened his mouth wider while the hand with the photograph edged toward his back pocket.

"What's that?" she said.

"It ain't nothin'," he muttered and handed it to her automatically.

It was a photograph of a girl of about twelve in a white dress. She had blond hair with a wreath in it and she looked forward out of light eyes that were bland and composed. "Who is this child?" Mrs. McIntyre asked.

"She his cousin," the boy said in a high voice.

"Well what are you doing with it?" she asked.

"She going to mah me," he said in an even higher voice.

"Marry you!" she shrieked.

"I pays half to get her over here," he said. "I pays him three dollars a week. She bigger now. She his cousin. She don't care who she mah she so glad to get away from there." The high voice seemed to shoot up like a nervous jet of sound and then fall flat as he watched her face. Her eyes were the color of blue granite when the glare falls on it, but she was not looking at him. She was looking down the road where the distant sound of the tractor could be heard.

"I don't reckon she goin to come nohow," the boy murmured.

"I'll see that you get every cent of your money back," she said in a toneless voice and turned and walked off, holding the photograph bent in two. There was nothing about her small stiff figure to indicate that she was shaken.

As soon as she got in the house, she lay down on her bed and shut her eyes and pressed her hand over her heart as if she were trying to keep it in place. Her mouth opened and she made two or three dry little sounds. Then after a minute she sat up and said aloud, "They're all the same. It's always been like this," and she fell back flat again. "Twenty years of being beaten and done in and they even robbed his grave!" and remembering that, she began to cry quietly, wiping her eyes every now and then with the hem of her smock.

What she had thought of was the angel over the Judge's grave. This had been a naked granite cherub that the old man had seen in the city one day in a tombstone store window. He had been taken with it at once, partly because its face reminded him of his wife and partly because he wanted a genuine work of art over his grave. He had come home with it sitting on the green plush train seat beside him. Mrs. McIntyre had never noticed the resemblance to herself. She had always thought it hideous but when the Herrins stole it off the old man's grave, she was shocked and outraged. Mrs. Herrin had thought it very pretty and had walked to the graveyard frequently to see it, and when the Herrins left the angel left with them, all but its toes, for the ax old man Herrin had used to break it off with had struck slightly too high. Mrs. McIntyre had never been able to afford to have it replaced.

When she had cried all she could, she got up and went into the back hall, a closet-like space that was dark and quiet as a chapel and sat down on the edge of the Judge's black mechanical chair with her elbow on his desk. This was a giant roll-top piece of furniture pocked with pigeon holes full of dusty papers. Old bankbooks and ledgers were stacked in the half-open drawers and there was a small safe, empty but locked, set like a tabernacle in the center of it. She had left this part of the house unchanged since the old man's time. It was a kind of memorial to him, sacred because he had conducted his business here. With the slightest tilt one way or the other, the chair gave a rusty skeletal groan that sounded something like him when he had complained of his poverty. It had been his first principle to talk as if he were the poorest man in the world and she followed it, not only because he had but because it was true. When she sat with her intense constricted face turned toward the empty safe, she knew there was nobody poorer in the world than she was.

She sat motionless at the desk for ten or fifteen minutes and then as if she had gained some strength, she got up and got in her car and drove to the cornfield.

The road ran through a shadowy pine thicket and ended on top of a hill that rolled fan-wise down and up again in a broad expanse of tasseled green. Mr. Guizac was cutting from the outside of the field in a circular path to the center where the graveyard was all but hidden by the corn, and she could see him on the high far side of the slope, mounted on the tractor with the cutter and wagon behind him. From time to time, he had to get to the tractor and climb in the wagon to spread the silage because the Negro had not arrived. She watched impatiently, standing in front of her black coupe with her arms folded under her smock, while he progressed slowly around the rim of the field, gradually getting close enough for her to wave to him to get down. He stopped the machine and jumped off and came running forward, wiping his red jaw with a piece of grease rag.

"I want to talk to you," she said and beckoned him to the edge of the thicket where it was shady. He took off the cap and followed her, smiling, but his smile faded when she turned and faced him. Her eyebrows, thin and fierce as a spider's leg, had drawn together ominously and the deep vertical pit had plunged down from under the red bangs into the bridge of her nose. She removed the bent picture from her pocket and handed it to him silently. Then she stepped back and said, "Mr. Guizac! You would bring this poor innocent child over here and try to marry her to a half-witted thieving black stinking nigger! What kind of a monster are you!"

He took the photograph with a slowly returning smile. "My cousin," he said. "She twelve here. First Communion. Six-ten now."

Monster! she said to herself and looked at him as if she were seeing him for the first time. His forehead and skull were white where they had been protected by his cap but the rest of his face was red and bristled with short yellow hairs. His eyes were like two bright nails behind his gold-rimmed spectacles that had been mended over the nose with haywire. His whole face looked as if it might have been patched together out of several others. "Mr. Guizac," she said, beginning slowly and then speaking faster until she ended breathless in the middle of a word, "that nigger cannot have a white wife from Europe. You can't talk to a nigger that way. You'll excite him and besides it can't be done. Maybe it can be done in Poland but it can't be done here and you'll have to stop. It's all foolishness. That nigger don't have a grain of sense and you'll excite . . ."

"She in camp three year," he said.

"Your cousin," she said in a positive voice, "cannot come over here and marry one of my Negroes."

"She six-ten year," he said. "From Poland. Mamma die, pappa die. She wait in camp. Three camp." He pulled a wallet from his pocket and fingered through it and took out another picture of the same girl, a few years older, dressed in something dark and shapeless. She was standing against a wall with a short woman who apparently had no teeth. "She mamma," he said, pointing to the woman. "She die in two camp."

"Mr. Guizac," Mrs. McIntyre said, pushing the picture back at him, "I will not have my niggers upset. I cannot run this place without my niggers. I can run it without you but not without them and if you mention this girl to Sulk again, you won't have a job with me. Do you understand?"

His face showed no comprehension. He seemed to be piecing all these words together in his mind to make a thought.

Mrs. McIntyre remembered Mrs. Shortley's words: "He understands everything, he only pretends he don't so as to do exactly as he pleases," and her face regained the look of shocked wrath she had begun with. "I cannot understand how a man who calls himself a Christian," she said, "could bring a poor innocent girl over here and marry her to something like that. I cannot understand it. I cannot!" and she shook her head and looked into the distance with a pained blue gaze.

After a second he shrugged and let his arms drop as if he were tired. "She no care black," he said. "She in camp three year."

Mrs. McIntyre felt a peculiar weakness behind her knees. "Mr. Guizac," she said. "I don't want to have to speak to you about this again. If I do, you'll have to find another place yourself. Do you understand?"

The patched face did not say. She had the impression that he didn't see her there. "This is my place," she said. "I say who will come here and who won't."

"Ya," he said and put back on his cap.

"I am not responsible for the world's misery," she said as an afterthought.

"Ya," he said.

"You have a good job. You should be grateful to be here," she added, "but I'm not sure you are."

"Ya," he said and gave his little shrug and turned back to the tractor.

She watched him get on and maneuver the machine into the corn again. When he had passed her and rounded the turn, she climbed to the top of the slope and stood with her arms folded and looked out grimly over the field. "They're all the same," she muttered, "whether they come from

Poland or Tennessee. I've handled Herrins and Ringfields and Shortleys and I can handle a Guizac," and she narrowed her gaze until it closed entirely around the diminishing figure on the tractor as if she were watching him through a gunsight. All her life she had been fighting the world's overflow and now she had it in the form of a Pole. "You're just like all the rest of them," she said, "—only smart and thrifty and energetic but so am I. And this is my place," and she stood there, a small black-hatted, black-smocked figure with an aging cherubic face, and folded her arms as if she were equal to anything. But her heart was beating as if some interior violence had already been done to her. She opened her eyes to include the whole field so that the figure on the tractor was no larger than a grasshopper in her widened view.

She stood there for some time. There was a slight breeze and the corn trembled in great waves on both sides of the slope. The big cutter, with its monotonous roar, continued to shoot it pulverized into the wagon in a steady spurt of fodder. By nightfall, the Displaced Person would have worked his way around and around until there would be nothing on either side of the two hills but the stubble, and down in the center, risen like a little island, the graveyard where the Judge lay grinning under his desecrated monument.

III

The priest, with his long bland face supported on one finger, had been talking for ten minutes about Purgatory while Mrs. McIntyre squinted furiously at him from an opposite chair. They were drinking ginger ale on her front porch and she had kept rattling the ice in her glass, rattling her beads, rattling her braclet like an impatient pony jingling its harness. There is no moral obligation to keep him, she was saying under her breath, there is absolutely no moral obligation. Suddenly she lurched up and her voice fell across his brogue like a drill into a mechanical saw. "Listen!" she said, "I'm not theological. I'm practical! I want to talk to you about something practical!"

"Arrrrrrr," he groaned, grating to a halt.

She had put at least a finger of whisky in her own ginger ale so that she would be able to endure his full-length visit and she sat down awkwardly, finding the chair closer to her than she had expected. "Mr. Guizac is not satisfactory," she said.

The old man raised his eyebrows in mock wonder.

"He's extra," she said. "He doesn't fit in. I have to have somebody who fits in."

The priest carefully turned his hat on his knees. He had a little trick of waiting a second silently and then swinging the conversation back into his own paths. He was about eighty. She had never known a priest until she had gone to see this one on the business of getting her the Displaced Person. After he had got her the Pole, he had used the business introduction to try to convert her—just as she had supposed he would.

"Give him time," the old man said. "He'll learn to fit in. Where is that beautiful birrrrd of yours?" he asked and then said, "Arrrrr, I see him!" and stood up and looked out over the lawn where the peacock and the two hens were stepping at a strained attention, their long necks ruffled, the cock's violent blue and the hens' silver-green, glinting in the late afternoon sun.

"Mr. Guizac," Mrs. McIntyre continued, bearing down with a flat steady voice, "is very efficient. I'll admit that. But he doesn't understand how to get on with my niggers and they don't like him. I can't have my niggers run off. And I don't like his attitude. He's not in the least grateful for being here."

The priest had his hand on the screen door and he opened it, ready to make his escape. "Arrrr, I must be off," he murmured.

"I tell you if I had a white man who understood the Negroes, I'd have to let Mr. Guizac go," she said and stood up again.

He turned then and looked her in the face. "He has nowhere to go," he said. Then he said, "Dear lady, I know you well enough to know you wouldn't turn him out for a trifle!" and without waiting for an answer, he raised his hand and gave her his blessing in a rumbling voice.

She smiled angrily and said, "I didn't create his situation, of course."

The priest let his eyes wander toward the birds. They had reached the middle of the lawn. The cock stopped suddenly and curving his neck backwards, he raised his tail and spread it with a shimmering timbrous noise. Tiers of small pregnant suns floated in a green-gold haze over his head. The priest stood transfixed, his jaw slack. Mrs. McIntyre wondered where she had ever seen such an idiotic old man. "Christ will come like that!" he said in a loud gay voice and wiped his hand over his mouth and stood there, gaping.

Mrs. McIntyre's face assumed a set puritanical expression and she reddened. Christ in the conversation embarrassed her the way sex had her mother. "It is not my responsibility that Mr. Guizac has nowhere to go," she said. "I don't find myself responsible for all the extra people in the world."

The old man didn't seem to hear her. His attention was fixed on the cock who was taking minute steps backward, his head against the spread tail. "The Transfiguration," he murmured.

She had no idea what he was talking about. "Mr. Guizac didn't have to come here in the first place," she said, giving him a hard look.

The cock lowered his tail and began to pick grass.

"He didn't have to come in the first place," she repeated, emphasizing each word.

The old man smiled absently. "He came to redeem us," he said and blandly reached for her hand and shook it and said he must go.

If Mr. Shortley had not returned a few weeks later, she would have gone out looking for a new man to hire. She had not wanted him back but when she saw the familiar black automobile drive up the road and stop by the side of the house, she had the feeling that she was the one returning, after a long miserable trip, to her own place. She realized all at once that it was Mrs. Shortley she had been missing. She had had no one to talk to since Mrs. Shortley left, and she ran to the door, expecting to see her heaving herself up the steps.

Mr. Shortley stood there alone. He had on a black felt hat and a shirt with red and blue palm trees designed in it but the hollows in his long bitten blistered face were deeper than they had been a month ago.

"Well!" she said. "Where is Mrs. Shortley?"

Mr. Shortley didn't say anything. The change in his face seemed to have come from the inside; he looked like a man who had gone for a long time without water. "She was God's own angel," he said in a loud voice. "She was the sweetest woman in the world."

"Where is she?" Mrs. McIntyre murmured.

"Daid," he said. "She had herself a stroke on the day she left out of here." There was a corpse-like composure about his face. "I figure that Pole killed her," he said. "She seen through him from the first. She known he come from the devil. She told me so."

It took Mrs. McIntyre three days to get over Mrs. Shortley's death. She told herself that anyone would have thought they were kin. She rehired Mr. Shortley to do farm work though actually she didn't want him without his wife. She told him she was going to give thirty days' notice to the Displaced Person at the end of the month and that then he could have his job back in the dairy. Mr. Shortley preferred the dairy job but he was willing to wait. He said it would give him some satisfaction to see the Pole leave the place, and Mrs. McIntyre said it would give her a great deal of satisfaction. She confessed that she should have been content with the help she had in the first place and not have been reaching into other parts of the world for it. Mr. Shortley said he never had cared for foreigners since he had been in the first world's war and seen what they were like. He said he had seen all kinds then but that none of them were like us. He said he recalled the face of one man who had thrown a hand-grenade at him and that the man had had little round eye-glasses exactly like Mr. Guizac's.

"But Mr. Guizac is a Pole, he's not German," Mrs. McIntyre said.

"It ain't a great deal of difference in them two kinds," Mr. Shortley had explained.

The Negroes were pleased to see Mr. Shortley back. The Displaced Person had expected them to work as hard as he worked himself, whereas Mr. Shortley recognized their limitations. He had never been a very good worker himself with Mrs. Shortley to keep him in line, but without her, he was even more forgetful and slow. The Pole worked as fiercely as ever and seemed to have no inkling that he was about to be fired. Mrs. McIntyre saw jobs done in a short time that she had thought would never get done at all. Still she was resolved to get rid of him. The sight of his small stiff figure moving quickly here and there had come to be the most irritating sight on the place for her, and she felt she had been tricked by the old priest. He had said there was no legal obligation for her to keep the Displaced Person if he was not satisfactory, but then he had brought up the moral one.

She meant to tell him that *her* moral obligation was to her own people, to Mr. Shortley, who had fought in the world war for his country and not to Mr. Guizac who had merely arrived here to take advantage of whatever he could. She felt she must have this out with the priest before she fired the Displaced Person. When the first of the month came and the priest hadn't called, she put off giving the Pole notice for a little longer.

Mr. Shortley told himself that he should have known all along that no woman was going to do what she said she was when she said she was. He didn't know how long he could afford to put up with her shilly-shallying. He thought himself that she was going soft and was afraid to turn the Pole out for fear he would have a hard time getting another place. He could tell her the truth about this: that if she let him go, in three years he would own his own house and have a television aerial sitting on top of it. As a matter of policy, Mr. Shortley began to come to her back door every evening to put certain facts before her. "A white man sometimes don't get the consideration a nigger gets," he said, "but that don't matter because he's still white, but sometimes," and here he would pause and look off into the distance, "a man that's fought and bled and died in the service of his native land don't get the consideration of one of them like them he was fighting. I ast you: is that right?" When he asked her such questions he could watch her face and tell he was making an impression. She didn't look too well these days. He noticed lines around her eyes that hadn't been there when he and Mrs. Shortley had been the only white help on the place. Whenever he thought of Mrs. Shortley, he felt his heart go down like an old bucket into a dry well.

The old priest kept away as if he had been frightened by his last visit but finally, seeing that the Displaced Person had not been fired, he ventured to call again to take up giving Mrs. McIntyre instructions where he remembered leaving them off. She had not asked to be instructed but he instructed anyway, forcing a little definition of one of the sacraments or of some dogma into each conversation he had, no matter with whom. He sat on her porch, taking no notice of her partly mocking, partly outraged expression as she sat shaking her foot, waiting for an opportunity to drive a wedge into his talk. "For," he was saying, as if he spoke of something that had happened yesterday in town, "when God sent his Only Begotten Son, Jesus Christ Our Lord"—he slightly bowed his head—"as a Redeemer to mankind, He . . ."

"Father Flynn!" she said in a voice that made him jump. "I want to talk to you about something serious!"

The skin under the old man's right eye flinched.

"As far as I'm concerned," she said and glared at him fiercely, "Christ was just another D. P."

He raised his hands slightly and let them drop on his knees. "Arrrrrr," he murmured as if he were considering this.

"I'm going to let that man go," she said. "I don't have any obligation to him. My obligation is to the people who've done something for their country, not to the ones who've just come over to take advantage of what they can get," and she began to talk rapidly, remembering all her arguments. The priest's attention seemed to retire to some private oratory to wait until she got through. Once or twice his gaze roved out onto the lawn as if he were hunting some means of escape but she didn't stop. She told him how she had been hanging onto this place for thirty years, always just barely making it against people who came from nowhere and were going nowhere, who didn't want anything but an automobile. She said she had found out they were the same whether they came from Poland or Tennessee. When the Guizacs got ready, she said, they would not hesitate to leave her. She told him how the people who looked rich were the poorest of all because they had the most to keep up. She asked him how he thought she paid her feed bills. She told him she would like to have her house done over but she couldn't afford it. She couldn't even afford to have the monument restored over her husband's grave. She asked him if he would like to guess what her insurance amounted to for the year. Finally she asked him if he thought she was made of money and the old man suddenly let out a great ugly bellow as if this were a comical question.

When the visit was over, she felt let down, though she had clearly triumphed over him. She made up her mind now that on the first of the month, she would give the Displaced Person his thirty days' notice and she told Mr. Shortley so.

Mr. Shortley didn't say anything. His wife had been the only woman he was ever acquainted with who was never scared off from doing what she said. She said the Pole had been sent by the devil and the priest. Mr. Shortley had no doubt that the priest had got some peculiar control over Mrs. McIntyre and that before long she would start attending his Masses. She looked as if something was wearing her down from the inside. She was thinner and more fidgety and not as sharp as she used to be. She would look at a milk can now and not see how dirty it was and he had seen her lips move when she was not talking. The Pole never did anything the wrong way but all the same he was very irritating to her. Mr. Shortley himself did things as he pleased—not always her way—but she didn't seem to notice. She had noticed though that the Pole and all his family were getting fat; she pointed out to Mr. Shortley that the hollows had come out of their cheeks and that they saved every cent they made. "Yes'm, and one of these days he'll be able to buy and sell you out," Mr. Shortley had ventured to say, and he could tell that the statement had shaken her.

"I'm just waiting for the first," she had said.

Mr. Shortley waited too and the first came and went and she didn't fire him. He could have told anybody how it would be. He was not a violent man but he hated to see a woman done in by a foreigner. He felt that that was one thing a man couldn't stand by and see happen.

There was no reason Mrs. McIntyre should not fire Mr. Guizac at once but she put it off from day to day. She was worried about her bills and about her health. She didn't sleep at night or when she did she dreamed about the Displaced Person. She had never discharged any one before; they had all left her. One night she dreamed that Mr. Guizac and his family were moving into her house and that she was moving in with Mr. Shortley. This was too much for her and she woke up and didn't sleep again for several nights; and one night she dreamed that the priest came to call and droned on and on, saying, "Dear lady, I know your tender heart won't suffer you to turn the porrrrr man out. Think of the thousands of them, think of the ovens and the boxcars and the camps and the sick children and Christ Our Lord."

"He's extra and he's upset the balance around here," she said, "and I'm a logical practical woman and there are no ovens here and no camps and no Christ Our Lord and when he leaves, he'll make more money. He'll work at the mill and buy a car and don't talk to me—all they want is a car."

"The ovens and the boxcars and the sick children," droned the priest, "and our dear Lord."

"Just one too many," she said.

The next morning, she made up her mind while she was eating her breakfast that she would give him his notice at once, and she stood up and walked out of the kitchen and down the road with her table napkin still in her hand. Mr. Guizac was spraying the barn, standing in his swaybacked way with one hand on his hip. He turned off the hose and gave her an impatient kind of attention as if she were interfering with his work. She had not thought of what she would say to him, she had merely come. She stood in the barn door, looking severely at the wet spotless floor and the dripping stanchions. "Ya goot?" he said.

"Mr. Guizac," she said, "I can barely meet my obligations now." Then she said in a louder, stronger voice, emphasizing each word, "I have bills to pay."

"I too," Mr. Guizac said. "Much bills, little money," and he shrugged.

At the other end of the barn, she saw a long beak-nosed shadow glide like a snake halfway up the sunlit open door and stop; and somewhere behind her, she was aware of a silence where the sound of the Negroes shoveling had come a minute before. "This is my place," she said angrily. "All of you are extra. Each and every one of you are extra!"

"Ya," Mr. Guizac said and turned on the hose again.

She wiped her mouth with the napkin she had in her hand and walked off, as if she had accomplished what she came for.

Mr. Shortley's shadow withdrew from the door and he leaned against the side of the barn and lit half of a cigarette that he took out of his pocket. There was nothing for him to do now but wait on the hand of God to strike, but he knew one thing: he was not going to wait with his mouth shut.

Starting that morning, he began to complain and to state his side of the case to every person he saw, black or white. He complained in the grocery store and at the courthouse and on the street corner and directly to Mrs. McIntyre herself, for there was nothing underhanded about him. If the Pole could have understood what he had to say, he would have said it to him too. "All men was created free and equal," he said to Mrs. McIntyre, "and I risked my life and limb to prove it. Gone over there and fought and bled and died and come back on over here and find out who's got my job—just exactly who I been fighting. It was a hand-grenade come that near to killing me and I seen who throwed it—little man with eye-glasses just like his. Might have bought them at the same store. Small world," and he gave a bitter little laugh. Since he didn't have Mrs. Shortley to do the talking any more, he had started doing it himself and had found that he had a gift for it. He had the power of making other people see his logic. He talked a good deal to the Negroes.

"Whyn't you go back to Africa?" he asked Sulk one morning as they were cleaning out the silo. "That's your country, ain't it?"

"I ain't goin there," the boy said. "They might eat me up."

"Well, if you behave yourself it isn't any reason you can't stay here," Mr. Shortley said kindly. "Because you didn't run away from nowhere. Your granddaddy was bought. He didn't have a thing to do with coming. It's the people that run away from where they come from that I ain't got any use for."

"I never felt no need to travel," the Negro said.

"Well," Mr. Shortley said, "if I was going to travel again, it would be to either China or Africa. You go to either of them two places and you can tell right away what the difference is between you and them. You go to these other places and the only way you can tell is if they say something. And then you can't always tell because about half of them know the English language. That's where we make our mistake," he said, "—letting all them people onto English. There'd be a heap less trouble if everybody only knew his own language. My wife said knowing two languages was like having eyes in the back of your head. You couldn't put nothing over on her."

"You sho couldn't," the boy muttered, and then he added, "She was fine. She was sho fine. I never known a finer white woman than her."

Mr. Shortley turned in the opposite direction and worked silently for a while. After a few minutes he leaned up and tapped the colored boy on the shoulder with the handle of his shovel. For a second he only looked at him while a great deal of meaning gathered in his wet eyes. Then he said softly, "Revenge is mine, saith the Lord."

Mrs. McIntyre found that everybody in town knew Mr. Shortley's version of her business and that everyone was critical of her conduct. She began to understand that she had a moral obligation to fire the Pole and that she was shirking it because she found it hard to do. She could not stand the increasing guilt any longer and on a cold Saturday morning, she started off after breakfast to fire him. She walked down to the machine shed where she heard him cranking up the tractor.

There was a heavy frost on the ground that made the fields look like the rough backs of sheep; the sun was almost silver and the woods stuck up like dry bristles on the sky line. The countryside seemed to be receding from the little circle of noise around the shed. Mr. Guizac was squatting on the ground beside the small tractor, putting in a part. Mrs. McIntyre hoped to get the fields turned over while he still had thirty days to work for her. The colored boy was standing by with some tools in his hand and Mr. Shortley was under the shed about to get up on the large tractor and back it out. She meant to wait until he and the Negro got out of the way before she began her unpleasant duty.

She stood watching Mr. Guizac, stamping her feet on the hard ground, for the cold was climbing like a paralysis up her feet and legs. She had on a heavy black coat and a red head-kerchief with her black hat pulled down on top of it to keep the glare out of her eyes. Under the black brim her face had an abstracted look and once or twice her lips moved silently. Mr. Guizac shouted over the noise of the tractor for the Negro to hand him a screwdriver and when he got it, he turned over on his back on the icy ground and reached up under the machine. She could not see his face, only his feet and legs and trunk sticking impudently out from the side of the tractor. He had on rubber boots that were cracked and splashed with mud. He raised one knee and then lowered it and turned himself slightly. Of all the things she resented about him, she resented most that he hadn't left of his own accord.

Mr. Shortley had got on the large tractor and was backing it out from under the shed. He seemed to be warmed by it as if its heat and strength sent impulses up through him that he obeyed instantly. He had headed it toward the small tractor but he braked it on a slight incline and jumped off and turned back toward the shed. Mrs. McIntyre was looking fixedly at Mr. Guizac's legs lying flat on the ground now. She heard the brake on the large tractor slip and, looking up, she saw it move forward, calculating its own path. Later she remembered that she had seen the Negro jump silently out of the way as if a spring in the earth had released him and that she had seen Mr. Shortley turn his head with incredible slowness and stare silently over his shoulder and that she had started to shout to the Displaced Person but that she had not. She had felt her eyes and Mr. Shortley's eyes and the Negro's eyes come together in one look that froze them in collusion forever, and she had heard the little noise the Pole made as the tractor wheel broke his backbone. The two men ran forward to help and she fainted.

She remembered, when she came to, running somewhere, perhaps into the house and out again but she could not remember what for or if she had fainted again when she got there. When she finally came back to where the tractors were, the ambulance had arrived. Mr. Guizac's body was covered with the bent bodies of his wife and two children and by a black one which hung over him, murmuring words she didn't understand. At first she thought this must be the doctor but then with a feeling of annoyance she recognized the priest, who had come with the ambulance and was slipping something into the crushed man's mouth. After a minute he stood up and she looked first at his bloody pants legs and then at his face which was not averted from her but was as withdrawn and expressionless as the rest of the countryside. She only stared at him for she was too shocked by her experience to be quite herself. Her mind was not taking hold of all that was happening. She felt she was in some foreign country where the people bent over the body were natives, and she watched like a stranger while the dead man was carried away in the ambulance.

That evening Mr. Shortley left without notice to look for a new position and the Negro, Sulk, was taken with a sudden desire to see more of the world and set off for the southern part of the state. The old man Astor could not work without company. Mrs. McIntyre hardly noticed that she had no help left for she came down with a nervous affliction and had to go to the hospital. When she came back, she saw that the place would be too much for her to run now and she turned her cows over to a professional auctioneer (who sold them at a loss) and retired to live on what she had, while she tried to save her declining health. A numbness developed in one of her legs and her hands and head began to jiggle and eventually she had to stay in bed all the time with only a colored woman to wait on her. Her eyesight grew steadily worse and she lost her voice altogether. Not many people remembered to come out to the country to see her except the old priest. He came regularly once a week with a bag of breadcrumbs and, after he had fed these to the peacock, he would come in and sit by the side of her bed and explain the doctrines of the Church.

QUESTIONS

1. What details—in the opening scene, for instance—serve to bring out Mrs. Shortley's ignorance? Is Mr. Shortley better informed than his wife about the world at large?

2. How far does Mrs. McIntyre's attitude towards the Guizacs differ from Mrs. Shortley's, and how far does it parallel it? In each case, what are the motives that lie behind the attitude?

3. How is the peacock used as a focus for indicating differences of perception among the characters?

4. What do you make of Mrs. Shortley's vision in the pasture? What caused it, do you think?

5. In what ways could it be said that Mrs. Shortley is present in the story right to the end? At what point in the story had she suggested that disaster might overtake Mr. Guizac? How important is the Judge in the story, and what seems to you to be his function?

6. At the end of the story Mrs. McIntyre is described in the following sentence: "She felt she was in some foreign country where the people bent over the body were natives, and she watched like a stranger while the dead man was carried away in the ambulance." What reversal of values and of position is indicated by this sentence?

7. How far may the story be seen as a Christian parable?